HOW MANY MEN WOULD MAKE A MOCKERY OF HER NEED FOR LOVE?

Edward—
handsome, wealthy, sophisticated, who in a Paris
hotel room turned Sybil's dream of love into a
shattering nightmare

Jonathan—
the young doctor who saved Sybil from the abyss of
total despair, yet whom she was forced to drive away
though it broke her heart

Geoffrey—
a man who had everything, and offered to share it all
with Sybil, if only she would agree to fit his image
of what a wife should be

Carter—
the talented, tormented writer with whom Sybil began
what she thought was an innocent flirtation, until it
threatened to wreck her marriage and her life

Also by Thérèse Martini
(written under the pseudonym of Alison King),
and available from Popular Library:

THE DREAMER, LOST IN TERROR

To Love AND Beyond

by Thérèse Martini

POPULAR LIBRARY • NEW YORK

Published by Popular Library, CBS Publications,
CBS Consumer Publishing, a Division of CBS Inc.

October, 1977

Copyright © 1977 by Teri Martini

ISBN: 0-445-04092-0

To Louise
with Love and Admiration

PART ONE

I

She found what she wanted in the Village: three small rooms in a three-story walk-up. The street was not strictly residential, though few streets were in New York. Small stores lined the sidewalk. Some were the front rooms of made-over brownstones. The small apartment building was between a shoemaker with a large neon shoe above the door and a drug store with a dusty window. By the time she arrived it was afternoon. Three children, holding hands were strung across the pavement precariously balanced on roller skates which grated noisily on the bumpy pavement. She side-stepped quickly.

"Hey, watch it, lady!"

The shaggy-haired boy on the end shouted at her, as she gained the steps of the building just in time. He couldn't have been more than ten years old, but he had a tough, city look that made him appear older. He gave her a Puckish grin and she smiled back shakily. He seemed to be enjoying himself and he hadn't meant to be rude. She had inadvertently interrupted his fun.

She was struck by the fear that this might be her Ned ten years from now. Where would she be ten years from now? Where would they both be? Sybil Eldridge Ashford had come a long way from home.

Papa, poor Papa! What would he think of his daughter if he knew where she was now and what she had done? The last time she had seen him he didn't know her at all.

7

He looked right at her and called her Alicia. He spoke, too, of her mother as though she were alive and not dead almost thirteen years. His younger daughter no longer existed for him. He lived completely in the world of the past before Sybil had come into it.

"You did this to him, you know."

Alicia's voice was low with fury. She'd even allowed her anger to register on her beautiful face. She took great care not to exhibit anything but the mildest emotions. They created lines and Alicia was acutely conscious of the aging process. She was thirty-six and she looked ten years younger only because she was ever vigilant. No one disputed the fact that she was one of the most beautiful women in Philadelphia society. She did not intend to relinquish her position for years to come.

When the sisters faced each other in the drawing room of the Eldridge home, Sybil thought what Alicia said might well be true. Driven by despair she had gone to her father and tried to tell him the truth about Edward. She described only some of what she had suffered at her husband's hands. Her father was shocked and deeply concerned. Of course, he had been angry, too, terribly angry. He insisted she stay the night. He would not hear of her returning to Edward.

Sometime during that night it had happened. The stroke left him paralyzed and without memory of her.

The sisters confronted each other the next day. They presented quite a contrast. Alicia's auburn hair seemed to be touched with fire. Her long green eyes with their heavy, sultry lids, were narrowed to slits. Sybil's coloring was entirely different. She had black hair like her father and she'd inherited his deep blue eyes.

"You are responsible."

Alicia persisted in her accusation. "I told you not to go to him with your insane tale. I begged you."

"I had to. I had to for Ned's sake."

Sybil tried to keep her voice from being too shrill and she gripped the back of the Chippendale chair that stood before the terrace doors.

8

"Oh, God! I think you are mad! You really believe that, don't you? Edward thinks you've been unbalanced since Paris, since your pregnancy began. It happens to some women. I should have expected it to happen to you. You were always impossible. Always! Heaven knows I tried to be a mother to you. I tried to advise you and give you what you needed. But it was no use, no use at all."

"That's not true, Alicia. That's not true. You gave me nothing that I really needed."

She was shouting now, but she didn't care. She wanted Alicia to know that she knew the truth.

Until the year of her debut her sister had taken very little interest in Sybil. Until then Sybil lived a comfortable, if somewhat lonely existence, with her father. Papa was not the most lively of companions, but she loved and admired him. When Mama died Alicia was married to Montgomery Ransome and living in her own home so there were only Sybil and her father in the gracious Eldridge mansion.

At first, Papa seemed to take little notice of her and left her to the care of a governess. He had loved his wife very much and felt her loss keenly. Gradually he had formed the habit of allowing his younger daughter to dine with him. He found her an intelligent, charming, unobtrusive child and seemed to prefer her company to that of the many friends who sought to comfort him.

She listened with awe to everything he said and gradually, as she grew older, he would take her into his study and teach her about his hobby, genealogy. She spent the pleasant evenings sewing while he worked. She was particularly artistic they said at school. Her delicate embroidery and careful stitching were praised by her teachers.

By the time she was sixteen she had gotten to like her life the way it was. She was driven to and from Miss Alben's School for Young Ladies each day. The evenings she spent with her father and weekends with the grandson of her mother's old friend.

Ronald Baldwin was completing his second year at

Princeton. He was thoughtful and gentle, though his appearance was not impressive. He was tall and thin with a pale complexion, pale brown hair and pale blue eyes. But his voice was strong and he had a nice touch of humor. He wrote poetry that she did not always understand, but she thought she understood him and would probably marry him someday.

Alicia had other ideas. The magic year of Sybil's debut seemed to transform her into a person worthy of her sister's attention. Alicia began to visit the Eldridge home every day, beginning in early June after Sybil's seventeenth birthday.

"We must begin preparing for the most important event of your life. Your social debut cannot be taken lightly. It's possible that you could be quite a success. You have a splendid figure. Your face will certainly do, thank goodness. All that remains is for you to meet the right people."

Until that very moment she had never thought of being a social success. Now she saw that Alicia almost revered that sort of thing and for the first time she thought it possible to win her sister's friendship. Beautiful, cool, and aloof, Alicia had been a mystery to her for years. How wonderful if now they could begin to be close!

"Can you tell me why it is you squint your eyes like that, Sybil?"

She rubbed her eyes self-consciously. She had not realized she was squinting.

"I think they must be tired," she said apologetically. "I stayed up quite late last night sewing a layette for the Needlework Guild. They do marvelous work, Alicia. So many poor families would have nothing for their babies when they come."

Alicia's lips formed a disapproving line.

"You'll have to give up your sewing for awhile. And you must do something about that eager way of talking. It's best to be aloof. Men find that intriguing."

She readily accepted this advice and was not even hurt

10

by the criticism. It was flattering to be noticed at all by her sister.

Alicia began to plan Sybil's entire social life. She was taken on calls, introduced to numerous people and treated to concerts and ballets always in the company of Alicia or Alicia and Monty and, sometimes, her father. There was hardly any time at all to see Ronald. She didn't mind at first. Everything was so exciting and everyone seemed to be very pleased with her.

"You've blossomed into a beautiful young woman," her father told her. "Your mother would have been so proud of you."

She glowed with these rare words of praise. She knew her father loved her, but he so seldom actually said anything. Now she wanted to go on doing exactly what was expected of her if it would bring her the admiration and affection of her family.

It wasn't until they were making up the guest list for her coming out ball that she began to think that Alicia's desires were not necessarily her own.

"Who is Ronald Baldwin? Not Olivia Baldwin's grandson! It hardly seems worthwhile including him." Alicia gazed questioningly at her sister.

Ordinarily Sybil would have followed Alicia's lead and agreed at once just to please her. She was still, after all, a little in awe of her older sister and uncertain about her own judgment. But they were talking about Ronald.

"He is my dearest friend. I'm very fond of him. I wouldn't feel right if he were not at my ball."

There was a moment's pause while Alicia took in this unexpected resistance. She seemed to be weighing the wisdom of challenging it. Then she shrugged and gave in. The strength of Sybil's loyalty must have been obvious.

"Very well. If you like. But remember this, Sybil. In choosing a husband one looks for a man, not a boy. Ronald Baldwin is a boy."

Sybil was annoyed. Did Alicia intend to dictate her choice in husbands along with everything else? Besides, she didn't even know Ronald. How could she presume to

11

judge him? When it came to husbands, Sybil intended to select her own.

And then without knowing it, she fell in love with the very man Alicia would have selected herself.

Edward Ashford had been living at Coply Corners for only three months when he approached Montgomery Ransome with an investment idea that sounded highly intriguing. Born and raised as the member of an old, distinguished family, Monty never had to worry about money until he married Alicia. Monty's dark good looks, polished manners, and respected family name were not enough for his wife. She had expensive tastes and he was hard pressed to satisfy them. He knew next to nothing about business and when he did dabble in the market he chose the worst possible time which ended disastrously in the crash. He'd been particularly cautious ever since. But half a year later he met Edward at his club and was terribly impressed. Edward was visiting Colonel Havermeyer and looking about for congenial business partners, he said. He was in mining and seemed to have an unlimited supply of money when money everywhere was scarce. Colonel Havermeyer seemed awfully fond of him. Edward had served under him in France in 1917. What mattered was the Colonel vouched for him, trusted him. Monty invited Edward to dinner and Alicia found him acceptable. She saw to it he received an invitation to her sister's ball.

Sybil didn't even remember dancing with him. She'd had so many partners. They'd all been terribly flattering. Her debut was a greater success than anyone dreamed. In the days that followed, a confusing number of invitations began to arrive. She seemed to have captured the interest of Jason Skinner and Aaron Rutherford.

"What plums!" Alicia said. "Everyone's talking about you, Sybil. I thought it would be like this. You have only to make the right choice."

She looked pleased and proud, as though she had created Sybil in her own image and was congratulating herself on a job well done. She took every opportunity to discuss possibilities. These discussions depressed the

12

younger woman. She thought both men Alicia called "plums" were conceited prigs. She was surprised they had even condescended to notice her. What she really wanted was to fall in love. Once she thought she loved Ronald. She certainly was fond of him, but that wasn't being in love. Where was the man she could be in love with?

And then on a cool autumn day when the air was so clear the world seemed to glow with deep jewel colors, she met Edward. Ruby and amber leaves of tall trees were outlined sharply against an amethyst sky as she rode through the Pennsylvania woods toward the river. She thought she was alone and hadn't bothered about her appearance. When a tree branch knocked off her hat, she let it go. She'd find it on the way back. She reached up and unpinned her dark hair which she now wore in a neat roll at the nape of her neck like Alicia. She set her hair free and let the wind play with it as she used to when she was younger, before she had become aware of her many social responsibilities. She must have been riding for nearly an hour when she heard a horseman behind her. He was keeping pace with her as if he were following her. It occurred to her that it was Ronald, who might have come home early for the weekend. She seldom saw anyone else on these rough paths through the woods. Most riders stuck to the bridle paths behind the estates, but she liked the privacy and the feeling of untouched nature. She decided to tease Ronald a bit and urged her horse swiftly forward toward Sommers' Point. He'd never keep up with her. He'd told her often enough that she rode recklessly and begged her to be more cautious. Ronald seldom took chances himself. When she reached her goal and realized her pursuer was still with her, she was amazed. What had come over Ronald? She dismounted in the clearing above the river and turned to face him, laughing and breathless. She felt her cheeks glowing with the exercise and fresh air.

Instead of Ronald she found she was face to face with a stranger. He, too, had dismounted and walked to meet her, his hat in his hand. He was tall, over six feet. He had

13

dark heavy eyebrows above equally dark almost black eyes that gazed at her with frank admiration.

"Surely you are the goddess, Diana, not Sybil Eldridge at all. No mere mortal can ride like that."

She smiled with pleasure at the compliment and found she could not take her eyes from his. Was she staring? Had they met before? She thought she would have remembered those disturbing eyes. His features were too heavy to be thought handsome, but this was an attractive man who had something more than smooth, regular features. There was the excitement of strength and dominance.

He told her frankly that he'd been following her.

"I called several times at your home, but you weren't in. This seemed the simplest solution. I had to see you again."

She was flattered but confused since she didn't remember him.

He smiled knowingly. He had full sensuous lips.

"You danced with me on the evening of your debut. I see you don't remember me and I must confess my pride is hurt."

She tried for a moment to recall, but it was no use. She reached up to smooth away the strands of hair that had blown across her face. She was embarrassingly aware of how disheveled she must look without her hat and with her hair loose.

"Oh, let it blow free, please," he said. "You have no idea how lovely you look just that way."

She felt herself blushing. Who was this man? He seemed to be a stranger and yet she had the feeling that she knew him, knew that he, like her, enjoyed and indulged in unconventional behavior at times. Alicia would never approve of this casual meeting.

"I'm sorry that I don't remember you," she said and meant it sincerely. "Won't you tell me your name?"

Edward Ashford! Edward Ashford!

She repeated it to herself again and again in the days to come. For Edward Ashford began to be a part of her life.

She invited him to tea that first day and to her surprise Alicia approved of him. Her father liked him, too. Edward knew something of genealogy and even knew of Woodrow Eldridge's work, a fact that amazed Sybil.

"I've come across several of your papers, sir, in the library," he said. "Your work is very much admired."

Edward was respectful and proper with her father, charmingly polite and flattering with Alicia, and friendly and indulgent with Monty, advising him carefully in business matters. With Sybil he was gentle and adoring.

He accompanied her to the opera at the Academy of Music one night not long afterwards. Alicia and Monty discreetly saw to it that they had the family box to themselves during intermission.

Edward took her hands and she looked into those dark, disturbing eyes. She was trembling with anticipation at what he might be about to say, for she already knew she was at last in love and had no clear idea of what she could do about it.

"I'm too old to play games," he told her. "I'm twenty-nine, but I feel much older. I've led a different sort of life from the men you've known. Forgive me for being impatient. I've fallen in love with you, Sybil. I think I've loved you from the moment I saw you in that golden gown at your ball. But the day we went riding, I knew. I want to marry you, if you'll have me."

If she would have him! If! How could there be any question?

She'd known him only a month and yet there did not seem a time she had not known him. He was part of her now. Everything she did, every experience was colored by what Edward would think when she shared her thoughts with him. They seemed to share everything and she could not imagine her life without him. He was attentive and solicitous. No day went by that he did not send her a little gift: flowers, candy, a silk scarf, books. She had read very little beyond the approved works for young ladies at Miss Alben's School. He introduced her to the world of Hemingway and Fitzgerald. He asked her advice on the deco-

15

rating of his new home at Coply Corners. He'd bought the estate at a fraction of its cost.

"I want to make it a showplace with you the very center jewel in the crown, my darling."

He'd never had a real home. His mother died like hers when he was young. He wandered from place to place with his father, who grew more and more affluent as his mining interests in Colorado increased. Edward had little formal education until his father sent him east to study. And then he'd only spent two years at college, dropping out because he felt he didn't belong among the cultured scions of old, established families.

"I want to establish a family of my own. I've been lonely, Sybil. I can't tell you how lonely."

She thought she knew and her tenderness for him grew. Behind the façade of confident strength lay the boy who had been hurt and rejected. She would make it all up to him.

Whenever he was near she felt a quickening of all her senses. His touch thrilled her and she made excuses to stand close to him. The warmth and excitement that emanated from his body intoxicated her. When he took her in his arms and kissed her that night after the opera she trembled with a passion she had not realized existed in her. For the first time she knew what it meant to desire someone.

They were married almost a year to the day after they met. She thought her father was pleased and happy for her, but he came into her room before the ceremony looking so grave she thought she should be having misgivings herself.

"You are really going to be happy then," he said, putting his hands on her shoulders and looking deeply into the blue eyes that so closely matched his own.

"But of course, Papa. I love Edward very much."

She was surprised to see how frail he looked. His white hair looked thinner and his cheeks had an odd pallor. But he smiled then and his face came alive again.

"That's all that matters," he said, kissing her tenderly.

16

"I'll miss my sweet, loving companion. Forgive your old father his weakness."

Her wedding was like a fairy tale come true. The reception was held in the Eldridge ballroom. The women wore velvet gowns of blue and red and emerald green. In the background were the discreet strains of Mozart and Handel. There were the men in their cutaways and Edward, more attractive and exciting than any of them. It did not seem possible that the joyful bride and groom would not live happily ever after.

It all ended so differently. She'd had to run from Edward, from all of them for her own sake and for Ned's.

She awoke in the small dark room. The air was stifling. At first she did not know where she was. Gradually the crib beside her began to take shape. Ned was sleeping peacefully. She could hear his soft breathing. They were safe in their New York apartment and Edward was far away.

Then what had awakened her? Something outside? Some noise in the alley below the third-floor window? Hadn't the Lindbergh baby been stolen from a second-floor bedroom? But the noise was closer, in one of the other rooms perhaps. She sat up, straining to hear. No, it had not stopped. She slid from the bed and tiptoed barefoot to the bedroom door. Some light from the street made its way past the scarred, crooked shades on the living room windows. She was able to make out the furniture, or at least the humpbacked mounds she knew were the chairs and sofa. The lamps poked their heads out of the round-shouldered tables like nosy people and Sybil, mouth dry and heart pounding, switched one of them on and sighed with relief to see the now familiar objects. There was no threat here, but the tapping persisted.

It was not coming from the door, as she had first suspected, but the kitchen. The kitchen! The thought that came to mind made her sick with revulsion. What if there were rats or mice? Afraid to know for certain and yet unable to go back to bed without knowing, she walked to

17

the kitchen door, reached inside, and snapped on the overhead light. At once the room came to life. The cupboards were neatly closed and the tubs, drainboard and table were shining clean and as empty as she had left them.

With maddening precision the tapping continued, loudly and unabashed. Ned's diapers, which she had not the strength to wring out thoroughly, were dripping their excess water into the tubs.

She sank down onto one of the chairs and stared in disbelief. Why hadn't she thought of the diapers? She had let the demon of fear possess her. She'd come this far. She mustn't give up now.

Once again she got into bed. It was going to be all right. She'd been in New York only four days and she'd found a comfortable place to stay with a gruff, but surprisingly sympathetic superintendent. And she had made a friend.

Yesterday the superintendent, Mrs. Ina Philips, led Sybil up the steep stairway to the third floor. An assortment of odors hung in the air: cabbage, freshly baked bread, burnt coffee, and the strong pungent smell of disinfectant. The stairs were clean and she saw no sign of dust in the cracks. She decided the building was reasonably well-kept. By the time they reached the top, she had made up her mind.

"Thirty-five dollars a month furnished, linens, dishes, heat, and hot water," the superintendent told her in a bored, flat tone. Only her eyes were alert and curious. "This one has its own john. We got another one empty on the floor below, but you gotta share the hall facilities with the other families. That's why this one's five dollars extra. We don't mind kids here. Not every place will take 'em," she added, looking her prospective tenant over carefully, trying to size her up.

Sybil had explained about Ned, her three-month old son. She said she was a widow and gave no further information. Under Mrs. Philips's shrewd gaze, she was

18

acutely aware of her mink-trimmed coat and hat. They didn't fit the part she meant to play.

She looked around at the over-stuffed chairs, the paint chipped white walls, and the scarred wooden table in the kitchen. In the bedroom was a double bed which seemed to take up nearly all the floor space. Somehow a four-drawer dresser was squeezed in beside a narrow window that looked out onto an alley below and the stone wall of another building beyond that. On the other side of the bed there would be just enough room for a crib. With a little imagination and a good deal of courage something could be done with the place.

"I'll take it, Mrs. Philips. When may I move in?"

The superintendent shrugged. She was fiftyish and plump. Her dyed red hair was in curlers, though it was the middle of the afternoon.

"Today if you want. That'll be two months in advance," she said firmly, almost as if she expected an argument.

"Of course."

Sybil handed over the seventy dollars, pausing only long enough to wait for a receipt before leaving to find the furniture store to buy a crib for Ned. She walked along the narrow streets and came upon a place that bought and sold clothing. She paused to look inside and caught a glimpse of her own reflection in the window. She saw what Mrs. Philips had seen, a young woman of nineteen with dark hair and deep blue eyes whose broadtail mink-trimmed coat and hat immediately betrayed her background.

She hardly stopped to think beyond the fact that she must change her appearance at once and entered the shop. The coat brought $75, hardly a fraction of its value, but she came away with a forest green cloth coat which, though not particularly stylish, was warm and inconspicuous. With the money she was able to buy Ned a new crib and still had cash left over to add to her rapidly dwindling supply.

She spent the entire first day in her apartment working

to make it livable. She carried Ned with her to a local store and bought disinfectants and cleaning utensils of every description. It was necessary to make two trips to carry them all. On her second trip, Mrs. Philips called to her from the open door of her apartment on the first floor. Sybil felt the woman had been waiting for an opportunity to talk.

"Mornin', Mrs. Anderson. That your baby?"

Anderson was the name she'd decided to use. She wanted desperately to put down her heavy package, or Ned, or both, but she walked over to chat. Mrs. Philips had not yet changed from her nightgown and wore a faded blue wrapper over it. The curlers had been removed from her hair and tiny, springy curls covered her head.

"Yes, this is Ned."

Lulled by the motion of the walk to the store, he had fallen asleep against her shoulder. Now he stirred restlessly. At any minute he would begin to cry. It was time for his bottle.

The older woman reached out her arms. "Could I hold him?"

Sybil didn't see why not. Her arms were aching. Mrs. Philips held Ned with almost professional care. He opened his eyes sleepily and seemed to smile up at her. There was more of Edward in him than there was of her. His eyes had gone from blue to brown and his red-gold hair would probably darken. Still, he was her son, too, and she thought she saw something of herself in his face, the shape of the mouth and the hint of a dimple in his left cheek.

"They're cute when they're small," Mrs. Philips said. "I have a daughter, though you'd never know it. She never bothers with me. Never even calls me up to see if I'm dead or alive. The only pleasure she ever gave me was when she was a baby. That's when she needed me. Hope yours turns out better than mine."

She was about to give Ned back when she noticed Sybil's bundle.

"Let me carry him upstairs for you. You went to the

20

store and you don't have no carriage or nothin'?" A shade of suspicion crept into her voice.

"Some of my things haven't come yet." Sybil invented the explanation quickly. She would need a carriage, but the idea of spending any more money right now frightened her. What little she had would have to last until she found work.

Mrs. Philips said nothing until they had climbed the two flights of stairs.

"There's a carriage down the basement. Somebody must have left it here a long time ago. Wanna use it until your stuff comes?"

The offer was so welcome that it nearly brought tears to her eyes.

"Why, that would be wonderful, if you're sure it's all right."

"Oh, yeah. It's just down there gathering dust. I'll get it for you this afternoon and clean it up a bit. You can keep it behind the stairs. No one will touch it there."

When Sybil set her bundle down on the kitchen table, her arms were free to take Ned again. Mrs. Philips seemed reluctant to give him up.

"There's nothin' like the warm, sweet feel of a baby. You know, I'd be glad to take care of him for you sometimes. Wouldn't cost you much if you wanted to leave him with me for a whole day. Fifty cents a day is all I'd charge you. I mean, if there was some place you wanted to go or something," she finished hopefully.

It occurred to Sybil that the other woman might welcome the money. Perhaps she'd been thinking about this since yesterday when she'd heard about Ned.

Sybil knew someone would have to care for Ned once she started working. The offer seemed almost providential. Of course, she'd have to make sure the woman was reliable first. She must be careful not to commit herself.

"I'll remember that."

The superintendent nodded. "Just let me know when you need me. The truth is they don't pay me hardly any-

21

thing for this job. You get a roof over your head and that's something, but not much in the way of cash. So I try to pick up a few dollars here and there. They say things'll get better. I'm counting on this Roosevelt. He can pull us out of this here Depression if anyone can. If he gets elected this November, well, come next year we should see better times in 1933. They can't be any worse and that's for sure."

Sybil was surprised to hear Franklin Roosevelt spoken of in such admiring tones. In Philadelphia society his possible election was considered an economic disaster and his party platform synonymous with Socialism.

Ned began to whimper then and Mrs. Philips returned him to his mother. Still, she did not go, but gazed at Sybil thoughtfully.

"You know, people say that New York City is a hard, cold place. Don't you believe it. People here have as much heart as anywhere else. You're going to be all right," she said and gave her a reassuring look.

Sybil's heart leapt with gratitude at this kindness, but she was disconcerted, too. It was almost as if Mrs. Philips knew. But she couldn't really know. That Sybil was alone and rather frightened was probably obvious. But no one could possibly guess the whole truth.

After a lunch of soup and toast she washed everything: floors, shelves, and dishes. When she pushed aside the heavy floral-printed drapes in the living room to get at the windows, she was horrified by the shower of dust that fell on her and the grimy feel of the cloth. She took them down and decided to replace them with something light and easily washable.

By evening she was exhausted; her hands burned terribly from the unaccustomed cleaning fluids, but she was satisfied the place was clean. She made a simple meal for herself of rice and browned butter, a memory from her early childhood when her governess would make this for her on Sunday evenings. She bathed Ned in the bathroom sink and put him to bed in the new, brightly painted yellow crib. It was the one cheerful spot of color in the bed-

22

room. There were no curtains on the window and a white chenille throw covered the bed.

She did not mind the stark bedroom as much as the garish colors in the living room. The sofa and two chairs were covered in varying shades of yellow, green, and orange. There were two square end tables, two lamps with gold fringed shades, and a rectangular coffee table of indeterminate dark wood. On the floor was a faded green carpet.

She made herself some coffee and sank onto the lumpy, but soft, cushions of the sofa. She kicked off her shoes and lifted her feet onto the coffee table.

What luxury! Her back was stiff and her arm and leg muscles ached terribly. She closed her eyes and let her mind drift. She was too tired to think of anything, not Edward, or her sister, Alicia, or even her poor father who lay so still in his darkened room, attended by quiet, efficient nurses.

She might have slept if it had not been for the sudden intrusion of loud angry voices. Instantly her eyes flew open and she was terrified. She imagined that Edward and Alicia were there, right in the apartment. Having discovered her, they were berating her bitterly. Startled, she looked about the empty living room feeling slightly disoriented. Her heart pounded furiously and she felt badly shaken.

Somewhere a man and woman were shouting at one another. Where? Upstairs? Next door? A door slammed and there was the sound of running in the hall and then silence. She hurried into the bedroom to see if the noise had disturbed Ned, but he was sleeping peacefully on his tummy, a small fist holding a blue rattle, the one toy she had managed to take with her.

She tiptoed from the room and stood motionless before the door to the hallway. She heard nothing, but she had to be sure no one was there. Surely even Edward could not have gone into action so quickly. She had no doubt her husband would hire people to look for her. But first he would have to realize she was missing. At the moment

23

he should still think she was visiting friends in Washington. She thought this would give her at least a week. Still, she had to make sure there was no one watching outside her door or she would imagine all kinds of things.

Slowly, her hands trembling, she undid the chain lock and opened her door. She found she was nearly face to face with a girl about her own age or perhaps a little older who was peeking out from the open door across the hall. The girl had platinum blonde hair and blue-gray eyes fringed with lashes darkened by thick mascara. When she saw Sybil, she, too, was at first surprised and then she laughed heartily, throwing her door open wide.

"Nobody's dead or dying," she said in a high, almost childish voice. "One of these days though—" She paused and rolled her eyes dramatically. "They're crazy Hungarians, the Saxons. Fight and make up. Fight and make up. It's all they do. You'll get used to it, just like me. I'm Marlene Grant," she said, striding across the hall and holding out her hand. "We're neighbors."

The relief Sybil felt at finding there was nothing to fear was doubled by the friendly overture of this girl. She smiled with genuine pleasure as she took Marlene's hand.

"I'm very pleased to meet you. I'm Sybil Anderson."

"And you moved in this morning. You've got a three or four month old kid, you're a lady and you're crazy clean."

Sybil was amazed by this astonishing fund of information. Did everyone in the building know about her? Marlene had a good laugh and shook her head. Her lips were very red and a similar color tipped her nails. She was small, shorter than Sybil's 5 feet 6 inches, and she had an excellent figure.

"The Phantom knows all," she said, dropping her voice mysteriously.

"The Phantom?" Sybil had no idea what the girl meant. She liked her instinctively. Marlene was friendly and pretty in a rather flamboyant way. She was wearing a sleek costume of red satin slacks and a flowing blouse of the same material.

"Philips, the Phantom. Sees all. Knows all. Tells everything. Don't confide any secrets unless you want the world to know your business."

"Oh!" She felt suddenly very young and inexperienced.

"No kidding? You have a baby?" Marlene asked, smiling disarmingly. "I love babies, all babies, as long as they're not yelling and as long as they're not mine."

"Ned's a good baby. He hardly cries at all. Would you like to see him?" she offered hopefully. How comforting it would be to have such cheerful company!

"Love it!" Marlene turned to pull the door of her apartment shut behind her. In three strides she walked into Sybil's living room. "Hey," she said and whistled softly. "You really are crazy clean. This place hasn't looked this good in a century. Going to have the curtains cleaned? Good idea. Mother Hubbard never touched them, nor the windows. Mrs. Hubbard was the last tenant. A widow, with plenty of time on her hands and nothing to do. She went through every cent of her husband's insurance money and then, when there was nothing left, she went to live with her married daughter. Good luck to both of them. The daughter's stingy and the mother's a spendthrift."

Marlene paused and looked expectantly at Sybil.

"Oh, Ned's in here," Sybil said. She'd become so fascinated by what her neighbor was saying, she'd almost forgotten. She led Marlene into the bedroom. The light from the living room touched Ned's red-gold hair and he stirred and sighed softly in his sleep.

"Precious," Marlene whispered and won Sybil's heart.

"Would you like some coffee? It's just made."

"Love it." The girl settled herself comfortably in the living room.

In the kitchen Sybil found the only other cup without a crack in it. She wished she had something else to offer. There was only the coffee. Her guest didn't seem to mind and she took it black.

"Saves money all around," she said. "If I were you, I'd get rid of those drapes altogether."

25

"I plan to. Only I don't quite know how. Do I just return them to Mrs. Philips?"

Marlene nodded. "I would. But then you'll need something on the windows. Macy's would be your best bet. They have everything."

"Do they? I'll go tomorrow."

If she had tried, she couldn't have described the effect Marlene was having on her. For the first time in days the knot of fear deep within her had diminished. She began to feel more hopeful. Here was someone else who had presumably made it alone in the city. She would have given worlds to know how Marlene had done it, but she was too polite to ask.

The other girl seemed to read her mind.

"You know, I've been living here two years and you're the first person who didn't start right in and ask me a million questions. You know. 'Where are you from? Are you married? Why not? Where do you work?' The whole thing."

"I suppose that's because I don't like questions myself." Sybil smiled shyly. "But I am curious," she admitted.

Marlene gave a good-natured laugh. "We got something in common then. But I don't mind telling you. It's no secret. It's just I don't like folks prying. I've been on my own since I was fifteen. My stepfather threw me out of the house. Too many mouths to feed when his own kids started to come." She shrugged philosophically. "I couldn't stand him anyway. I was big for my age and able to pass for older, so I got a job and a place to stay. I've been my own boss for years and I like it."

She paused to sip her coffee. "Now you don't have to tell me a thing at all that you don't want to. It's not like I need to know a person's pedigree. If I like them, I like them and that's all I need to know. You take you and me. We could get to be really good friends and I don't need to know who your husband was, or why you're here, or any of that. We could really get to be good friends without that. Do you have any cigarettes, honey?" Marlene asked,

26

drumming her long, red-tipped fingers nervously on the coffee table. She seemed to be constantly in motion.

Sybil was apologetic. "I'm awfully sorry. I don't smoke."

"Never mind," Marlene said, sitting back and folding her arms. "It's O.K. I smoke too much anyway. And you shouldn't start. You get dependent on them, if you know what I mean." She swallowed the rest of her coffee and got up. "Here I am chattering on and on and you must be dead. Tell you what. Tomorrow's Saturday. I only work half day. If you like, I'll help you buy the drapes and then we'll put them up together. It'll be fun. And we'll have lunch, too, a kind of picnic, right here around one o'clock before we go. It'll sort of be my welcome to you to the neighborhood. I mean, I don't bake or cook or anything, so I can't bring you a pie. What do you say?"

She was overwhelmed by the offer. Marlene was presenting her with untold riches, friendship, food, advice, and the benefit of her experience. It was almost too much.

It was thoughts of Marlene and the soft rhythm of Ned's even breathing that finally lulled her to sleep once more.

When Ned awoke the next morning and began to cry in earnest, she was up and ready for him. Sun poured through the living room windows and she began to feel cheerful and not half as tired as she expected.

In the afternoon Marlene took her to Macy's.

"We'll take turns carrying the baby," she said. "No sense paying the Phantom to take care of him when we can do it ourselves. She's reliable, in case you were wondering. She takes care of other children in the building. Believe it or not, the kids are crazy about her."

They took a subway, something she had been too frightened to do alone. But Marlene rode the trains easily, leading the way up and down dark, dank stairways and through sliding doors that opened and shut automatically with no care for the safety of slow, unsuspecting passengers who were likely to be crushed, snapped at, or simply left behind. The cars rocketed through the black tunnels screaming the advent of their approach. Through it all,

27

Ned slept and they arrived at last at Macy's department store.

Of all the colorful drapes from which she might choose, she selected the palest, sheerest, gold, in a most simple design.

"That's what you want?" Marlene asked.

She nodded.

"I want to be able to let in as much light as possible and I'd like to use the very palest touch of color."

"Honest? You're sure? I mean you could have one of these prints. Or, how about some of those with ruffles?"

Marlene shifted Ned to her other hip while Sybil fingered the silk gauze. It was light and soft and she thought easily washable.

"No, this is perfect! It's what I was looking for."

"Well, we'd be crazy to buy them here then, if that's what you want."

"But why?"

"Because anyone can make something as simple as this for a fraction of the cost."

"Make them?" She hadn't thought of making the curtains, but the idea appealed to her. Only it seemed a rather large project. She'd only worked on small, delicate pieces before.

"Sure we can make them. I'll help. Believe me it'll be worth the effort. Look at the price on these."

"Oh, my! Nine dollars a pair. I didn't realize—" she began. Of course they were far too expensive. She couldn't possibly afford them. That was over half a month's rent for two windows.

"Come on. Chin up. You'll have your drapes and not half as skimpy as these. They say they'll fit a standard window. Ha! Just about. Follow me."

Sybil took Ned, who had begun to whimper. She thought he was too warm in the store. She had bundled him up against the raw autumn weather, but the artificial heat in the store was something she didn't think to provide for. She opened his yellow blanket and unbuttoned his sweater.

For less than five dollars they were able to buy more than enough of what they would need of the pale gold silk gauze. Marlene seemed to know exactly what she was doing, giving out the information about yardage to the saleswoman and buying matching thread.

When they got home, Ned was crying steadily. Sybil made him comfortable, fed him, and put him down in his crib, while Marlene unfolded the material on the living room floor. She brought shears, pins, and a measuring tape from her own apartment. She was expert at what she was doing.

"I haven't worked at the House of Arnaud for two years for nothing," she said proudly. "I keep my eyes open and I learn a lot."

The House of Arnaud, she explained, was an exclusive custom dress house which catered to the very rich, and Marlene was a seamstress there. She made nineteen dollars a week and spent every cent she made, mostly on clothes and makeup and "good times".

"I love the movies. I go every week. Sometimes twice a week, especially when I have a date like tonight. I met him at a dance hall uptown. Joey's a great dancer. Maybe we'll go dancing after the movie tonight," she told Sybil and smiled and hummed to herself as she began basting pleats in place.

They worked right through the dinner hour, pausing only long enough to care for the baby. Marlene came into the bathroom and sat on the edge of the tub basting while Sybil bathed Ned in the sink.

Ned loved his bath and played happily in the confined space, splashing and talking his own language. Sybil played and laughed with him.

"You're a good mother," Marlene said after watching them together.

"I want to be." She wrapped Ned in a towel and carried him into the bedroom where she began powdering and diapering him. Ned was her life. She meant to make his world for him. He was the one thing that was totally and completely hers.

"I wouldn't have the patience myself," Marlene told her. "Don't get me wrong. I think babies are adorable. But I had all I want of them for a lifetime. Being the oldest in a family of seven did that to me. Handling the diapers and the vomit and the crying in the night— That's not for me. Never again."

She was amazed. She thought there was nothing more wonderful than this tiny miracle to which she had given life.

"But someday you'll want to marry and then—" she began.

Marlene bent to bite off the end of the thread and then shook her head.

"Oho! Not me! You won't catch me being a slave for some fancy fellow. What for? I can have all the good times I want without that. As long as there are guys with money willing to spend it on me, I'm going to steer clear of that kind of life. Like I told you, I'm my own boss and I like it that way. And kids? Well, they're cute when they're babies, but once they start developing minds of their own, watch out! In the end they're all ungrateful little bastards. Oh, say! Look at the time!" she exclaimed, glancing at her watch. "Joey will be here in an hour."

She held up the panel on which she'd been working and examined her seams with a practiced eye.

"Not bad for all handwork," she said. "It would go faster if we had a machine, but this will be better in the end. And you do nice work, too."

"Well, I enjoy it," she admitted. Her work was every bit as fine as Marlene's.

"I'm going to run now, honey. But I'll help you tomorrow. The other panels are just like these and fit right onto the rods you already have. Didn't I tell you it would be easy?"

The finished pleated panel looked beautiful. They had stretched it smoothly over two chairs and Sybil stepped back to admire it.

"The seams still have to be pressed. Look, that's what you can do," Marlene said. "Press out the seams and try

30

the one panel. It'll keep you out of trouble while I'm gone. Don't move a muscle." She was gone and back within seconds carrying a clumsy ironing board and an iron.

"You can set this up right here. Just be sure you don't make the iron too hot. Test it first on a corner of the material. O.K.?"

"Have a good time," Sybil said almost wistfully. It wasn't that she herself wanted to go out, but she had gotten pleasantly used to her new friend's company.

"Thanks, Hon. I always do." Marlene blew her a kiss as she left.

Without her the living room seemed suddenly empty and lonely. Sybil decided she could not simply sit and brood. Funny, until now she hadn't really thought about being lonely. Perhaps there had not been time. She'd had so many other things to think about. And there was still the problem of a job. She had to have a job. Starting Monday she'd have to begin looking. But what would she be looking for? And how would she begin to talk to people she really didn't know? How could she ask these total strangers to give her work, to pay her for doing something she could not define? She felt the panic she had been so careful to control begin to rise. Horrified, she decided she must fight it. She'd do what Marlene suggested, press the seams of the completed panel. The ironing board was big and heavy, but she managed to set it up. She arranged the sheer panel over the board and began with the corner of the upper pleating.

It had taken them roughly five hours to complete the panel. It took her only seconds to ruin it. She stared in disbelief as she lifted the iron and saw the square of burned material clinging to it. The sharp scorched odor of cloth reached her nostrils and brought tears of despair to her eyes. What had she done?

She cried out and set the iron on its heel. How could she have let this happen? Hadn't Marlene warned her? All their hard work destroyed!

She sank down onto the sofa and wept. She had not

31

wept once since coming to the city. She'd faced every challenge stoically. Now she gave herself totally to despair over something relatively unimportant.

She did not know how long she sat, sobbing uncontrollably, but gradually her sobs lessened and she wiped her eyes and blew her nose. Crying never helped matters. You'd think she of all people would have learned that. She got up and went to the ironing board to examine the ruined panel. It was the upper right-hand corner that was destroyed, a patch about the size of a three inch square had been burned out. She glanced at the other three floor-length panels Marlene had cut out and pinned. There was still material left over. She looked from the panels to the windows and then back again. The rods were metal spears held in place by two metal rosettes. An idea began to form in her mind. Yes, she could imagine just how it would look. Using wrapping paper and the stub of a pencil she sketched her idea. The finished product would look graceful and elegant. From the leftover material she could cut an elongated triangle. It would be draped over the top of the rod, its folds fastened over the metal rosettes. It would give a finished look to the top of the panels and hide the damage.

She measured and cut carefully. It had become very important to her, almost symbolic, that she succeed in this. She'd made a foolish mistake, but everything was not lost.

It was after midnight when she finished hemming the valance. Her eyes burned badly from the poor light and the close work, but she was satisfied that she had done a good job. There was still the pressing. This time she was more cautious. She used a diaper between the precious curtain and the uncertain heat of the iron. And when, after a slight struggle with the rod, she managed to put up the panel and drape the valance, she caught her breath in wonder at the beauty of her handiwork. The sheer gold material seemed to light up the room. The window, covered by an old, sun-faded shade, was partially hidden.

During the day, she'd roll the shade all the way up until it disappeared. The draped valance fell perfectly and she thought the appearance of the room was improved immeasurably. She sat down on the sofa and simply stared in admiration. She'd done it! Perhaps she had not done it all alone, but a good deal of the work was hers and the design of the valance meant everything. She felt accomplished and tremendously fulfilled.

This must be the way an artist feels, after facing an empty canvas and creating something entirely his own. She felt heady with success. Sheer exhaustion kept her from beginning work on the next two panels. That would have to wait until morning. Wouldn't Marlene be surprised, though? Nothing kept her awake that night. In nearly twelve hours she hadn't given Edward a thought.

Marlene arrived at her door sometime after noon with a coffee cake, still warm from the bakery, and wearing her red satin slacks. The vestiges of last night's make-up, which she had neglected to remove, clung to her eyes and lips and her blonde hair was wound up in a black turban. She looked like something out of the Arabian Nights and she said she felt rotten. There was the sweet, stale aroma of gin about her and she said her head was splitting. But when she saw the drape, she seemed to forget everything else.

"I don't believe it! I absolutely cannot believe it! Why it looks like a movie set. It's gorgeous! Whatever made you think of it? I think you've got hidden talents."

Sybil was almost as pleased now as she had been in the first realization of her success.

Marlene eyed her thoughtfully.

"Look, honey," she said at last, "this may not be any of my business and you can just say so if it's not, but do you need a job? I mean, were you figuring on getting a job? If I'm prying, just tell me to shut up and I will, I really will. Oh, this head!" She took a long sip of the hot black liquid in her cup, but went on watching Sybil's face, though wincing dramatically. "Will I be glad when those clods in Washington do something about this prohibition! Bathtub gin is going to kill me yet," she muttered half to herself. "Honestly, honey, I don't mean to be nosy, but if you do need a job, maybe I can help."

"I need a job. I need one badly, Marlene."

Marlene's gaze did not waver. "O.K. Then you're gonna get a job and, believe me, that's hard these days. But you can do what I do and from the looks of things," she added, nodding toward the drapes, "you can do it better."

They both looked admiringly at the sheer folds of gold that draped the window.

"How—how would I go about getting a job like yours?" Sybil asked, hardly daring to believe she'd be so lucky. She had visions of herself standing in long employment lines like those she'd seen in the newsreels. She'd thought it would take weeks to find a suitable position, if she could find one at all. She'd thought she could look into art. She'd always been artistic. Perhaps she could find a place with a newspaper or a magazine. She confided this now, a bit shyly.

"Oh, honey!" Marlene shook her head. "Unless you know somebody—" she began.

"I don't!"

"Then forget it. Those places are turning people out. And then there are the unions. You gotta pay to get in them."

She thought of her dwindling supply of cash and shook her head. Marlene probably knew what she was talking about.

"Well, what do you think I should do?"

"Can you wait a couple of weeks?"

She hesitated. Only this morning she'd counted what was left of her cash, sixty-nine dollars and twenty-two cents. That was all there was between her and disaster. The rent was paid for two months. It was just a matter of being careful.

"Yes," she said slowly.

34

"Well, then, there just might be something at Arnaud's. It's a custom house so we don't bother with unions. And I think I know where there might be an opening." She nodded. "Yes, I think I do."

II

Gradually she became accustomed to her new surroundings. She slept all through the nights without being awakened by some unfamiliar sound. In two and a half weeks Edward had not found her and she allowed herself cautious relief. Still, she was suspicious of strangers, especially men, she saw in the street. Several times she thought she and Ned were being followed when they went out to the store. Nothing ever came of these incidents and she set them down to her lingering fear. She thought she was reasonably safe. It would be hard to recognize Sybil Eldridge Ashford now.

It was a very different looking Sybil she saw reflected in her mirror these days. Shorter hair and bangs had changed her appearance and were much more stylish, according to Marlene.

"You look just like Claudette Colbert. I'd give anything for that natural wave of yours."

She was pleased with the change herself, but she knew her father would never have approved. He was terribly conservative. "Bobbed" hair and loose women would have been coupled in his mind.

Poor Papa! How she wished she could see him even if he didn't know her! The doctor said there was no hope of recovery, none at all, but her father might linger for months, perhaps years. Or, he could die suddenly and she'd never know. The hardest thing of all was accepting that. She tried to think of him as he had been when he was well and happy, happy for her and his grandson, too, before she'd tried to tell him the truth. Her own guilt never left her. If she hadn't tried to tell him, would he be well today? It was something she'd have to learn to live with all her life.

The job Marlene spoke of came through three weeks later. Sybil was terribly nervous that first day. Marlene provided her with shears, needles, and a thimble.

"No girl comes in without her own. That way they can tell you worked before. If anyone asks, say you're from Chicago and worked for a private dressmaker. They never bother to check and if you do good work, they'll be satisfied. Just keep your eyes open, watch the others, and try to stay one step ahead. That way the draper can't complain about you."

The seamstresses at Arnaud's sat in groups of eight or nine at tables in a long, dismal room where the outside light somehow never quite penetrated the layers of grime on the bare windows. Naked electric bulbs glared down on them from overhead so no girl could use poor lighting as an excuse for poor stitching. Sybil felt completely exposed and was certain the draper and the fitter had eyes only for her. No one seemed to take much notice of her at all at first and the work was simple enough. She slipped easily into the daily routine.

But nothing could have prepared her for what working and caring for Ned at the same time would really be like. At five months he changed from a sweet, docile creature to a cranky terror. He began teething. Though Mrs. Philips did not complain about his daytime behavior, Sybil found the nights nearly impossible. He seemed to cry constantly and she never got a good night's sleep. After nearly three months of working at Arnaud's by day and walking the floor with Ned at night, she wondered if she'd be able to go on at all.

On top of everything else the fitter, Annette Levere, had taken a dislike to her for no apparent reason. She was constantly singling her out. Today Sybil seemed to be all thumbs. She leaned over to pick up the cushion of pins she'd dropped for the fourth time that morning. She straightened up quickly. That was a mistake. The whole room suddenly seemed to be on an angle. Lord, she felt weak. She had to make it come right. The room seemed to be turning around her. She bit her lip and dug her nails into the palms of her hands. Slowly the long tables settled back, the spinning stopped, and she drew a shaky sigh of relief.

"Is anything wrong, Sybil?"

She looked up cautiously at the sharp tone. Sudden movements caused dizziness, she knew. Annette Levere was standing over her, dark eyes searching for any sign of weakness or laziness. Girls were fired for taking a forbidden cigarette break in the bathroom. Relaxation or illness were not tolerated.

"No, Miss Levere, nothing is wrong," she said, forcing a confidence into her voice that she did not feel. After a moment the fitter moved on.

"Bitch!"

The word slipped softly from Marlene's lips, but lost none of its emotional impact. She sat opposite Sybil and her mere physical presence lent a support that the younger girl could never have done without.

"If you like, I'll finish for you," Marlene whispered. "What did you do? Come out without breakfast?"

"Just coffee." Neither girl had taken her eyes from her work. Their lips hardly moved as they spoke and they could not be heard two feet away above the whir of the sewing machines. "There wasn't time for anything else."

"You should make time," Marlene advised. "You're nothing but skin and bone. You can't afford to be sick."

"I know."

Marlene made a nearly imperceptible movement with her finger, signaling the approach of the fitter again. The girls fell silent. Sybil could feel Miss Levere staring at her, almost daring her to make the slightest error or display some sign of weakness. She did not lift her head from her work. The black velvet jacket she was lining with silk felt smooth and delicate to her roughened hands. Sometimes she thought she would damage the delicate material she worked on and she would be dismissed because of that. There was little she could do about the rough, chapped skin. Her hands, it seemed, were always in water. Ned's need for clean diapers was endless.

The sharp clanging of a bell brought an abrupt halt to all work.

"Come on. You need a change. Bring your lunch," Marlene said.

She looked at her friend in surprise.

"Where could we go?"

"You'll see. Just come."

She didn't know if she should go. They usually spent each lunch hour eating right there at the tables with the other girls, conserving their strength and leaving only long enough to go to the bathroom.

Well, perhaps she did need a change. It might clear her head and keep her from falling asleep. Oh, how she would like to sleep one night through till morning without waking to Ned's insistent cries.

She gathered up her things and followed Marlene to the back stairs. The girls were not allowed to use the front elevators reserved for customers. So it was the freight elevator or the stairs. Marlene preferred the stairs since one of the elevator operators had taken to pinching her. Marlene's well-rounded figure and the saucy, flirtatious look in her eye were a temptation to most men.

The girls stepped outside into the clear December sunshine. They walked three blocks at a brisk pace and entered an old stone building.

"Where are we?" Sybil asked.

"It's the hall of St. Vincent's church. They give out free coffee and soup every day. Joey told me about it last night. He heard about it at Mass on Sunday. Would you believe it? Joey's a Catholic!" She shook her head. "You could have knocked me over."

Marlene had confided that Joey really interested her. He had money to spend and connections, though she wasn't too clear about what sort of connections.

"I wouldn't mind hanging on to him for awhile. He's a good dancer and a real classy dresser, hundred dollar suits with velvet collars. Nothin' chintzy about Joey. He's willing to spend. Yeah, you can really have good times with Joey."

While Marlene chattered on, Sybil looked around her. There were long wooden tables and chairs set up through the hall, cafeteria style. The room was crowded mostly with men. But there was a table with women at the far end, half a block, it seemed, from the soup and coffee. Black-robed nuns and priests hovered about greeting everyone cheerfully.

Marlene laughed, suddenly suspending her narrative to take in the expression on her friend's face.

"Bet you never thought you'd find yourself in a place like this?"

Sybil smiled and relaxed for the first time that day.

"No, I guess I never did."

Marlene opened her lunch bag.

"This is ham and cheese. What have you got?"

"Leftover meat loaf."

"Mmm! I love your meat loaf. Swap you half," Marlene said, already making the exchange. "Variety's the spice of life, as they say. I'll get the soup and coffee."

"You know," Marlene said, lighting a cigarette when they were through, "Levere's jealous of you. I've come to that conclusion."

"Jealous? Of me? Why?" She was astonished. She saw Annette Levere as a threat to her, not the other way around.

"You caught Arnaud's eye, as they say, and anyone who catches Arnaud's eye is in for trouble with Levere."

"But that's impossible."

"Not really," Marlene said. "Look at it this way." She took a long languid drag on her cigarette the way she'd seen glamorous stars smoke in the movies. She had a number of little, affected mannerisms she'd picked up from movie stars she admired. She used a cigarette holder and constantly pushed at the waves of her smoothly marcelled hair. She pursed her cupid's bow mouth when she was thinking, making her lips look even fuller. Whenever she thought a man was looking she'd smooth the material of her tight fitting clothes over her breasts to her waist and then down over her hips in imitation of Jean Harlow.

"Everyone knows how Levere got promoted to fitter. She's no damn good. Can't even get a sleeve in right and she's a fitter! Ever ask yourself why? Easy. She hops into bed with Arnaud."

"Really?" Sybil wondered how Marlene could know such a thing.

Was it possible? She thought of the thin, wiry Monsieur Arnaud, who had built his business on a shrewd combination of old world charm and talent. He knew how to adapt the latest designs to his customers' tastes. Some of the richest women in the city were his clients coming back year after year to replenish their already full wardrobes. Monsieur Arnaud must be past seventy, nervous and ascetic. She never thought of him as a lover. Wasn't there a time when such activity would no longer interest a man?

"Not till they're dead, honey," Marlene said, shrewdly reading her thought. "Not till they're dead, and Arnaud is far from that."

"But how would he have noticed me?"

Marlene leaned forward.

"Remember that calico printed cotton, meant to be so casual for Mrs. Thorpe?"

She nodded.

"Who fitted the sleeves after La Thorpe made such a fuss last week?"

"I did."

"And who stood by anxiously watching and waiting?"

"Oh!"

She recalled that Monsieur Arnaud had made her extremely nervous by leaning against the wall, arms folded and frowning ferociously while she worked to baste the sleeves in place. She had volunteered to do this when Miss Levere, exploding into a temper tantrum, had locked herself in the bathroom and refused to come out.

41

"Levere wasn't so dumb. She knew she couldn't do the job, so she hid until it was all over. That gave Arnaud plenty of time to watch and admire you." Marlene nodded triumphantly. "I bet somebody told Levere. All she needs is an excuse to get rid of you. She might not even wait for an excuse, but make something up."

"Oh, Marlene, what can I do? I need this job."

"Of course you do," Marlene said promptly. "That's why if anything happens, you're going to have to appeal to Arnaud. I'm a pretty good judge of men and it's my opinion he's developed a case on you. All you have to do when Levere pulls her stunt is go to him. Mark my words, honey, it's Levere who'll get the gate, as they say, not you."

All afternoon her thoughts were a jumble. When M. Arnaud entered the sewing room, she was not aware of him until he touched her on the shoulder.

"You are the girl who fits sleeves so well, no?"

She started and cast Marlene a helpless glance which the other girl responded to with a quick wink.

"Yes, sir."

She was afraid to look at him, but finally raised her eyes to his face. His skin was thin and wrinkled like crumpled paper, but his eyes were bright and his gaze intense.

"Come with me, if you please."

It was not possible to refuse, but she wished she could. After what Marlene said, she was apprehensive. She followed M. Arnaud past the long tables, past the other girls who watched with ill-disguised curiosity, and finally past Miss Levere herself whose dark eyes glared venom. He led her out of the workrooms to his studio which was light and spacious, but littered with large sketches in various stages of completion on desks, on the floor, and on table tops. In one corner was a dressmaker's dummy. The bodice and skirt of a white satin gown had been fitted, but only one sleeve was in. He snatched up a sketch and pointed to it.

"Well, can you do it?"

His eyes roved her face and then her figure, taking in every curve.

"You want me to fit the sleeve?"

He nodded, stepped closer to her. They were almost touching. She had all she could do to keep from moving away.

"Yes, when they are prepared, you will fit the sleeves, no?"

His eyes glittered and he thrust his face close to hers. His colorless lips formed a smile.

"If you like," she said. Couldn't he have asked her this in the sewing room?

"Ah!" His smile revealed little white teeth. They seemed somehow too small.

He tossed aside the sketch and reached out thin hands suddenly to grasp her shoulders.

"The fabric will flow like so and like so. You understand, no?"

His hands caressed her upper arms as he demonstrated the line he meant to achieve. Was it only an accident that they also touched her breasts?

She stepped back slowly. She did not want to offend him.

"Yes, I understand."

"Ah! Bon! Bon!"

He was grinning, leering openly at her now. All she wanted was to move away, to go outside where the others were. She moved toward the door and he came with her, putting his arm possessively about her shoulders. He was no taller than she and almost fragile looking. She did not feel physically threatened, only demeaned and disgusted.

Just before he opened the door for her, he unexpectedly planted a dry kiss on her cheek and then turned her to face him.

"You are intelligent as well as beautiful. Until tomorrow, eh?"

She did not answer, but hurried along the dark corridors to the sewing room. She did not even want to think about tomorrow. How could she face him again? But how could she refuse? She needed this job.

43

When she returned Marlene raised her brows quizzically. Sybil shook her head. She couldn't talk here.

She worked feverishly all afternoon in an effort to complete her assigned tasks. By four-thirty she was exhausted. It was then Miss Levere decided to strike. Sybil was called away from her table to assist the fitter in the dressing room.

The woman being fitted had a stern face and was buxom. She was standing on a raised pedestal staring with distaste at the hemline of her new tweed walking suit. Sybil vaguely remembered lining the skirt with pale green taffeta.

"There it is! Just as I told you. It simply hangs irregularly in the back. I can't possibly take it this way."

This, Sybil knew, was the fault of the fitter who was now using her as a scapegoat.

Head bowed she knelt, holding pins between pursed lips as she worked directed by Miss Levere.

"If Madame will not find it too tiresome, we can measure and stitch the hem within the hour," said Miss Levere. "The caliber of help one finds today is very low, I'm afraid." She tapped Sybil sharply on the shoulder with a yardstick. "Not that way! Can't you see it is not even?"

Sybil winced. The reminder was unnecessarily sharp, but she dared not protest. She went on working, measuring and carefully marking the hemline with pins. There was not a thing wrong with her measurements.

"You, girl! Look at me when I speak to you."

Sybil moved much more suddenly than she meant to. Straightening her back, she looked up into the furious dark eyes. At once a wave of dizziness overwhelmed her. She reached out blindly and grasped the nearest object to steady herself. This was the pedestal on which Mrs. Bancroft stood. The room whirled around her and Sybil gave a smothered cry before she sank into unconsciousness.

She slept for two solid days. Her nights were filled with

Ned's crying and discomfort. But the days were hers. She slept while Mrs. Philips kept Ned. The dirty diapers simply piled up in the tub. She needed to rest before she started looking for another job. Would she even be able to find one? The entire setup at Arnaud's had been so perfect and it couldn't have been easier with Marlene there to smooth the way.

On the evening of the second day, Marlene came in carrying an aromatic delicatessen dinner of garlic bread, roast beef, macaroni salad, and a bottle of red wine Joey had given her. She also seemed to be filled with suppressed excitement.

"We're celebrating!"

Sybil, who had been feeling more and more depressed, could not imagine why. Marlene simply waved all questions aside and smiled mysteriously.

"Wait'll you hear what happened at Arnaud's today. Just wait! Eat up first, though. Let's bring the table in here and light those candles you're so nuts about. Come on, help me carry it."

They brought the table from the kitchen and set it in the middle of the living room, covering it with a yellow paper cloth with Happy Birthday written all over it. Marlene had gotten several of them at a half-price sale at Woolworth's. They used water glass tumblers for the wine and ate by candlelight.

Sybil had become more and more puzzled by Marlene's high spirits. Things couldn't be worse, she thought. So why was Marlene so excited.

"To success," Marlene said, raising her glass in a toast. "Have I got some news for you!"

"Marlene, if it's about talking to M. Arnaud to get my job back—" she began uncertainly. "I really couldn't do that. I mean, I know that your advice is sound, but I—"

She felt she was blushing. The thought of offering herself in place of Miss Levere, well, it was out of the question.

"Oh, I know that, honey," Marlene said, waving the protest aside with a red-tipped hand.

45

She refused to say another thing until they had completed their meal. Then she found a cigarette in the bottom of her bag. "My last one," she said. "Got to enjoy it until payday. Well, to get on with it. Remember Mrs. Thorpe, the one with the sleeves you fitted?"

"How could I forget?"

Marlene nodded. "She was in today and there was a terrible row. She didn't like anything Arnaud showed her. Can you imagine? Not one thing! That wouldn't have been so bad, but then she asked him the unforgivable question. I thought he'd have a stroke, honest."

"What did she ask?"

"She'd been to the theater the night before and she asked Arnaud if he would adapt a gown she saw in the second act of the play. And she wanted it pronto. You know how Arnaud prides himself on his own designs. Well, when she made her suggestion, he all but threw her out. It insulted him, see? Well, I happened to be outside the model's dressing room ironing and so I heard the whole thing. I even heard her leave in a huff and ring for the elevator. Well, you should have seen me move. I was down those back stairs in nothing flat, no kidding, and I just caught her coming out the front of the building."

Marlene paused to take a drag on her neglected cigarette.

" 'Mrs. Thorpe, you don't know me, but I work at Arnaud's,' I tell her. 'I happen to know a very good seamstress who could make that dress for you so you'd have it in time for that weekend party.'

"She stared at me, you know the way they do with that haughty, 'I don't need any look.' When she heard she could have the dress by Saturday, that got her."

" 'Who is this seamstress?' she asks.

" 'Well,' I said, 'you remember the girl who fitted your sleeves last week? That girl.'

" 'Oh?' she says, looking real interested.

" 'Of course, she'd have to see the dress and on our salaries we don't get to the theater much.'

" 'Hmm!' she says.

46

"And the next thing I know she's promising to send her chauffeur over with a ticket to the show."

Marlene held it up triumphantly. "Tonight's performance. Curtain in an hour. You'll just have time to make it."

"Me? Oh, Marlene, I couldn't. I mean, there's Ned," protested Sybil.

"You think I can't look after Ned? I know all about babies. Now, hurry and get dressed."

"But I don't know that I *could* copy the dress just from seeing it."

"You never know until you try. Look what you did with those drapes, and you made your own blouses and skirts for work from just studying mine. I know you can do it, honey."

Sybil hesitated. The idea was exciting.

"What about material? I mean we'd have to buy it and—"

Marlene reached into her purse and produced a fifty-dollar bill.

"A little advance and I know a wholesale place over on Seventh Avenue where they owe me a favor. So you see, it's no use putting up roadblocks. We've got it made. Come on. Get dressed."

There didn't seem to be any reason not to go.

When Sybil came out of her bedroom fifteen minutes later, wearing her only blue wool dress with a single strand of real pearls, Marlene whistled softly.

"You sure have got class. Somebody's liable to mistake you for one of the stars."

She laughed self-consciously. She did look good, though thin. But then, it was fashionable to be thin. She was hardly the well-rounded girl she had been, but her figure was still well-proportioned. The planes of her face were excellent and her large blue eyes were haunting.

"Make no mistake, honey," Marlene said, walking her to the door, "this could lead to something big. She'll pay as much as a hundred dollars for the dress over and above the material. Who knows, it could lead to other or-

47

ders. Maybe we could start something on our own. You could be with Ned all day and work on your own time."

It sounded too good to be true, but Sybil did not discount the possibility. Marlene had been right about so many things.

"If Ned wakes up before I get back, there's a bottle for him in the icebox."

"I'll find it," Marlene promised, giving her a gentle shove and sending her on her way.

She took an uptown bus and then walked over the last two blocks. The streets were crowded with evening theatergoers, chauffeur-driven cars, and taxis. The men and women in evening clothes milled around under the marquees. Even in difficult economic times there were always the very rich who somehow weathered the storm. How well she knew the easy, thoughtless lives they lived, wondering only where their next moment of entertainment would come from, unhampered by any really worries. Now with practiced eye she studied the clothes. Women in long gowns, with low-cut necklines and swirling satin skirts, their shoulders swathed in every kind of fur, stood around the brightly lighted lobbies with their escorts. They smoked long cigarettes attached to longer cigarette holders. She felt conspicuous in her simple blue wool dress. Everyone seemed to be in pairs. She gave her ticket to an usher and was quickly shown to a seat in the orchestra, an excellent seat in the center section. She supposed Mrs. Thorpe had every intention of allowing her to examine the dress at close range. She decided to make the most of her opportunity to relax and enjoy herself. It had been weeks since she'd thought of anything but work and Ned.

"I beg your pardon."

A tall, broad-shouldered man of about thirty took the empty seat beside her jostling her arm.

"Perfectly all right," she murmured and shifted in her seat, looking up only briefly.

She became aware finally that the man was gazing at her as she read her program and suddenly she was frightened. Why was he staring? Did he think he knew her? Was he very deliberately trying to place her? She tried to remember what she'd seen of him in her brief glance. He might simply be looking for a pickup. What could she expect? She'd come to the theater at night alone. Probably that was all it was. She tried to relax again.

The theater was filling up. She glanced at the boxes curiously. She wondered how many people they might accommodate.

"Exclusive, aren't they?" the man beside her asked. "I wonder who they are, don't you?"

She froze. Was his voice familiar?

"Not really," she said and resumed her perusal of her program.

He seemed to take the rebuff seriously and to her relief did not speak again until the first intermission, although she did feel he was watching her.

As the lights came up, he turned to her. He smiled engagingly.

"I know we haven't been properly introduced, but you see I'm just visiting the city from Milwaukee. New York's rather a lonely place when you don't know anyone. My name is Paul Bingham and I wonder if you'd join me during intermission. Perhaps you'd like a drink, some champagne?

She raised large, luminous eyes to his. He was good-looking and well-mannered in the way so many men she had known were. He was friendly and seemed to find her attractive. She thought she should feel pleased and flattered. Instead, she felt threatened.

"No, thank you. I don't drink," she said and opened her program to the biographical notes on the actors.

"Oh," he said helplessly. "Well, then—" He paused. "Well, then, if you'll excuse me—"

She did not look up and he left abruptly. Paul Bingham was not a name she knew. Perhaps he was just what he said he was. She hadn't meant to hurt his feelings. She could have been more gracious. But she was never completely free of her fear of being discovered. How awful it was to have to look upon every stranger as having sinister motives! Would it never end? Poor Mr. Bingham! He appeared to be so sincere. It might have been pleasant to talk with him if only she could be sure— She didn't finish the thought. Wasn't this what they called paranoia? And yet she couldn't help herself. How long would Edward go on looking for her? It had been three months. Would he give up after a year? Two years? It seemed like a life sentence. Or would she eventually have to face him? And lose Ned? No! She couldn't! She wouldn't!

Mr. Bingham did not return to his seat until the lights dimmed for the second act. And then she was so intent on studying the dress she had come to see, she hardly noticed him. The gown had an Empire line. The hem was raised in front and curved gently down in back. The fabric was crushed velvet in a primrose shade. The wide sleeves were lined with blue satin. She sketched in the margin of her program and when the curtain came down and the lights went up, she was quite sure she had all the information she needed.

"I think I should apologize."

He had turned in his seat and was gazing intently at her. Now what? she wondered nervously.

"What I mean was, I know it isn't strictly proper to suggest spending the intermission together. That is, when we don't actually know one another, but I thought I'd at least make the effort. And at first, just for a moment there, I thought I did know you, that we had met before. I realize I was wrong. I—I can see you aren't here merely for entertainment," he added, indicating the sketches she had made.

She quickly folded the program in half and tucked it into her bag.

"I can assure you, Mr. Bingham, no apology is necessary."

The fact that he admitted he found her familiar threw her into a near panic. She rose and he was instantly on his feet and standing in the aisle.

"If you will excuse me," she said and made her way purposefully past him. Only when she was outside and walking down Broadway did she feel safe again. He wasn't following her. She carried with her the memory of the hurt, puzzled expression on his face. Probably he thought she was unbalanced. She couldn't blame him. Her behavior was anything but normal.

"Back so soon?" Marlene greeted her.

"I left after the second act. I was worried about Ned," she lied. She didn't like to lie to Marlene, who was so straightforward and trusting. What have I become? she thought. The lies came easily to her lips now. They hadn't at first. She felt she lived a kind of dual existence, the person she was and the person she pretended to be. Wasn't there some danger in becoming confused herself and ending up as a shallow, haunted creature? She'd become increasingly aware of this as she grew to know and like Marlene. There were times when she wanted to voice an opinion or respond spontaneously to something her new friend said, but she resisted the temptation, knowing she must weigh her words carefully for fear they would give away too much. Sometimes she wondered why Marlene bothered with her at all. The older girl must find her terribly reserved, too reserved to be interesting. But Marlene did seem to like her. She gave her time and her emotional support generously. And she enjoyed Ned, no matter what she said about not wanting to be bothered with babies.

She offered Marlene her sketches.

"Hey, they're good, real good. You're an artist."

"Oh, no," she protested. "But they do show all I need, I think."

"No, really! You're good. They look like the real thing," Marlene flipped quickly through the program.

Sybil had sketched the dress from every conceivable angle. Looking at them with Marlene, she saw they were good, almost professional. She had, during the long, lonely months of her pregnancy, often amused herself by copying sketches from fashion magazines Alicia kept bringing her under the mistaken notion Sybil would want an entirely new wardrobe after the baby was born.

"What do you think we'll need? I mean to make up the gown?"

Sybil sat down on the sofa and began estimating the amount of material that would be necessary.

"There's thread and the tiny buttons up the back, too. And we'd need Mrs. Thorpe's measurements. Oh, Marlene, would she come here for a fitting?"

"She hates fittings. At Arnaud's we worked with her form, remember?"

"But we don't have that." Sybil began to see insurmountable problems. "And—and a machine. We can't do it all by hand. We'd never get finished."

"Don't worry, will you, honey? I've got it all planned. Tomorrow, when no one's looking, I get Mrs. Thorpe's measurements from Arnaud's. Then I get sick, see, and leave early. I go over to my friend on Seventh Avenue and pick up what we need and on the way back I stop in at a secondhand place and rent a portable sewing machine. Mrs. Thorpe says she'll pay all expenses and these are expenses. Anyway, by tomorrow night we'll be ready to go. And next week, say Wednesday or Thursday, Mrs. Thorpe can come by for the final fitting. Everything's going to work out fine. She'll love it. You'll see."

Sybil tried to imagine every step of the project going smoothly. She'd have to make her own pattern. How could she drape the material accurately without a dummy? What if Marlene couldn't get what they needed?

"And your job, Marlene! Your job at Arnaud's. If they think you're sick, they're liable to let you go. Miss Levere knows we were friends. She can't be any too pleased with anyone she associates with me."

"Listen, I've lost jobs before. So what! I'm still here. And besides, what difference will it make? Like I said, this could work into something real good for both of us. We won't need Arnaud or anybody else," Marlene finished emphatically. She picked up the list. "Is this it now?"

"I think so."

She did not want to dampen Marlene's enthusiasm, but anything could go wrong, anything at all. What if Mrs. Thorpe was not pleased? What if she asked for her fifty dollars back after they'd spent it?

"Don't look like that, kid," Marlene said. "You're getting lines in your forehead for nothing. One thing you've got to learn in this world is you have to take chances. Big chances, big pay-offs. Take it from me, we can do this. What you need now is a good night's sleep! Tomorrow you can start on the pattern, just the general lines until I get back with the measurements. Don't worry about a thing. We're going to make this. I've got a feeling, a real good feeling."

She tried to take Marlene's advice. How wonderful if they could pull it off! A hundred dollars between them. That would be three weeks' wages. And she'd have earned it without leaving the house! She wished she had Marlene's optimistic enthusiasm. She knew she was far more cautious and easily frightened by the unknown than her friend. Marlene plunged recklessly ahead on almost any project. She enjoyed herself so much more than Sybil, never allowing herself to be bothered by dire possibilities that never materialized and if any of them did, she simply shrugged them off as temporary setbacks. She was willing to take life as it came on its own terms. Sybil longed to imitate her friend's easygoing nature. Would Marlene have been frightened by poor Paul Bingham? Probably not. She'd have accepted him at face value and enjoyed the intermission in his company. How much more pleasant the evening would have been for her than it had been for Sybil! But then Marlene had nothing to hide. Still, even before Edward, she knew she had been too timid and rather afraid of life. Was it possible to change now? She wanted to. Leaving her husband was certainly the first step, but it wasn't enough, not nearly enough.

She slept badly that night and toward morning she had a terrible dream. She was at the theater again, seated beside Paul Bingham. He spoke to her, introducing him-

53

self as he had. But his friendly, open smile was gone. His gaze was triumphant. He grasped her arm roughly as the lights went up for intermission and dragged her from her seat. They began to struggle violently. She cried out, but the unseeing eyes of the people around her brought no response. His face seemed to melt away like a mask. She found she was staring into Edward's dark eyes.

"Now, my dear, there's no sense making a scene. Of course, you're coming back with me, you and my son," he said, his voice cold and unrelenting.

She awoke to hear someone knocking at her door. Her hands were clenched into fists and she felt as though there was a heavy weight on her chest. She glanced at the clock. It was past eight. She'd overslept. Ned was whimpering in the crib beside her bed and someone was at the door.

"Mrs. Anderson! Mrs. Anderson!"

Her head cleared. It wasn't Edward, nor an emissary from him. It was only Mrs. Philips. She snatched up her robe and hurried to the door.

Mrs. Philips looked worried.

"Gee, I thought somethin' happened to you when you didn't come down at eight. I thought maybe you got sick again and was too weak to get up. So I thought I'd just check. Are you O.K.? You want me to take the baby today?"

The concern was sincere and she was grateful. The superintendent had taken a motherly interest in her since the first week she'd been there. She hesitated now wondering if she should spend the fifty cents. After all, she was well enough to care for Ned now herself. But without the baby to look after, she'd have the entire day to concentrate on the problem of Mrs. Thorpe's dress. Yes, she'd do it! It might be that she'd be spending the money needlessly, but then again it might not. What had her friend said about taking chances and winning big? Marlene would not have had to think twice.

All morning she worked on the sketches she'd made the night before, front, back, and side views. She began to see the dress in parts and thought she was ready to experiment with a pattern made out of newspaper. She'd take some of the discarded newspapers that piled up in the back hall. The threat of Edward faded from her consciousness. She deliberately tried to imagine what success with Mrs. Thorpe might mean to them. All sorts of pleasant possibilities came to mind. She went downstairs through the empty halls. It certainly was quiet this time of day. The children were all in school, husbands at work, and the housewives busy with chores or simply enjoying the peaceful time in front of their radios. She sometimes thought she would like to have a radio just for the company of adult voices when she was home alone with Ned and Marlene was off on a date. The price of a radio made that out of the question at the moment, but perhaps not permanently now.

The back hall was dark. Once again the exit light had burned out. There must be a defect in the fixture because it happened so often and Mrs. Philips was slow about replacing the bulbs. Sybil nearly stumbled over the papers before she saw them. They were stacked up knee high before the back door. She picked up an armful and started toward the stairs.

"All of them? You're going to take all those?"

At first she was not sure who had spoken. Because she was not expecting to meet anyone in the hall at this hour, let alone a man, she was startled, but she sternly kept her fears in check until she knew for a fact there was reason to be afraid. That's what Marlene would have done.

"I—I beg your pardon," she said, peering up at him. She couldn't see his face clearly. He was tall, over six feet, she judged, and well-built.

"Yes, I think you should. I really think you should beg my pardon."

His voice was deep and vibrant. Was he laughing?

"Madam, step out here into the light," he ordered. "I'm curious to see what you look like. Anyone with such a voracious intellectual appetite must be unique. When do you plan to have time to read all those newspapers and

55

how long does it take you? Now, I can go through the *Tribune*, essential information and one or two frills in oh, say, forty-five minutes. But you have several papers there and duplicates, too, I'll bet."

He was young, early twenties probably. He had a wide, generous mouth and laughing brown eyes. It was those clear, honest eyes that told her she had nothing to fear from him. His hair was light brown and a bit on the shaggy side. It was thick and wavy, but in need of the professional touch of a barber. A heavy lock fell across his forehead and he brushed it aside impatiently as he gazed down at her. She knew she looked particularly well that morning. She had brushed the waves of her dark hair with particular care. Not that she had any reason to look her best. She just felt better when she did. Even when she knew she'd be staying in the house alone all day with Ned, she was dressed and well-groomed. And so she was wearing the blue skirt and white blouse she had made herself, and she knew she looked attractive. But the effect she had on this man was somewhat more than she expected.

"My word!" he said softly as she moved into the light. "My word," he repeated and grinned broadly. "You're beautiful! Will you marry me?"

She blushed with surprise and could think of nothing to say. There was something infectious about his cheerful nonsense and Sybil found herself slowly smiling back at him.

"Ah!" he cried. "Madam, that smile! You take my breath away. Can such loveliness be real, or is it all a dream?"

He reached out and covered her hand with his.

She felt an unexpected response and was surprised by the thrill of pleasure she felt at his touch.

"Warm flesh! She lives! But where does she live, I wonder. Here? Say you live here, dear lady. Say we share this humble roof."

She laughed. What a charming tease he was!

"Yes," she said, "we do. And I'm sorry if I took too much paper. But there is plenty more back there."

"Ah, she speaks and her voice is like music!" he said, sighing rapturously, then fixing her with a suspicious look.

"Plenty more papers back there, eh? The bottom of the pile, you mean. Last week's papers! Last month's even! It's yesterday's papers I want and it's yesterday's papers you have," he said giving up his light, joking tone and pointing to the dateline. He had long sensitive fingers. Sybil thought he might be an artist or a musician.

"Oh," she said, beginning to realize what he was after. "You want to *read* the news."

"Why, yes, exactly," he said, looking vastly surprised at her obvious lack of understanding. "Don't you?"

"No! That is, I do like to keep up with the news when I can, only I want the papers for a very different purpose today. Please take what you like of these. I'll go and get more. Anything will do for me."

She turned over the entire batch she'd just picked up to him and went back for more.

"Hey, gosh! I didn't mean—" he began helplessly.

"No, no," she said when he hurried after her. "I wouldn't want you to neglect your reading. Think of how much more knowledgeable you'll be after going through all those." She smiled mischievously. "At forty-five minutes a paper, that should take you all day and keep you out of trouble."

She squeezed past him with her new bundle of papers and started up the stairs.

"Wait! Don't go!" he called after her anxiously. "I don't even know your name. I'm Jonathan Rogers," he added after a moment, "and I really think I've fallen in love with you. I can feel it right here," he said dramatically touching his blue sweater in the general area of his heart.

"Hmm! You're certain it isn't indigestion, Mr. Rogers?"

"It's Dr. Rogers. I'm interning at Mercy Hospital. Won't you tell me your name?"

She continued up the stairs while he looked up at her hopefully. He certainly was persistent. She knew he'd be hurt for all his light-hearted nonsense if she did not tell him her name. More than that she *wanted* to tell him her name.

"It's Sybil," she said, smiling down at him. "Sybil Anderson." And she was rewarded by his delighted grin.

He blew her a kiss. "Bless you, Sybil Anderson. I'll remember this morning all my life, the morning that we met."

She knew he continued to watch her, what he could see of her, through the slats of the staircase, until she reached the third floor and let herself into her apartment. She was humming to herself as she began work on the pattern. Funny, she hadn't done that in ages. A chance meeting with a stranger had given her this lift. Well, bless that stranger. Bless Jonathan Rogers! He'd put her in a cheerful mood. Made her feel optimistic. She wasn't sure exactly why but there was something about him. He exuded self-confidence. Perhaps he was awfully good at what he did. He was a doctor, he said. Well, he'd be a good one. He'd charm his patients into recovering if nothing else. She wouldn't mind having someone like Jonathan Rogers charm her into recovering. For too long she'd been trapped in the vise of fear, unable to permit herself even a moment's happiness without casting apprehensive looks over her shoulder or feeling guilty. That was no way to live. And it was not a healthy atmosphere in which to bring up her son. She was determined that today would mark the beginning of an entirely new approach.

The new Sybil believed in her ability to solve the problem of Mrs. Thorpe's dress. By evening she'd done it.

She even devised a way of fashioning a kind of dressmaker's dummy out of newspaper. The pattern she had made would suffice temporarily, but she'd want to try it in muslin first before cutting into the precious material.

The pale afternoon sun faded and she was forced to switch on the lamps. She rubbed her eyes and admitted to herself that she was tired. She went down to Mrs. Philips's to get Ned. He was happily sitting in the middle of the kitchen floor banging pots and pans with a huge wooden spoon.

"Kids don't need expensive toys. You just give 'em something they can make noise with and they're happy as clams. Say, you feeling better?" asked Mrs. Philips, looking closely at her. "You look better. It's good to see you smile again. There for awhile—" she shrugged. "Well, but you're all right now. And you're young. That's the thing. You can't keep young folks down for long."

No, you can't, thought Sybil. I have everything on my side. I'll never let myself get into such a state again.

"Oh, I'm much better, thank you," she said aloud. "Doesn't Ned look happy? You really have a way with children, Mrs. Philips."

She placed two quarters for Mrs. Philips' services on the crowded kitchen table as she always did. Somehow she felt embarrassed about putting it directly into the superintendent's hand. She bent to pick up Ned and Mrs. Philips hooked the strap of the diaper bag over Sybil's arm.

"Well, then, you'll be going back to work tomorrow," she said, as she walked Sybil to the door. "It won't be so bad, your first day back since it's Saturday and only half a day," she added encouragingly.

Sybil did not have the heart to tell her there was no job to go back to. If things worked out as planned maybe Mrs. Philips would never have to know.

"Thanks, Mrs. Philips. Thank you for everything."

She could hardly wait now for Marlene to get home, but it was nearly seven before there was any sign of her.

Ned was already in bed and she was just settling down to dinner when she heard the sound of loud laughter in the lower hall. There were heavy footsteps on the stairs and then Marlene's voice calling to her to open the door.

"Make way! Make way!" Marlene yelled, motioning her to stand back as a broad-shouldered, stubby, red-faced man stepped through the door clutching a portable sewing machine in his arms.

"Where do you want it? I'm like to bust a gut with this thing. Even my toes is strained," he said.

Marlene's laughter was enthusiastic.

"You're a riot, Joey. Isn't he a riot, Sybil?"

Sybil quickly removed the bowl of artificial flowers and two ash trays from the coffee table. Joey promptly plunked the machine down and collapsed onto the sofa.

"Well, there you are, goils. How you're gonna get that back to Brady's, I won't tell you. Must weigh a ton."

"Oh, Joey, you're somethin'!" Marlene cried. "Isn't he somethin', Sybil? He carried that six blocks and up the stairs and everything. Joey's got muscles on muscles. Right, Joey?"

Joey nodded and reached for a pack of Camels in his pocket. "Oh, yeah! That's me. Mr. Muscles. So this is your friend Sybil."

Joey had small dark eyes in a round flushed face. He had not bothered to take off his overcoat and the velvet collar hunched awkwardly about his thick neck. He gave Sybil an appraising look, his gaze resting briefly on her face, her breasts, and lingering on her hips, until she felt herself blushing with embarrassment at his open admiration. So this was Joey Ferguson! She'd heard so much about him she thought she knew him already. Somehow he didn't look much like Marlene's description of him. Marlene was fond of comparing him to movie stars like Richard Arlen and Robert Montgomery, whom he did not resemble at all. He had a loud voice and a good-natured grin. He seemed pleased to be able to do them a favor.

"Hey, kid, don't I get a drink after all that?" Joey demanded, fixing Marlene with a commanding glare.

"You sure do, Joey. You sure do. Just wait right there. I'll be right back. Don't move a muscle."

"Boy, you don't have to tell me that. I wasn't plannin' to move nothin' at all, unless your friend here was willing." He winked roguishly at Sybil. "Say, she's quite a looker. You oughta be in pictures, kid. You and Marlene!"

Sybil smiled self-consciously, but Marlene whooped

60

with laughter as she rushed out the door and across the hall.

"Didn't I tell you Joey's a scream, Sybil? Get the glasses. I'll get the booze."

Sybil went into the kitchen and returned with three water tumblers and a bowl of chopped ice. She didn't quite know what to say to Joey. She'd never met anyone like him before.

"What's that for?" he asked suspiciously, pointing to the ice.

"Why, I thought— That is, Marlene likes ice in her drink—" she began.

"Ha! That's a hot one! Hey, Marlene, since when you been putting ice in your rye?"

"Since always," Marlene said, placing a bottle of gin and a bottle of rye next to the portable sewing machine. "You don't think I drink the way you do every night, do you?"

Joey shrugged. "Drinkin's drinkin'. You're gonna dilute it with ice, why bother? That the stuff I got you?" he asked, indicating the bottles.

"What else?" asked Marlene.

"Well, all right then. Rye all around?" he asked and then went ahead and poured three rather healthy drinks, ignoring the ice.

Sybil, who never drank anything but wine, stared at the amber liquid and wondered where Joey had gotten it and how safe it was. Of course, Marlene had been surviving on a diet of Joey's gin and rye for months. When Marlene and Joey raised their glasses, she felt she must make a show of drinking, too, or be thought impolite.

"Here's mud in your eye, princess," he said and winked at Sybil.

She smiled back shyly and raised her glass. The next thing she knew, the unfamiliar liquid was burning her lips and throat. She thought for a moment she would never be able to speak again as the fiery substance seemed to consume her entire consciousness. It brought tears to her eyes. She choked and coughed and was forced to rush into the kitchen for water.

She heard Joey and Marlene roaring with laughter as she tried to overcome the impulse to retch right there in the sink. At last she was able to compose herself and return to the others, though she was terribly embarrassed. She felt warm all over now that the whiskey had suffused her body and though that was a pleasant sensation, she could not imagine putting herself through the discomfort of sipping the awful stuff again.

"Why didn't you say it was your first time?" Joey asked, leaning forward and helpfully dropping two pieces of ice into her drink. "You can't drink it straight the first time. Hey, you know, this place is classy," he said looking around. "Maybe I could get to like it here."

"Oh, Joey," Marlene squealed. "You slay me, you really do." She had taken off her coat and sat very straight, the fabric of her white satin blouse pulled taut over her rounded breasts.

Joey sighed and drained his glass.

"Well, kiddies, much as I'd like to stay, Uncle Joey's got to be going. Got to see a man about a dog, as they say."

He stood up and the girls stood, too.

"Don't take any wooden nickels, princess," he said and reached out to chuck Sybil under the chin.

"Thank you so much for carrying the machine up for us," she had the presence of mind to say.

"Oh, it was nothin', kid. Just took ten years off my life, as they say."

"Will I see you tomorrow night, Joey?" Marlene asked, as she walked with him to the door.

"Yeah, why not? We'll take in a movie. Hey why don't you bring the princess along, if she has nothing better to do," he said.

"Sure, if she wants to," Marlene said, glancing uncertainly back at Sybil, who shook her head frantically. Marlene wouldn't want her intruding on a date.

"Thanks, but I have to care for my baby," she managed to say.

"Baby!" Joey turned to stare at her and then raised his brows. "Baby!" he repeated. "Well, what do ya know? You got a baby?" He seemed to be revising his assessment of her.

"Yes. My son is nearly six months old, so you see I'm rather tied to the house."

"Oh, yeah," Joey said. "Be seein' you both, I guess." He shook his head. "A baby? She don't look old enough to have no baby."

What was he really thinking? What would any man think when he knew? It was hard to say. Joey's round face registered something like amazement and disbelief. When the idea sank in he seemed to withdraw a little. The fact that she was encumbered by a child did that. He seemed to regard her with awe. She could hardly be insulted by Joey's sudden change in attitude, but she wondered how Jonathan Rogers would have reacted to the news that she had a baby. How foolish to think of him! Their light-hearted exchange that morning meant nothing and yet here she was thinking of him again. She wondered what Dr. Rogers would think of her situation. Would he, too, suddenly find her less interesting? Would he look upon Ned as an impediment? Briefly she wondered what it would be like to be carefree like Marlene and was instantly sorry that the thought had ever crossed her mind. She felt as though she had betrayed her child. Guilt nearly choked her so that she was only able to smile and nod as Joey said good-bye.

"I'll walk you to the front door, Joey." Marlene slipped her arm through his and leaned against him.

Sybil took her glass and Joey's and rinsed them out in the sink allowing the water to run freely. The smell of the liquor made her feel slightly ill and she wished she didn't have to leave Marlene's glass out. But Marlene might want the rest of her drink. She wondered idly how long it took to get used to liquor, to be able to drink and enjoy it. This seemed the mark of the sophisticate and she wished she could achieve it quickly. To Joey she appeared to be terribly young, a mere child herself. She lacked maturity and the authority that went with it. This she saw as a drawback. Who would take her seriously if she and Marlene ever did go into business for themselves?

"I got everything!" Marlene announced when she returned, opening the bundle she'd dropped on a chair. "Everything!" Her usually perfectly outlined lips were slightly smeared and Sybil realized she and Joey had made use of the privacy of the darkened hallway.

"What did you think of Joey?" Marlene asked, pausing in her efforts to untie the string that fastened the bundle.

"Oh, he's very—interesting," Sybil told her. "It was awfully good of him to carry that machine up here."

"Yeah, he's got a soft heart," Marlene said happily. "He'd do anything for a friend and he liked you. Did you notice?" There wasn't the faintest suspicion of jealousy in Marlene's voice. She was simply very pleased her friends got on so well.

"You said you got everything?" Sybil asked.

"Oh, yeah!" Marlene opened her purse and pulled out a crumpled paper. "Mrs. Thorpe's measurements!"

"You did get them!"

Sybil glanced at the paper. They were pretty much as she suspected.

"I think we can do it, Marlene." She couldn't keep the excitement from her voice. "I've pretty much figured it all out. And look at this."

She went to the closet and got the paper form she'd made.

Marlene giggled.

"Hey! Looks just like her. So we're all set."

There was something in her friend's voice despite the laughter that made Sybil look at her more closely. What had happened to Marlene's enthusiasm of last night? A thin line had appeared between her penciled brows.

"Is anything wrong?" Sybil asked, suddenly anxious.

"Aw! They caught me snitching La Thorpe's measurements."

"Oh, no! Who did? What happened?"

"Well, you might know it was Levere. She's been watching me like a hawk since you left, looking out for one false move, as they say. Today she got what she wanted. We're both on the street, honey. So now we've got to make good for both of us."

Marlene gave her a sheepish grin.

"I guess I shoulda been more careful, but, well, you know. I was fed up there. And Levere sure hasn't made it easy. Aw, honey, don't look like that. It's not the end of the world. We're gonna make it. You'll see."

They both looked ruefully at Mrs. Thorpe's plump, paper form. Sybil's determination to remain cheerful in spite of everything melted away.

"It looks like we're going to have to. Marlene, I feel responsible. If it weren't for me, you'd still have a job."

"Yeah, but we wouldn't have Mrs. Thorpe," Marlene pointed out, once again finding the bright side. "She was impressed with you, not me. Come on. What do you say we eat? I'll go out and get something. Then we can get to work."

"No, no! Save your money. I have something ready."

It was nearly midnight when they began cutting into the precious velvet. Marlene did the actual cutting on the kitchen table using Sybil's muslin pattern.

"Let's quit for tonight," she said when the pieces were neatly laid out and ready for basting. "I couldn't see to sew now anyhow."

Sybil quickly agreed, crawling into bed a short time later, only to be awakened by Ned's indignant cries. She walked the living room floor with him for what seemed like hours, glancing out from time to time at the deserted street. A wind had come up and, as she watched, the first feathery flakes of snow began to fall. Across the street darkened store fronts stared back at her. Christmas garlands trimmed with silver tinsel decorated even the shabbiest window.

Ned's first Christmas and I don't have a tree for him, she thought. Poor baby! She had all but forgotten about

Christmas. Thank goodness he wouldn't know the difference. Next year she'd have to have something. Yes, next year at this time there'd be something. The main thing now was to succeed with Mrs. Thorpe.

Softly she began to hum "Silent Night." It was lost on the baby. He slept peacefully in her arms, a warm, soft bundle of new life. She loved him with all her heart and meant to make his life a happy and comfortable one. How could she have ever thought of being free of Ned?

Marlene, on the other hand, saw the baby as a tremendous asset which surprised then shocked Sybil. It was Marlene's attitude towards Ned that triggered their first real quarrel.

"She'll come tomorrow at eleven," Marlene announced a week later. Mrs. Thorpe had given her a number to call.

"Here? She'd really come here?"

The third floor walk-up hardly seemed to be their customer's style.

Marlene shrugged. "Why not? She wants the dress. She's gonna dazzle all those fancy friends of hers. She'll go anywhere, as long as she gets it."

"I thought maybe she'd want us to go to her."

Sybil had imagined them being let into the Thorpe home through the service entrance.

"Me too, but maybe she wants to see the setup here. Er—and speaking of setup. Let's have her come to your place. It's got more class than mine. And it wouldn't be a bad idea to let her see the baby."

"Really? Why?" Sybil asked, unable to imagine why Mrs. Thorpe would be interested in Ned.

Marlene was way ahead of her. "It wouldn't hurt to let her know there's a baby."

Sybil was surprised and shocked by the suggestion.

"But that's trading on sympathy!"

Marlene shrugged.

"Every little bit helps."

Sybil could not agree. It seemed like begging and she hated the idea. She drew herself up stiffly.

"I don't want Mrs. Thorpe to feel sorry for me. I want

her to like my work. I'm willing to work and work hard. I won't accept charity, not ever."

She'd grown angry and her words came out in a short burst of indignation.

Marlene hesitated, then laughed and shook her head.

"Forget I mentioned it. It isn't important."

But she couldn't forget because the next day when Mrs. Thorpe came for her fitting, she was so delighted with the dress that she paid them on the spot and then, before she left, slipped another bill into Sybil's hand.

"For the baby, my dear. For Christmas," she said, smiling for all the world like a benevolent angel.

Sybil was too mortified to do anything but mumble a weak thank you. Marlene, she realized, must have told. There hadn't been a peep out of Ned, who slept peacefully in the bedroom.

Mrs. Thorpe had not left the living room during her fitting. Sybil made tea and set out cups on the coffee table, but their customer refused the offer, preferring to get on with the fitting at once. She removed her fox-trimmed coat and allowed Marlene to help her out of her dress. The gown hung in the hall closet, seams carefully basted. Marlene brought the cheval glass from her bedroom for Mrs. Thorpe's use.

She stood in the center of the floor, twisting and turning before the mirror.

"I really can't see the back," she complained in her rich, throaty voice.

The scent of her perfume filled the room. Her coiffure was perfect as usual and seemed to have been done in imitation of Lynn Fontanne, whom she resembled, though she was shorter and heavier. Still, the dress was flattering and Mrs. Thorpe was pleased.

"You girls are both with Arnaud's?" she asked, after Marlene thought to bring the wall mirror from her dresser and held so that Mrs. Thorpe could examine the back view.

"We were," Marlene said, before Sybil could answer. "We've decided to strike out on our own."

"How very enterprising! But with business the way it is, are you sure you should?"

The question seemed to be asked for the sake of politeness rather than any real desire to know. Mrs. Thorpe couldn't begin to understand their financial plight and couldn't be expected to care even if she did. She was like every spoiled, wealthy woman in the world, sailing serenely through life without ever really being touched by it.

I was almost like that, Sybil thought. I was certainly well on my way to being a Mrs. Thorpe.

"It's a kind of necessity really, ma'am," Marlene explained. "We haven't any choice. We were neither of us happy at Arnaud's."

Mrs. Thorpe frowned briefly.

"I can well imagine. I found the designs and the workmanship very disappointing. Now this—" She fingered the velvet. "I'm very happy with this. Perhaps we could make an arrangement. Yes, I think we might," she said with decision. "The dress is perfect as it is. When will you be able to complete it?"

"By tomorrow easily," Marlene said.

"Splendid! Then I'll send my chauffeur by in the afternoon. You won't need me again. I don't see why we can't do business together, do you? I'll be in touch."

They helped her dress and when she left, she pressed the bill into Sybil's hand. It was ten dollars. Ten dollars worth of charity for her baby. She didn't know when she had been so humiliated and Marlene could not begin to understand why.

"It's a little bonus. Don't be like that, Sybil," Marlene pleaded.

"You told her about Ned!" Sybil flung the accusation at her bitterly. "I don't want to be the object of her charity. Why can't you understand that?"

She could not explain to Marlene the extent of her fury, but in the back of her mind she could picture herself piously telling Alicia what good work the Needlework Guild did for the poor and needy. Had she once actually seen the "poor and needy" of whom she spoke? Had she once tried to find out who they were or what they thought or felt? The resentment she felt towards Mrs. Thorpe doubled because of the disgust she felt towards herself and she was helpless against it. It was as though she were outside herself observing her own behavior with disapproval, but unable to do anything about it.

She threw the ten-dollar bill on the floor and strode stiffly into the kitchen where she began boiling water for Ned's diapers. After a moment Marlene followed her. She stood in the doorway and for a time said nothing. Sybil's eyes smarted with useless tears. She didn't know if she could ever speak to Marlene again.

"I'm sorry. Gee, honey, let's not fight. I just thought— Boy, it was a dumb move. But I really thought a little sympathy would help. We probably would have got along just as well without it. The whole thing was dumb and I'm sorry. You got your pride. I can't blame you for that. I was just so scared—I mean, we need the money. Please don't be mad."

Sybil, who had begun transferring diapers from the pail into the tub, turned to look at her friend's anxious face. She did look frightened and hurt as well. Marlene knew what it was to be poor and alone and perhaps even hungry, something Sybil had never had to face. They had a different approach to life and they hardly valued the same things. And yet they had grown quite close because Marlene was warm-hearted and generous. How foolish to let pride come between them! Marlene had far more experience than she and had acted out of fear and desperation. Sybil could not blame her for that. She forced her own guilt, as well as her pride, into the recesses of her mind. What was she accusing Marlene of after all? Simply being human?

"You know what I'm going to do with that ten dollars?" she asked at last. "I'm going to make Christmas for Ned." Soon they were both happily making plans.

III

Early on the morning of Christmas Eve she went looking for a tree.

"Don't pay more than fifty cents for anything,". Marlene advised. She'd volunteered to stay with Ned. "I want to do my hair and nails anyway. This is going to be one heck of a good holiday season. Things are looking up all around." She began singing a familiar Christmas carol completely off key.

Things were, as Marlene said, looking up. Mrs. Thorpe had given them orders for two more dresses, one of which was to be ready for New Year's. If this kept up, life would be much easier.

Mr. Barbarini was selling trees outside his grocery store. They were stacked against the brick wall in clumps of three and four and roped off from the sidewalk. His son, Gino, a boy of about twelve, was standing outside, ringing a brass hand bell vigorously and singing out his wares.

"Get your genuine Christmas trees here!"

He grinned broadly when he saw Sybil. He had a broken tooth right in front.

"Snapped it off on Frankie Laszlo's head," he'd told her once. "That kid's got a thick skull."

Dark curls sprang from beneath his red knitted cap and onto his forehead.

"Hi ya, Mrs. Anderson. Merry Christmas. How's the holy terror?"

70

He'd christened Ned the holy terror ever since the day Sybil set the baby down on the counter and he'd grabbed the bottom can in a soup display. The whole thing toppled down with a tremendous crash, frightening Ned into loud, hysterical cries and creating mayhem in Mr. Barbarini's store. Sybil had been terribly embarrassed, but Mrs. Barbarini took Ned and quieted him expertly while Gino and Sybil rebuilt the display.

"I gotta six of my own," said Mrs. Barbarini. "This one he'sa gotta healthy lungs."

She smiled at Sybil and they'd all been friends ever since. Gino always offered to hold Ned out of reach of precarious displays while Sybil shopped.

"Merry Christmas, Gino. He's fine. I'm looking for a tree for him."

"Oh, boy! I got just the thing. Nice six-foot balsam. Only a dollar and a half for you."

"Robber!" said one of the customers in a good-natured tone. "Don't pay it. He can make a better bargain than that."

Sybil turned to look with a pleased smile at the man who had spoken. Since the day she had met him over the newspapers in the back hall, she hadn't seen Jonathan Rogers. That was nearly two weeks ago, but she knew his voice at once. It was obvious he did not recognize her. She had bundled up against the cold in her green cloth coat and Marlene's fox fur hat. This all but hid her face. But when he looked into her eyes, Jonathan grinned with pleasure.

"I don't believe it!' he cried. "You're still here. I thought sure you'd vanish while I was gone. Merry Christmas, Sybil Anderson, am I glad to see you!"

Before she knew what was happening, Jonathan grasped her by the shoulders and planted a kiss on her forehead.

"There, you can't ever leave me now. I'll have to make an honest woman of you. Here, young man," he said, slipping his arm firmly about her waist and turning to Gino. "This is the woman I love. Trot out the best tree

71

you've got. Er—" he said, dropping his voice. "How much did you want to spend?"

"Fifty cents," she said, laughing up into his dark eyes. They were deep brown with little flecks of gold. Once again, she was swept up in the warmth of his charm and good humor and she allowed herself to enjoy every minute of it.

"There you are, my boy. Money is no object. We'll be happy to go as high as fifty cents."

"Aw, come on, mister. Give me a break. I gotta sell at least half these trees before we cut the prices. Ma'am, you think this tree is worth a buck and a half, don't you?"

Gino held it out at arm's length for her appraisal.

"It is a little thin through the middle, Gino," she said, acutely aware of the pressure of Jonathan's body against hers. He did not seem to have any intention of releasing her and she made no move to pull away.

"There's a badly damaged branch down there towards the bottom," Jonathan pointed out.

"You could tie it on," Gino said quickly.

"Not the same," returned Jonathan. "No, all in all, I'd say this tree was barely worth fifty cents."

"A dollar! A dollar at least," Gino squealed.

"Hmm! What do you think?" Jonathan asked in an undertone.

"I like it," she whispered. "Very much. But a dollar's too high."

"Seventy-five," Jonathan suggested to Gino.

"I'm gettin' fleeced!" Gino protested. "Mrs. Anderson, have a heart!"

"*Mrs.* Anderson!"

She felt Jonathan's arm stiffen suddenly. "*Mrs.* Anderson," he repeated and she felt her throat tighten with a disappointment she never expected she'd feel. He was beginning to look just the way Joey had when he'd learned about Ned.

"Is there a Mr. Anderson?" he asked.

"Oh, no, no!" she said quickly.

He grinned broadly, obviously relieved. How long, she

wondered, would that last? Sooner or later he'd learn about Ned. She felt suddenly deflated.

"We'll take the tree, Gino. Seventy-five cents. Our final offer!"

"Oh, but I only meant to pay—" she began, but Jonathan reached into his pocket and pressed a quarter into her gloved hand.

"My contribution," he said, "on the condition you let me share some of Christmas with you. I wasn't going to have a tree at all. It didn't seem worth it for one. What do you say?"

She hesitated.

"I couldn't have you do without Christmas." She smiled shyly up at him feeling hopeful again. He might not back off as Joey had after all. What was there about him that made her want so much to please him?

"Tie it up, Gino. We'll take it with us," he said.

"Good thing! You think you get delivery, too, for seventy-five cents?" Gino grumbled, but he was half grinning and when he tied string around the branches, he added an extra branch to replace the broken one.

"For the holy terror," he said.

"Who?" Jonathan asked, lifting the tree by the rope.

There it is, thought Sybil.

"I'm afraid you're in for a surprise," she told him, but she delayed mentioning Ned.

Jonathan followed her on her shopping rounds as though he had nothing else to do. They got two boxes of ornaments and a stand in a store around the corner.

"I've been away. Did you notice?" he asked, as she paid for her purchases.

"To tell you the truth," she said, "I only wondered once."

"But you wondered," he said grinning. "You did wonder. That's something. Gosh, it's nearly ten o'clock and I've got to be uptown in an hour. Let me bring the tree upstairs for you. You haven't forgotten your promise. I really would like to share some of Christmas with you. May I?"

She said nothing until they were outside her door. She knew it was now or never. It would be nice to spend some of the otherwise lonely hours of Christmas with Jonathan.

She turned to look up at him with serious eyes. She decided to be direct.

"I have a son," she said, "a six-month-old baby. He's the holy terror. Would you still like to spend Christmas with us?"

The first shock of surprise vanished quickly.

"Do I look like a man who doesn't like babies? Even now I am going to Mercy Hospital, where I will be on duty until six o'clock in the children's ward. After that I'm free and I'd very much like to spend the evening with you both."

The gay banter had left his voice and she could see he sincerely meant what he said.

"Come to dinner," she said. "It won't be much, but there'll be the tree."

"And you," he said. "And you. Until tonight, Sybil." He pressed the fingers of her gloved hand to his lips.

She watched him run lightly down the stairs. At the first landing he turned and called up to her, "Till tonight." And then she couldn't see him any more and the hallway looked just a little darker than before.

"Well, well, you sure do keep things to yourself," Marlene remarked, with a surprised grin, when she told her about Jonathan. "I'd be shouting it from the rooftops. He sounds nice and you met him right here."

"Oh, it isn't anything, just something to do on Christmas Eve. I'm afraid it could be awfully depressing to be alone tonight."

Marlene held up one red-tipped hand and surveyed the polish critically. Satisfied, she started on the other one.

"Is that the way you feel? Me? I never let myself get lonely. I just pick up and go to the movies. When I'm there I forget everything. You should try it."

"It wouldn't be as easy for me. There's Ned."

"Plenty of people bring babies to the movies," Marlene said, finishing the last nail and waving her hand in the air.

"Where are you going tonight?" Sybil settled herself in the chair by the window and picked up the bodice of Mrs. Thorpe's new dress. She was sewing silk flowers around the deep neckline.

"You know, I'm not really sure," Marlene admitted, frowning slightly. "Joey said it was a friend's place. Somebody who lives on the Island. He didn't say who. But I think this somebody is pretty important. I'm glad I met Joey. He takes me places I've never been. And he doesn't mind spending. Some guys are really chintzy. They take you out for a couple of drinks in some dive and they think they own you. Always pawing you and everything. All for a few lousy drinks. Now Joey, he really comes across. You don't mind givin' in to a guy like Joey."

"Giving in" was a phrase Marlene used quite often, but Sybil did not think her friend was as free with her favors as the words might imply. She could have Joey in her apartment all night, if she wanted, but she never did. Still, what did a man expect of a girl like Marlene, who was apparently completely on her own? What might a man expect of Sybil, for that matter? What about Jonathan? She really knew nothing about him except that she liked him instinctively. He cheered her, flattered her, and his optimism was contagious. Was that all one needed to know about a man one had invited into one's home?

"You know, honey, you should really be careful about who you invite to your place," Marlene said, unexpectedly voicing Sybil's thoughts. "I mean, if you're out, there it is, and you can walk away from it and go home if you want. But when you are home, it can be—well, it could be hard for you. You know, if you don't object, I think I'm gonna go down and have a little chat with The Phantom. What do you say? It can't hurt to know something about this Jonathan Rogers."

"Oh, Marlene! That sounds so—so—"

"So low-down sneaky?" Marlene asked. "Yeah, but better safe than sorry. The guy could be Jack the Ripper for all we know. And I'd feel better, if I knew you was safe tonight."

She grinned.

"You know, I worry about you, like you was my little sister. And here you are, been married and had a kid. I bet you could tell me stories." She paused expectantly, giving Sybil a curious look. It was the closest she had ever come to prying. When Sybil said nothing, she shrugged.

"O.K. O.K. I'm outta line. You'll tell me someday when you're ready, right? So I'll go downstairs now and see what I can learn."

Sybil didn't stop her. In a way, she was curious about Jonathan, too. It wouldn't hurt to verify her opinion of him. An hour later Marlene was back, flushed and walking a bit unsteadily.

"Never let it be said The Phantom doesn't have the Christmas spirit. If you ask me, she's got more than one and they come in bottles. We've been drinking Irish Coffee down there. It was worth it just for that. You'll be glad to hear that your boyfriend seems to be on the up and up. Good family, clean liver, hard worker. Been livin' here for a year on and off because he's mostly at the hospital. If he's got a wife stashed someplace nobody knows it. A real gentleman, according to The Phantom, so I think you're safe. Must be O.K. Whoo! This head! You know, I'm gonna have to take a little nap to sleep this off. She's got a heavy hand on the bottle, old Philips has, and could drink me under the table."

Marlene giggled. She had begun to slur her words. "Well, at least I'll be up to Joey when he gets here. He always has a couple first. What a night this is going to be! Merry Christmas all around!"

Later she stopped in to say good-bye before she went downstairs to meet Joey.

"He hates climbing the stairs and he's always so anxious to get moving. Hey, you look great, honey, really good!"

Sybil had fastened one of the red silk flowers from Mrs. Thorpe's new dress in her black, wavy hair. She was wearing her blue wool dress and the string of pearls. The Dresden blue of the dress brought out the color of her

76

eyes and made them look even larger. Her cheeks were flushed with excitement. The untrimmed tree, still tied with Gino's rope, leaned against the wall between the windows.

"I'm glad one of us is going to have a tree," Marlene said. "After what I paid for this dress, I couldn't afford even a little one."

Marlene had taken almost all of the profit from her share of the first dress they'd made for Mrs. Thorpe and put it into the black satin gown she'd gotten on sale at Bergdorf's through a friend who worked there. It was two sizes too big to begin with, but she and Sybil altered it until it fit in a sleek, curvaceous line over her breasts and hips. It had a low back and there was a kick pleat on the side that gave the skirt a little flare when Marlene walked in that self-conscious, sensuous manner she had.

"I give 'em what they want and they love it," she often said.

"Well, I'm off, honey. Merry, Merry Christmas to both of us," she embraced Sybil and impulsively kissed her cheek. "See you when I see you!"

Sybil watched from the window and saw Joey drive up in a shiny black car. There was another man in the front. He was almost an exact replica of Joey, including the soft, wide-brimmed, gray felt hat. Marlene sat between them. They pulled away from the curb, wheels squealing and Sybil thought she could imagine Marlene's high-pitched laughter as the men tried to impress her with witty remarks.

Marlene would make it her business to have fun tonight. In fact, she'd be the life of the party. Sybil thought she would not know how to begin to entertain two men at once. She only hoped she could show Jonathan a pleasant time tonight. She wondered what it was about her that had attracted Jonathan.

Other men had been attracted to her before. After her debut several very eligible men had come to call. And what had she offered them aside from a pleasant appearance and good manners? She knew why Edward had been interested because he'd told her. But the others, Aaron Rutherford and Jason Skinner, for instance. Had it merely been her obvious eligibility enhanced by excellent family background or had they seen something else? She wasn't sure what she did have to offer. At seventeen she'd hardly known herself. She'd simply been a starry-eyed, romantic girl. And now? What did she have to offer now? She hoped Jonathan would not be disappointed.

The buzzer rang promptly at seven. She kept Ned up just a little longer so that Jonathan could see him. The baby was sitting in the middle of the sofa, sucking on a piece of dry bread.

Jonathan was holding something behind his back which he refused to reveal right away.

"First I thought I'd bring you flowers, but they're so perishable. Then I thought of diamonds, but they're so cold. And then it came to me! The perfect gift. Practical, edible, and decorative!"

He whisked the package from behind his back.

"Popcorn!" he said triumphantly. "Still warm from the vendor's cart," he added.

Sybil laughed. "How thoughtful! And imaginative!"

"I thought so, too," he said without a trace of modesty.

"Bah!" said Ned loudly.

"What's this? What's this? A critic and not out of diapers yet?"

Jonathan strode past her and picked the baby up, holding him high over his head, much to Ned's delight.

"Madam, it is my professional opinion that this is a very healthy specimen, not too bright, mind you, but healthy."

"His name is Ned," she said, pleased that he really did seem to like babies.

"Ned, short for—?" he inquired.

For a moment, she did not answer. She didn't like to think of Ned being short for Edward and so she said, "Ned! Just Ned!"

If Jonathan noticed her hesitation, he did not show it.

"Well, pleased to make your acquaintance, Just Ned,"

he told the baby, whirling him around the room and coming to a stop before the tree.

"Take a good look at that, my friend. Not a very inspiring sight, is it? But just you wait until tomorrow. It will be transformed. Changed by some magic alchemy in the night. And voila! In the morning, your first Christmas tree."

"Bah!" Ned said.

Jonathan sighed. "There's no pleasing some children. Don't give up. He's young. He may still develop some taste. After all, his mother had the good sense to choose me as a dinner companion. I've left a few things out in the hall," he added. "I'll just go get them while you put sleepy head into his crib."

She took Ned inside with little hope that he'd go right to sleep, but he did not protest. Putting his head down he chanted softly to himself. "Bah! Bah! Bah!"

She smiled, rubbed his back and kissed his cheek tenderly before returning to the living room where Jonathan had set a bottle of red wine on the table and a small box wrapped in Christmas paper at her place.

"Oh, you shouldn't have!" she said. It had never occurred to her to find something for him.

"Of course, I should," Jonathan said, making himself comfortable in the large armchair. "But not to be opened until Christmas, of course. Sit down," he said, catching her hand as she went by, "and talk to me. I want to know everything about you, where you've been, where you're going, and why you love me."

Sybil laughed. She needn't have worried about the evening being dull for Jonathan. He simply made his own fun and he had enough energy and humor for them both.

"We'll talk over dinner. It's ready. Will you open the wine? We don't have very elegant glasses, I'm afraid."

"Don't I know it! My place is furnished, too."

She served lamb chops, baked potatoes, and beets because they were the color of the season. For dessert she'd made an apple pie. Lately she'd been experimenting with baking and found she was good at it. They ate by candlelight. Jonathan joked and told outrageous stories about his adventures in medical school.

"Now I know I can't live without you," he said when they'd finished their meal. "Do you have any idea what they feed interns at Mercy Hospital?"

He began to describe the tasteless, starchy diet, and went on to tell how he'd decided to come north to study medicine because New York was the fabled land of medical miracles. He was from Richmond, Virginia, and was fortunate that his family was able to pay a good deal of his expenses over and above the small salary he received as an intern.

"I couldn't stand living at the hospital. Even when you're off duty, you're on, if you know what I mean. I have one room on the first floor here. It's dark and small and cramped, but it's all mine. A quiet retreat, so to speak. I suppose you'd like to know something about me, I mean, since we're probably going to be married. Let me warn you, once I make up my mind, it's made up."

As they began setting up the tree, he kept up a running commentary.

"I have a mother who adores me, a father who hopes I won't end in a lunatic asylum, and a younger sister who is sure I will. My father's a country doctor, a G.P., but I want to be a surgeon and I'm going to be a great one someday. My mother is the only one who believes in me. Catherine, that's my sister, has calmed down a bit since her marriage. She has a son as old as Just Ned, in there," he said nodding toward the bedroom. "No lights on this tree?" he asked, after he'd finally fitted the stand to the trunk and gotten it to stand upright.

The scent of pine filled the room and Sybil was suddenly struck with the memory of other Christmases and other trees, resplendent with shiny glass balls and candles on every branch. And, of course, she thought of her father. Was he even alive? There was no way of having any news of him without giving herself away. She thought she'd come to terms with this problem, but Christmas Eve and the tree brought it all back.

"Hey, you're a million miles away," he said, coming to sit beside her on the sofa. She had begun to string popcorn in a chain, expertly weaving needle and thread through. She kept her eyes on her work, afraid they would betray her.

"It seems to me I've done an awful lot of talking," he said, finally. "Won't you tell me something about yourself? How long have you been in the city, for instance?"

"Since October."

"Since October," Jonathan repeated. "All that time and we never met," he laughed. "I know you think I'm quite mad. But Catherine, my sister, is wrong, you know. I'm not in the least mad. I'm simply spontaneous and sure of what I want. You'll see. The more you get to know me, the better you'll like me," he added complacently.

He reached over and took the popcorn chain from her hands.

"It's not finished," she protested.

"I know," he said. "But there's plenty of time. Let's talk about you, Sybil Anderson. You have beautiful hands," he said, holding them in his and gazing steadily into her eyes.

"What happened to Mr. Anderson? You don't look like a divorcee."

She caught her breath and felt herself flushing.

"I'm sorry," he said quickly, releasing her. "I don't mean to upset you, but I'm curious. Here you are, an obviously well-bred, beautiful young woman alone in the city with a very young child. What can have happened? Your husband— Is he— Are you a widow? Have you no family?"

He was, as he'd warned her, persistent.

She shook her head, but did not speak. How could she possibly explain her situation? What would he think if he knew?

"Well, I can see you don't want to talk about it." Frowning, he rose and began to pace the floor as he mulled the thought over. "All right," he decided at last, "we won't talk about it. We'll have another glass of wine,

81

we'll sing carols, we'll decorate the tree, and we'll live for tonight. How's that?" he asked, smiling down at her.

Tears came to her eyes and she blinked them away. It was almost the nicest Christmas gift she'd ever received.

"Thank you," she said, shakily, gazing up at him.

"I'm very generous," he whispered, as he drew her to her feet. "And you are very, very beautiful."

For a moment she thought he meant to kiss her and her lips trembled in anticipation. She was not sure that she wanted him to. His kindness had endeared him to her and she was feeling lonely on this of all special family evenings, but she was afraid.

He didn't try to kiss her. He seemed to know instinctively that she was unsure of herself. Instead, he touched her cheek with his fingertips.

"I can wait," he said and then turned toward the untrimmed tree. "We've only two hours till midnight. Will we make it?"

They worked steadily, stringing popcorn and wrapping the long chains around and around, touching every branch until the tree looked as if it had been covered with snow. Jonathan hung the new, brightly colored glass balls and they carefully separated and hung the strands of tinsel that shimmered in the lamp light.

"Who needs lights?" he asked. "When I was a boy in Richmond, we had candles, but they were dangerous and later we had lights, but the darn things were always going out. 'Not worth the money you pay for them,' my father always said. He was always concerned with the buck, you'll notice."

He sighed. "Crotchety as he is, he's as lovable as I am." He stepped back to survey his handiwork. "Not bad if I do say so myself. What do you say?"

"It's beautiful!"

"Now all we need is for Santa to come. I've an idea there are one or two things tucked around here for Ned."

"Well, just a few." She went to the hall closet and took out the presents she'd bought for Ned. There was a teddy bear, which took nearly all of the money Mrs. Thorpe had given her. But she'd managed to get a toy car and a pull toy in the shape of a duck that really quacked. There was no money for wrappings which, of course, wouldn't matter to Ned.

"Now it's Christmas!" Jonathan said with a satisfied grin. "They say Christmas is for children and I guess it is. When I think of Christmas past, I think of my childhood, don't you?"

"Yes, I do." She wished she could stop thinking of her childhood and her father. Her throat felt taut and she hoped she wasn't going to cry.

"Now, they weren't necessarily my happiest Christmases," Jonathan was saying. "I mean, Christmas present isn't bad at all. It holds the promise of Christmas yet to come. What do you want for Christmas, Sybil? For this Christmas and all the Christmases to come?"

It was an impossible question. She wanted to be with her father, safe and loved in her old home. But she wanted Ned, too. She couldn't have both and she couldn't go back.

"I suppose everyone wants happiness and security and friendship," she said slowly. "What do you want, Jonathan?"

"Love," he said simply. "I want love. I want someone for whom I can move mountains," he told her grandly. "And I want loyalty and affection in return. I don't think that's too much to ask, do you?"

Her lips trembled as she smiled at him. She was amazed how closely his thoughts echoed her own, but she had been too shy to voice them.

"No," she said softly. It was the very sort of love she had once dreamed would be hers. That all seemed so very long ago, as though it had happened to someone else and yet it was less than two years since she'd married Edward . . .

IV

For weeks she had been anticipating her wedding night. She'd tried to imagine the joy the actual physical union with Edward would bring. They drove to New York after the reception and arrived at their hotel just past ten o'clock.

She stood proudly at the desk beside Edward as he registered them as man and wife. If the clerk and the bellboys found the honeymoon couple amusing, she never noticed. The manager himself showed them to their suite and presented them with forbidden champagne. Sybil had not yet acquired a taste for the drink. It seemed bitter. Besides, her stomach had begun to feel uncertain.

"You must be tired, darling. Why don't you prepare to retire? I'll join you shortly," Edward said, pouring himself a second glass of champagne.

She found that a maid had unpacked her white lace and ribbon-trimmed nightgown and laid it out for her. The gown was elaborate and beautifully cut, almost like a ball gown. She knew how well it fit, for she had tried it on many times, standing before her mirror and imagining what Edward would think when he saw her wearing it.

She undressed and took a luxurious bath, slipped the gown over her head, and stood shimmering in a white cloud. She unpinned and brushed her hair. When she was ready, she glanced shyly at the huge double bed and decided it would be best to wait on the chaise. She felt a little breathless with excitement.

"Oh, Edward," she whispered aloud to the empty room. "I do love you so."

She waited for nearly an hour and when he did not come, she grew more and more anxious. What had he found to occupy him for so long?

Just as she decided to look for him, he came in. He had changed and was wearing a blue velvet robe and silk pajamas.

He held out his arms and she went to him at once.

"You are even more beautiful now than the day we met riding. Remember? I like your hair loose like that. The way a man's wife looks speaks for him. Did you know that, Sybil? And you are magnificent!"

She blushed with pleasure.

"I want to be beautiful for you, Edward."

"Well, you are, my dear. You are." But he frowned and fingered the ribbons of her gown.

"Isn't this all too much? You look the picture of chaste perfection, like something out of a magazine. What the well-dressed young bride will wear this season!"

She looked down in dismay.

"I—I thought you would be pleased."

"Pleased?" He shrugged and laughed, lifting her chin with his fingertips. "Never mind. Never mind."

He kissed her and his arms tightened around her. The criticism was forgotten in the exquisite pleasure of his touch. He lifted her and carried her to the bed. Trembling with excitement and a bit of apprehension, she lay still and watched him turn out the lights.

When he got into bed beside her, he pulled her close.

"Now," he said. "This is the moment we've been waiting for, isn't it?"

"Oh, yes, Edward."

She waited for his lips to seek hers. Instead she felt her gown pulled unceremoniously from her shoulders. His hands and then his lips sought her breasts. He was quick and not very gentle. She was not ready when the sudden thrust came and she cried out in surprise and pain.

He kissed her cheek afterwards.

"There, that wasn't half bad for the first time, was it?"

She did not know what to say. She felt too choked to speak. Was this the ecstasy of love-making? She'd felt nothing but pain. There was hardly time for emotion.

He rolled onto his side and in moments his slow, even breathing told her he was asleep. She stared miserably into the darkness, overwhelmed with disappointment. Why, it was almost as if he didn't love her at all. What had happened to her tender, solicitous Edward? He'd taken her almost casually. He had not spoken of love. He had not spoken at all. She felt suddenly lonely and rejected. Tears wet her cheeks and she turned her face to her pillow, afraid to wake him with her quiet sobs.

In the morning he woke her with a kiss. It was late for she'd been unable to sleep in the night. Only when the first rays of dawn touched the windows did she drift off. With consciousness, memory returned and she looked at Edward to see if he had somehow changed overnight.

"Better get dressed, my dear. We'll have to be boarding the ship soon. Breakfast is waiting."

He was already dressed and he smiled down indulgently at her. He was the same Edward. She became cautiously happy again. Perhaps this was all part of learning to be a wife.

Their crossing was pleasant. They met other interesting couples and indulged in shipboard activities. By day Edward was as attentive and charming as ever. He seemed to enjoy showing her off.

In Paris they dined at the finest restaurants, went to theaters, and saw all the tourist attractions. But there were days when he was preoccupied and distant. His newspapers and business plans took up much of his time. He no longer had time to listen with rapt attention when she spoke. Her thoughts did not seem to interest him as they once did. He spent hours sending cablegrams or talking on the telephone. He slipped at these times into another world, a world she knew so little about.

She grew to know what to expect of his love-making. Some nights he seemed more passionate than others, but he was always quick, too quick for her to derive much pleasure from the act other than having him completely to herself for that time at least. When he turned from her and slept, she lay awake, feeling unfulfilled and lonely. She wanted so much to know that she was loved and that she was important to him.

Had she failed him in some way? She thought she had and was miserable because of it. She loved him and was not content to wait for those moments when he had time to be affectionate. She knew he was ambitious and the time he spent telephoning and studying financial reports was calculated to improve his success.

They'd been in Paris three weeks when she gathered courage to speak to him of her feelings.

"What can I do to help you, in your business, I mean?" she asked one morning.

He gave her an odd look from beneath his heavy brows. "But you already help tremendously by being my wife."

It was a charming thing to say, so like him. He always knew the right thing to say. She smiled gratefully, but he did not respond with the warmth she expected. She was vaguely disquieted. She needed more than this. She wanted to participate in every aspect of his life.

"Edward, please tell me more about your business. If I understood more I might be able to be of some assistance."

"Assistance? You want to assist me in business?" He was amused and she was hurt. "What nonsense! Women, my dear Sybil, do not interfere in their husbands' businesses. They merely see to it that the social aspects of their lives run smoothly. It is up to you to see that we know the right people."

She was so surprised by his reply that she did not dare argue or explain that she did not mean to interfere. How could he have misunderstood her? They seemed so close in their thinking before they were married. Now she felt shut out. By afternoon she began to believe that she had been wrong to say anything at all. When she met Lady Waring at bridge, she saw a way to redeem herself.

She invited Lord and Lady Waring for cocktails. There were few titled guests at the hotel and Sybil thought Edward would be pleased. Everyone was vying for the attention of this couple. Ruth Waring seemed particularly friendly towards Sybil. She admired Sybil's skill at bridge.

"I think you have a mind like a man. I have the uncanny feeling that you could tell me every card I'm holding in my hand. How do you do it?" the older woman asked. Sybil turned the compliment aside modestly, saying she'd been playing for years which she had, acting as her father's partner. He'd been proud of her skill and never hesitated to ask her to join him when he had friends visit, even if the two other members were male and his contemporaries. She had to be good to play with them and found the bridge games with women rather tame by comparison.

Lady Waring wasn't much older than Sybil, perhaps five years. She seemed quite reserved at the bridge table, but later in the powder room they both had a good laugh over Mrs. Vandervere, who was terribly deaf and had to have each bid shouted at her.

Ruth and Allen Waring were on their honeymoon, too. Sybil thought she had found a friend. And then Edward spoiled everything by displaying a side of his nature she'd not suspected.

He was surprised, and she thought happy, when she introduced Lord and Lady Waring. He not only bought cocktails, but dinner and they planned to spend all of the next day sightseeing together.

In the afternoon they passed a jeweler's shop where a magnificent diamond necklace and bracelet were displayed in the center of the window.

Edward stopped.

"The very thing, Sybil, my darling!"

He had developed the habit of calling her "my darling" or "my love" in public. It embarrassed her. She caught Ruth's sidelong glance. The other woman's eyes revealed not envy, but pity. The look bewildered Sybil because she was not yet aware of Edward's intent. Ruth had evidently known at once.

"These gems need to be displayed properly on a beautiful woman. What do you think, Allen?"

It was difficult to know what Allen thought, he was so correct. Ruth was much more open.

They all went into the shop and Edward extravagantly bought the diamonds and presented them to his wife with a kiss.

"Surely we shall find something for Ruth, too. Select something, Ruth. You deserve to be swathed in jewels. Doesn't she, Allen?"

Allen was a thin brown-haired man with few assets other than his English title. He declined gracefully and Edward quickly accused him of being a poor sport.

"My wife would never forgive me if she were not able to bring home trunkfulls of jewels and gowns. Isn't that so, my love?"

Sybil, by this time had become too numb to deny this. Was it possible that Edward was simply insensitive or were his motives quite calculated? Was he deliberately trying to belittle the Warings? She could not think how to smooth over Allen's embarrassment or her own.

She saw her husband for the first time as the hurt and vengeful boy who had not been accepted at school by the sons of socially prominent families. This was not the Edward she thought she knew.

After the episode at the jewelers they saw very little of Lord and Lady Waring.

There were more jewels and gowns. Edward seemed intent upon using his wife to display his wealth. He urged her to visit the most expensive boutiques of Paris. Harriet Fuller, a round-faced, pleasant matron from Dallas took her to her first Paris showing.

Edward met Frank Fuller in the bar. The two men struck up an immediate friendship. Frank shared Edward's new passion for real estate. The Fullers became their constant companions.

Harriet had been to Paris before and she took Sybil under her wing.

"It's almost impossible to get to one of these spring showings, but Frank can pull a few strings. His father is a Congressman and we know people at the Embassy. They'll know who to approach. We'll get in somewhere, Patou, Vionnet, somewhere. Sybil honey, you're going to make their mannequins look like scarecrows. What a figure you have! Don't think I haven't caught my Frank staring at you! I don't mind as long as he comes home to me," she said complacently, "and he always does."

Sybil had not been aware that Frank was staring at her at all and she watched him carefully after that. It seemed to her that his interest was nothing more than friendly admiration mainly because Edward was constantly calling attention to her appearance which embarrassed her. She was glad Harriet was not jealous. Any woman might have been offended by Edward's behavior.

He did seem to like the Fullers and she was glad. She felt comfortable with Harriet who was down-to-earth and friendly. There were times she wanted to confide in her. The Fullers seemed so compatible and she longed to know the secret of their success, but she could never quite bring herself to speak of such personal matters.

They went to a showing at Vionnet in the Avenue Montaigne. There were more celebrities in the room than she'd ever seen in one place. Designers from London, Rome, and New York were there. Harriet located at least three film stars and two of the richest women in the world. Everyone sat on little gilt chairs while the mannequins paraded past. A beautifully cultured voice announced the model names in French and then in English. Afterwards, champagne was served. Harriet was dying to order at least one gown for herself and she urged the younger woman to do the same.

"Edward would want you to. And just think what a sensation you'll be when you get home!" She paused and looked at her closely. "You feelin' all right, Sybil honey? You look pale."

"I do feel a little faint," she answered uncertainly.

Harriet whisked her into the ladies room and made her sit down with her head between her legs until she felt better. Gently she pried from Sybil the symptoms that had been plaguing her lately. With each one Harriet exclaimed with joy and no surprise whatever.

"Why, I do believe you're in the family way! Oh, Sybil, congratulations!"

Impulsively Harriet hugged her, crushing her affectionately against the long rope of oversized beads that spilled over her full breasts.

"I know how happy I was when little Frankie was on the way and then Rob! Now, don't you worry about a thing. There's nothing to be afraid of nowadays."

But she was worried! A child? So soon? She didn't know if she were ready to have a child. What would Edward say? She'd assumed that he'd been doing something to prevent this. Her pregnancy might spoil their trip.

"You'll have to see a doctor! Do you know of anyone here?" Harriet asked.

She shook her head. "I—no."

"Well, never you mind. I do. We'll go together. You might feel a little funny this first time, don't you know? I'll arrange everything. And we won't tell the boys until we're certain. But I'm certain. What do you want, a boy or a girl?"

She didn't know. She could hardly take it all in. Perhaps her friend was wrong. But she wasn't. A week later the doctor confirmed Harriet's educated guess. There was to be a child.

Sybil stood before her mirror after receiving the news and stared at herself in disbelief. She looked no different than she had on her wedding day. Now she would grow heavy because there was a new life growing inside her. Slowly she began to accept this and a warm thrill of happiness suffused her body. She was going to be a mother. A tiny new life would come into the world, part of Edward and herself. Who could not help being pleased by such a miracle? She'd be a good mother, a companion to her child. She'd see that he was never, never lonely, as she and Edward had been.

She planned to tell her husband that night. Of course he would be happy. It was foolish to worry about that. He wanted children and why not begin their family now whether they had planned to or not. The child was something she could give Edward, something only she could do for him. She could hardly wait to see his face when she told him.

They had tickets to the opera that evening. How perfect! It was at another opera that Edward first told her he loved her. Perhaps the good news would penetrate his new preoccupation and bring them close together again; she was more excited than she'd been in weeks. When, at the last moment, Edward announced that an important business deal was pending and that he would not be able to go because of a vital telephone call, she was bitterly disappointed.

"You go, my darling. I don't want to spoil your evening, too. The Fullers will be glad to look after you."

"Oh, Edward, I would much rather be with you tonight," she protested. She had planned to wear her new Vionnet gown and the diamonds. She knew that would have pleased him.

"No, no! I insist. You go and enjoy yourself. There's nothing you can do for me here."

She went, but after the first act the nervous excitement she'd been feeling all day reached a peak. She felt ill and asked Frank to put her in a cab. This he did after some arguing from Harriet that they all should leave. Sybil refused to allow this and so she arrived alone at the hotel.

She expected to find Edward sitting by the phone, waiting impatiently, having smoked innumerable cigars.

The sitting room of their suite was thick with smoke, but Edward was not there. She thought at first he might have gone down to the lounge, but then she heard a sound in the next room. The drive home in the fresh, cool evening air had revived her. She was looking forward now to giving her husband the good news. She threw open the door to the bedroom and rushed in.

It took several seconds for her to realize that Edward was not alone. He was sitting on the side of the bed completely naked. Beside him was a young man, a boy really. She thought she recognized him as one of the waiters from the hotel dining room.

The shock was like a physical blow. She might have screamed and run from the room, but Edward was suddenly beside her, his hand firmly placed over her mouth. He pushed her roughly into a chair and warned her in a terrible voice not to cry out. He closed and locked the door, taking the key out so that there was no escape. Shock had paralyzed her. This was some horrible dream. This monster could not be Edward. His face was distorted with an emotion she had never seen before.

The horror of that night was engraved on her memory forever. She was forced to sit in a terrified stupor and watch while Edward made love to the boy. She covered her eyes with her hands, but she could not shut out the sounds. Her throat was too constricted to allow her to cry.

When he was through with the boy, he came to her, tearing her hands from her face and dragging her to her feet. His hard, demanding mouth was on hers, cutting off the scream that finally rose to her lips. She wanted to die of disgust and shame. She knew the boy looked on while Edward stripped her of her clothes because she could hear the low, hideous sound of his laughter.

Edward seemed aware of nothing but his desire. His face was flushed and his eyes glazed with unrestrained lust. Her helpless struggles only seemed to excite him more. He caught her wrists and held her hands behind her.

"The child!" She screamed in desperation. "My child! You'll hurt the baby."

Edward froze. He knelt above her, his naked body drenched in sweat. He had heard. His eyes focused on her at last.

"Child?" he whispered hoarsely. "Child? You're pregnant?"

She nodded miserably, sobbing now, painful wrenching sobs.

The boy was sent away and Edward came back to where she lay on the bed. He was wearing a robe and he looked quite composed. She was terrified of him, but she did not try to move away. She couldn't. He lifted her limp body so she rested more comfortably on the pillows. He pulled the sheet over her. When he bent and kissed her forehead, she shuddered and shrank from him. If only she did not feel so weak and dizzy, she would run from him and never come back.

He brought her some brandy and insisted she drink it. She was afraid to refuse him. She thought certainly he must be mad and would harm her. Would the child be mad, too? Dear God!

The brandy warmed and calmed her. When she was quiet, he began to talk.

"What happened tonight, won't happen again. It was wrong to bring the boy here. We could have met elsewhere. In the future, I'll be more discreet."

How could he look so sane and speak such madness?

"In the future—" The words broke from her lips, a harsh cry of horror. "You can't think that I can go on after—after—"

She couldn't finish.

"Nonsense, Sybil! It's not the end of the world. It's not even the end of a marriage. You're too inexperienced to realize that some men have different tastes. Some men enjoy the favors of other men as well as women."

She stared at him. She knew very little about sexual behavior when she married him. What she had seen here tonight was a revelation to her. Surely it was not normal.

"Why—why did you marry me?" she whispered. She had to know.

He got up and began to pace the room, his hands behind his back, his voice low and reasonable. The Edward she had seen minutes ago might never have been.

94

"Why not? You are very beautiful and you do give me pleasure sometimes."

"Then you don't love me. You never loved me."

The words took on meaning as she said them and she thought she could not bear the pain of knowing. It was a pain so strong that it cut her off from everything she'd ever known or believed in. She felt as if she had drifted far from the comfort of simple human compassion and waited in a limbo of non-being.

He did not answer at once and when he did, she knew he was telling the truth as he saw it.

"Love, my dear Sybil, is an illusion at best. I sought you out, yes. You attracted me, yes, and so did your social position. But I attracted you as well. You cannot deny that my financial status was very much in my favor. You and your family were shopping for a suitable husband. I was shopping for a wife. We made a bargain, a good one, I think."

He came to sit on the side of the bed. She hoped he wasn't going to touch her. He didn't.

"You haven't been unhappy, have you? I've treated you well, haven't I? Everyone we've met will vouch for that. Now just go to sleep and we'll forget what happened here tonight. I promise you nothing like it will happen again. I'll make arrangements for us to go home. I want my son to be born at home."

He actually believed what he was saying. He thought they could go on as if nothing had happened, as if she did not know what she now knew about him. He spoke of the baby as *his* son, not their son. He seemed to think she had no choice, no feelings, no rights. And what of their child? What chance would he have with such a father?

She raised herself on her elbows, clutching the sheet to her bare breasts.

"I won't stay with you," she told him. "I won't."

He laughed and she felt frightened and weak again.

"Don't be a fool, Sybil. Where would you go?"

"Home! Anywhere! I'll get a divorce."

"On what grounds?" he asked coolly. "Who would believe you? I'll deny everything. I'll say your pregnancy has unbalanced you. And what of my child? Do you think I'd let you have my child? No, no, my dear. Put the thought from your mind. You've made a bargain and I will hold you to it." The hard, glazed look came over his eyes again. "I do not intend to let you go."

He left her then, closing the door firmly behind him. He discounted her threat because he was certain she could not carry it out. He saw her as weak and completely ineffectual. His contempt only served to make her determination grow. Everything within her rebelled. She would leave him in the morning. She would find the fastest ship home. He thought no one would believe her, but there was her sister, Alicia. She could go to Alicia and to her father. She'd buy her ticket in the morning.

It was then the truth was borne in upon her with horrifying finality. No wonder Edward could be so confident. He was right. She was incapable of carrying out her threat. How could she buy a ticket? She had no money of her own at all. She had gone from the protection of her father to that of her husband with no in between. She did not have the means to be independent. She was as effectively trapped as if she had been imprisoned. She wasn't going anywhere without Edward.

Eventually she did find a means of escape. It took nearly a year of frustration, fear, and desperate unhappiness. Ned was born prematurely at the end of June. It had been a difficult pregnancy and she'd been sick most of the time, too sick to care what happened to her. But afterwards her strength returned and with it her determination to leave Edward. When it became obvious she would have to run away, she made her plans carefully, stealing the money she would need from the loose bills and coins that were strewn over the dresser when he emptied his pockets each night. He never noticed or even suspected her which was only another example of the contempt he felt for her intelligence. When she left, she had nearly four hundred dollars to get started and the knowledge that there was no turning back.

V

Summer came to New York. With the warmer weather Greenwich Village seemed to move outdoors. Striped awnings appeared over store fronts, and tables and benches loaded with merchandise filled the sidewalks beneath them during the day. There were trees, small trees with very few branches, but trees nonetheless, that gave the Village a small town aura so different from the rest of the city. Sybil seldom went uptown except for occasional trips to the wholesale fabric dealer on Seventh Avenue or to Broadway when Mrs. Thorpe sent over tickets. Even uptown New York had its charm, Sybil realized, now that she was no longer fighting for simple survival and had time to look around.

Jonathan said she acted like a tourist whenever they walked through Times Square at night. She only laughed and went right on gaping at the bright lights of commercial signs and theater marquees. This was, after all, the largest city in the world and she was still getting used to it. She found it fascinating and not frightening at all. Only occasionally did she walk through areas where there were long lines outside soup kitchens. Now and then the papers carried pictures of the tar paper shacks of shanty towns like the one in Riverside Park. Then she would become depressed and thankful, too, that she was, at least temporarily, secure at a time when life was very hard for most Americans.

On June 21 they celebrated Ned's first birthday. Sybil

baked a cake and iced it with yellow frosting. Marlene and Jonathan had big plans for the day. They'd been hiding something in Jonathan's apartment for weeks.

Sybil now found her life more pleasant and comfortable than she could ever have believed possible. True, there was still the endless daily chore of washing diapers. True, she still worked long hours, but these were at home. Mrs. Thorpe continued to give them dress orders regularly and, though she wasn't always prompt about payment, she was generous when she remembered, sometimes adding as much as a fifty-dollar bonus. Neither Marlene nor Sybil felt the need to look for any other work. And Marlene was full of big plans for the future.

"The smart thing would be to start our own shop. All we need is a little capital."

"Oh, Marlene, with thousands of people out of work and small businesses collapsing everywhere, how can you think of it?"

Sybil had been able to save some money. She did not think she wanted to risk what she'd worked so hard to save. Try as she would she could not completely imitate Marlene's carefree optimism entirely, though she'd improved, especially since Jonathan had come into her life. He and Marlene were very much alike in their hopeful attitude toward life and this had a tremendous effect on her. She worried far less than she had in the past and when she looked at herself she saw a reasonably happy young woman emerging, so different from the frightened child she'd been a year ago. But she still had serious moments of doubt. Financial security was one of her highest priorities and so she argued against Marlene's proposal that they actually set up a business of their own. There were too many risks. But Marlene was not easily discouraged.

"There's always ways to make money no matter how bad things seem. Look at the Thorpes and their friends. The really rich seem to make out no matter what. And then there's this Roosevelt. This New Deal sounds good to me."

Sybil's mainline Philadelphia background made her

conservative and she realized she was not as politically aware as her friends. Only recently had she begun to study the newspapers and realized that her knowledge of politics was almost nonexistent. She did not feel ready to have an opinion. Jonathan seemed determined to educate her. He shared Marlene's enthusiasm for the new President.

"He's just what the country needs, don't you see? Action, bold, decisive action," he said.

"But he's asking for so much power. Should one man have such power?" she asked.

"Spoken like a true Republican, my girl. See how you give yourself away?" He gave her a knowing look and then a mischievous grin. "Marlene and I will convert you yet. Who is it who had power in the past? The rich, the very rich. Do they even now appreciate the plight of the working classes? What about your Mrs. Thorpe? Who is more likely to look out for your interests, Mrs. Thorpe or F.D.R.? Aha! I can see you know the answer to that one. As for Roosevelt's gaining too much power, I'm not worried. The founding fathers provided us with a splendid system of checks and balances. To quote the great man himself, 'All we have to fear is fear itself.' Where's your faith in American democracy?"

Gradually she did come around to a new way of thinking. With Marlene she listened to the President's Fireside Chats on her friend's newly purchased radio. It wasn't long before she, too, began to be inspired by Roosevelt's courage and confidence. Perhaps Marlene's plan for a business of their own was not impossible.

There was no doubt Marlene herself needed a new interest. There'd been some long, lonely nights for her recently because late in May, Joey suddenly left town.

" 'So long, kid,' he says, just like that. 'Be seein' you around.' And off he goes, no explanation. Nothin'. I don't hear from him for weeks and then I meet Mike and he tells me there's a new operation in Chicago. Chicago! He couldn't tell me himself, the louse."

For a month Marlene spent her evenings alone at the

movies or in dance halls looking for somebody else. Nobody seemed to measure up to Joey. Sybil felt her friend's loneliness and wished that someone new would turn up. Marlene tried hard enough, but even she was becoming discouraged.

"One night stands, most of them," she said bitterly. "And no money to spend. Some guys even try to borrow from me! You're lucky, honey! You got a nice, dependable guy like young Doc. There's not much money there, but you can't go out a lot because of the kid, and I don't see him trying to mooch off you. Yeah, you could do a lot worse than young Doc."

Sybil had begun to believe that, too. Jonathan was very dear to her. She'd become very fond of his gentle, endearing qualities. She admired his strength and determination to succeed. He was devoted to his profession and more and more he seemed devoted to her and to Ned. She found that she depended upon him for advice and support. But more than that, the warmth of his affection for her was like a drug. The more she had of it, the more she needed. After Edward, she thought she would never be able to turn to any man again. But Jonathan's patience and infinite understanding disarmed her. He never tried to pry into her past after that first night and, like Marlene, accepted her for what she was.

They were friends, good friends and they were together as often as he could manage it, though this was barely once a week because of his work at the hospital. So far he had made no real physical demands on her, though he spoke of his affection for her in grand terms as he had from the first. Gradually, her feelings for him grew and she began to wonder how long either of them could be satisfied with their platonic relationship and thought it a blessing they did have so little time alone together. She wasn't sure how she would respond to Jonathan's love if he did make any overtures. There were times when she herself longed for something more, but the pain of her experience with Edward was always with her and she seemed unable to reach out to Jonathan. She still could not even confide in him or Marlene and was constantly aware of the barrier she had built between herself and her friends.

Jonathan arrived the evening of Ned's birthday wearing a party hat with a yellow feather stuck in the side.

How like him! thought Sybil, smiling fondly. He could rise to any occasion, make any moment memorable with his good-natured nonsense.

"Is there anyone, anyone at all celebrating a birthday here today?"

Sybil threw open the door wide so that he could see the party table covered with the paper birthday cloth and set for three. Ned would have to sit on her lap as usual.

"Yes, yes! This seems to be the right place. One moment, madam. I must summon my assistant."

He stepped across the hall and rapped briskly at Marlene's door.

"Come out, come out wherever you are!"

Marlene opened her door and before she could say anything he placed a pink party hat on her head and anchored it firmly with a rubber band beneath her chin.

Marlene screamed with laughter.

"Where'd you get them?"

"Leftovers from children's ward parties, what else?"

"One for you, madam," he said, placing a gilt crown atop Sybil's dark hair and planting a kiss on her forehead.

"Congratulations to you, little mother. The first year is the hardest they say. And here's another crown for old Ned, king for a day. Where is he hiding?"

Ned had pulled himself up and was standing on short, sturdy legs beside the sofa, clinging to the arm for support. He stared at everyone with round dark eyes. He had Edward's eyes. He seemed to have a pleasant disposition and he adored Jonathan. Sybil believed fervently in the stronger influence of environment over heredity. With any luck at all, Ned would become a healthy, normal man. Even now, almost a year later, Sybil could still recall, with frightening clarity, Edward's often terrifying behavior. Sometimes at night she'd awaken believing he was in bed beside her, reaching for her and the thought of his touch made her sick. Then she'd think of Jonathan, his gentleness, his kindness, and she knew in her heart that all men were not like Edward.

"Bah!" Jonathan said, stooping down to place the cardboard crown on the child's head.

"Bah! Bah!" Ned replied and gave him an angelic smile. The gilt crown promptly slid down and rested on his ears, temporarily covering his eyes as well and he howled with indignation.

"Uh—oh! Mama, can you do something about this?"

She quickly lifted Ned onto her lap and adjusted the crown.

"Now for the surprises! Assistant, are you ready?"

"Never more ready," Marlene said, giggling and flexing her muscles.

Together she and Jonathan disappeared beyond the door and returned seconds later carrying a brightly painted red high chair and a newly shellacked play pen.

"Oh!" Sybil exclaimed. "It's too much!"

She'd been thinking about buying them both, but hated to part with money for nonessentials.

"Don't think these are new," Jonathan told her. "Rejects from the hospital again. Would you believe I carried them both all the way downtown on the subway? Not on the same day, of course."

"We've been scraping and painting for weeks," Marlene said and held up her broken nails to prove it.

That, Sybil knew, was a real sacrifice and nearly cried with the joy of her appreciation. How lucky she was to have found two such wonderful friends!

Jonathan put the high chair beside her place at the table and helped Ned into it.

"Bring on the feast," he said, sitting down at his place and holding a knife and fork on end, ready for eating. Ned immediately pounded the tray in front of him.

"Bah!" he yelled.

"Another county heard from. I hate to mention this,

102

ladies and your highness, but I've got to leave in an hour. Believe it or not, I pulled duty for tonight of all nights."

"Aw, I thought you were going to get out of it," Marlene complained. She was as disappointed as Sybil.

"Ours is not to reason why!" he said, shaking his head.

In spite of Jonathan's early departure, the party was a great success. Ned, having been trained by Marlene to blow out matches, blew out the candle on his cake with only a little help from Jonathan.

Marlene stayed to help clean up and Ned allowed himself to be put to bed without protest. Sybil thought his cheeks seemed unusually warm and flushed, but set that down to the excitement.

"Let's celebrate," Marlene suggested. "I mean, it's your day, too. Let's go to the movies. There's a good picture at the Strand with Richard Arlen. What do you say? We'll get Mrs. Philips to come up here. I know you don't like to disturb Ned's sleep. I'll bring my radio over for her and she'll be happy. Come on. It'll be fun!"

"Well—" she hesitated. It would be fun to go out. This was a very special night and she'd been more disappointed than she expected when Jonathan announced he could not stay. It was as though she'd been hoping for something more of this evening. How like a proud father he had been tonight! Against all reason she had indulged herself, allowing her imagination free rein and imagined them all as a family group. But family and father suggested husband. What right had she to think of Jonathan as anything more than a good friend? Still, when he left she felt frustrated and somehow cheated. The movie would take her mind off herself and her confusion. "Mrs. Philips may have other plans," she said, hoping this wasn't true.

"I'll run down and ask her," Marlene offered before Sybil could change her mind.

The movie wasn't crowded so they got good seats.

"I want to see Richard Arlen up close. Wait'll you see him! You're gonna love him, believe me, honey. He's every girl's dream man."

Sybil was surprised to find that she quickly became so

103

absorbed in the story she forgot everything else. At the end, when she thought it was time to leave, Marlene persuaded her to stay and see the whole movie through again.

"That way you really get your money's worth."

She agreed, though there was a nagging feeling in the back of her mind that she probably should not be gone so long.

It was past midnight when they left the theater and walked back through the quiet Village streets.

"Didn't I tell you that Richard Arlen was dynamite? When he smiles I just melt. Did you ever notice that my Joey had a really terrific smile? There's a resemblance there, don't you think?" she asked wistfully.

"Well, maybe." She had noticed no real resemblance between Joey and Richard Arlen and thought Marlene was overly romanticizing Joey.

"I guess you wouldn't unless you knew him real well, the louse," Marlene added vehemently. "Boy, if he ever comes back— If he ever tries to see me, I'm gonna snap my fingers in his face like that."

Mrs. Philips was sleeping on the sofa when they came in. All the lights were on and the radio was playing soft dance music. There was an empty green bottle and a glass on the coffee table. Marlene sniffed and wrinkled her nose.

"Wine! Our superintendent likes her booze. No doubt about it."

Frowning, Sybil went immediately to look in on Ned. The sound of their voices had not awakened Mrs. Philips. What if Ned had cried out? During the day she had never known Mrs. Philips to drink alone and had no qualms whatsoever about leaving Ned with her.

She bent over the crib and leaned her cheek against Ned's. She felt as though she'd been burned and her heart nearly stopped beating from sheer terror.

"Marlene! Marlene!" She rushed into the living room, where a drowsy Mrs. Philips was blinking up at them both.

"What's wrong?"

"He's burning up. Ned's burning up. He's sick."

104

"He can't be. He was fine at dinner."

Marlene went into the bedroom and came out looking frightened.

"There wasn't a peep outa him. Not a peep," Mrs. Philips said. "He's a good baby. I love him like he was my own."

"He's a sick baby now," Marlene said. "Mrs. Philips, we think he has a fever."

"A fever? Naw! He's probably just a little warm. It's a warm night."

She rose unsteadily to her feet and headed for the bedroom. She came out, looking quite sober.

"Lordy, you're right. But don't be scared, now. It doesn't have to be anything bad. It doesn't have to be infantile paralysis or anything like that. I know they've been writing stories in the paper about infantile paralysis epidemics and all that, but it don't have to be that."

"Infantile paralysis!"

Sybil felt the blood drain from her face and her knees went weak. She sank down in the nearest chair.

"Infantile paralysis!" she repeated, too stricken to say anything else. She had a sudden vision of her Ned crawling about with braces on his legs forever, paralyzed like the victims she'd seen in the movie newsreel tonight, or confined to a wheel chair like the President himself. It could happen to anyone.

"Now, don't let's jump to conclusions," Marlene said.

"But he's so still and so hot," she cried, fighting hysteria. "Oh, Marlene, what am I going to do?"

"Where's that doctor friend of yours? He'll know what to do," Mrs. Philips said.

"He's at the hospital."

"Well, call him. You can use my phone."

"I'll do it," Marlene offered. "You stay with Ned."

Sybil sat without moving until Marlene returned. She was afraid to do anything.

"He's coming." Marlene put a comforting arm around her friend. "He's coming as fast as he can."

"But what can I do for Ned while we're waiting?"

"Nothing! He said not to do anything as long as Ned's asleep. If he wakes up, try to give him water. That's all."

They waited, taking turns going back and forth to look at Ned, who neither moved nor whimpered in his sleep. If I hadn't taken him away from Edward, if I hadn't come to New York, thought Sybil bitterly, this never would have happened. First Papa, now Ned!

When Jonathan came in he put his arm around her and she shuddered against his shoulder.

"It's going to be all right," he told her. "Let's have a look." Together they went into the bedroom.

With gentle, practiced hands he undressed and examined the baby, who whimpered slightly but never awoke.

"It happened so fast," she said. "Oh, I never should have gone out. Never!"

"Don't blame yourself, Sybil. These things always happen fast. Babies can run a terrible temperature very suddenly for the least little thing. And you can't blame yourself."

"But he seemed warm to me before I left. I thought it was the excitement, but it wasn't. Oh, Jonathan, what have I done?" She began to cry helplessly, hopelessly.

Jonathan shook down the thermometer briskly.

"Go inside and wait, Sybil," he told her in a firm, businesslike tone. "Tell Marlene to come in here. I want to talk to her."

She went obediently, her shoulders shaking with her shuddering sobs. She felt completely useless.

When Marlene came out, she spoke what words of comfort she could.

"I'm going to get some sleep now. He says you'll need me in the morning."

Jonathan joined her at last. She was sitting on the sofa, her head on her knees, trying to control herself. He came and sat beside her and took her into his arms. She went willingly.

"Sybil, darling, don't do this to yourself," he whispered. "I can't bear to see you suffer like this."

106

"Tell me the truth, Jonathan. Please, tell me the truth. Is it—is it infantile paralysis?"

He grasped her shoulders and held her from him so that he could look into her eyes.

"I don't honestly know. A number of things start like this. I've given him something to bring the fever down. We can only wait now and be brave."

"Oh, Jonathan, what would I do without you!"

She put her head on his shoulder and wept. He rocked her gently in his arms and she knew she never would have survived alone.

Ned's fever raged for two days. She could get him to drink very little. She and Marlene took turns tending him. Jonathan divided his time between the hospital and Ned's bedside. None of them slept very much and Sybil hardly at all.

If it was infantile paralysis, if Ned were going to need special medical attention, it would have to be the best and that would cost money, far more than she had. She thought with reluctance of her family. Would she have to turn to them, give up all the freedom she had earned and risk losing Ned entirely? For his sake she would do it, of course.

Late in the afternoon of the second day she went into the bedroom. She dipped a cloth in cool water and sponged his hot skin. If only he would open his eyes! If only he would look at her and smile his guileless smile. He slept on.

Wearily, she stretched out on the bed beside the crib and lay watching him. The burden of the work on Mrs. Thorpe's dresses had fallen to Marlene. Together they'd carried the sewing machine, which they now owned, into Marlene's apartment so not even the whirring of the wheel would disturb Ned. Mrs. Philips cooked soups and casseroles to tempt them all, but Sybil was beyond caring about food.

It was warm in the tiny bedroom even with the window wide open. She stared at Ned's flushed face willing him to get well. Her eyelids grew heavy and she slept.

She came back slowly as from a long distance. There was a familiar sound in the room. Someone was sitting beside her on the bed. She could feel the warmth of his body.

"Mama!"

"Mama! Mama!"

She was dreaming. Ned and Jonathan were playing. She could hear them so clearly through the pounding in her head.

"Sybil!"

She forced her eyes open. Jonathan was looking down at her, his face white and strained. Beside her there was an insistent rattle of wooden bars. She turned slightly. Her neck ached terribly. Ned was kneeling in his crib calling out to her.

"Mama!"

"He's all right, Sybil. The fever broke. He's going to be fine. Sleep! Sleep!"

She slept on and off for several days. Once she awoke and was alarmed to find that Ned's crib was not beside her bed.

She sat up and cried out. Jonathan was with her at once.

"Ned's with Marlene," he told her. "Rest, my darling. Rest."

But she would not close her eyes until Marlene appeared in the door with Ned. He looked completely recovered and full of energy. Tears of gratitude and relief slid down her cheeks. She slept. Her own recovery took longer. Her fear and the lack of sleep had weakened her more than she knew.

When at last she was strong enough, Jonathan took her for a walk in the park. She'd been ill for more than a week.

Everything along Washington Square looked new and very beautiful to Sybil. The neat brownstone houses that lined the street were more precious than ever. In the park the trees looked green and the grass more lush. They

108

sat on a bench and watched the people stroll in the afternoon sunshine.

"Smell the air, Jonathan," she said, delighted to be well and growing stronger and to know that Ned was healthy and energetic and likely to grow up that way, according to Jonathan. There was no need now to think of Edward or going to her family for help. She sniffed the air delightedly, laughing at herself as she did so, but finding it irresistible. "It's so fresh. Somehow fresh air doesn't ever seem to get into the apartment." She smiled up at him shyly.

Something between them had changed during the time she had been ill. An intimacy had developed of which she was very much aware. Even now he held her hand in his and the warmth and strength he communicated to her was a delight.

When he spoke his eyes were filled with tenderness.

"I suppose you know that we can't go on as before."

She looked deep into his eyes and saw there just what she had long suspected and what she herself had desired.

"I love you, Sybil. You must know that. Once I told you that what I wanted was a woman for whom I could move mountains. I have found her. All I ask is affection and loyalty in return. What I'm asking is that you marry me."

She turned away from him, trying to hide the tears that suddenly sprang to her eyes. Nearby a pigeon waddled along the path, cocking his head and looking at her with a faintly puzzled expression, as Jonathan must be looking at her. He put his hand on her shoulder and turned her to him. She could not look at him, but sat with her head bowed, weeping silently. What could she say to him? Now that it had come, what could she say or do? What right had she to love him or allow him to love her when she was married to Edward?

"What is it, Sybil? Isn't it time you told me?"

"I—I can't," she whispered. Fear of the truth being known, fear of having to deal with it still paralyzed her.

"Can't? Sybil, can't? I believe you do love me, whether

109

you realize it or not. I don't know what terrible experience you are keeping locked inside you, but whatever it is I want to share it with you. I want to share it and then help you to forget it. Let me do that, Sybil."

She looked up at him then and knew that the love in his eyes was echoed in her own heart. How could she ever have thought she had loved anyone before?

Gently he lifted her chin and with the greatest tenderness their lips met. She leaned toward him hungrily, slipping her arms around his neck. They were locked in an embrace filled with a passion and longing that nearly dissipated the fears of the past. When he released her, they were both shaken.

"I knew," he whispered. "I knew. Nothing can keep us apart now. Nothing. We'll be married. I have only a few months more of my internship here and then I'm going to take you away and care for you, cherish you—"

His voice shook with emotion and she reached up and touched his lips before he could continue. The sadness she felt at having to tell him what he must know mingled with the pure joy of her awareness of their love.

"I—I am not free to marry you, Jonathan."

A frown creased his wide forehead and she thought she could not bear the sudden pain in his eyes.

"Then there is a Mr. Anderson."

She nodded mutely, steeling herself against the anger he must feel at the deception she had practiced. She was not prepared for his reaction. He laughed.

"You little goose! You don't love him. You love me. It's only a matter of becoming legally free, don't you see? It's simply a matter of time, a year perhaps. What's a year? Oh, darling, nothing matters but that you love me."

He was so certain that against all reason she began to hope. And that night they became lovers. Marlene, who had been sitting with Ned, while they went to dinner, went sleepily back to her own apartment.

He took her into his arms and the kiss they had shared in the public park took on a greater depth of passion in the privacy of her living room. His gentle hand touched her breast and Sybil stiffened and pushed him away.

"Sybil, darling, you must not be afraid. I love you. And I want you. Have I frightened you?"

She turned from him with a choked cry. All the desperate fear and disgust of her life with Edward returned and she was suddenly terrified of Jonathan. He was a man with male appetites and desires. How Edward's appetites had humiliated her! Once she thought she had loved him, too.

Jonathan sat down on the sofa and held his arms out to her.

"I think I understand," he said. "Come here beside me."

"No," she cried, tormented by terrible memories. "It's no use. I can't."

What was she doing to him? To them both? She saw the pain of rejection in his eyes and felt it as her own. How could she describe the events that had left her emotionally crippled? She closed her eyes and tried to move away, but she couldn't. Her desire was stronger than she knew.

When she turned again to look at his dear face in the lamplight, she hesitated. She had the strongest feeling that he knew something of her turmoil without being told and in that moment she felt closer to him than she ever had to anyone else.

"Come here," he said quietly and she went to him. She thought she would do anything for him. Anything!

He kissed her lips, her neck, and then, unbuttoning her blouse, her breasts. Sybil slowly relaxed and gave herself up to the pleasure of his touch. He was gentle and infinitely patient and she found herself responding to him completely, lost in a depth of emotion she had never known. When at last they were united, she cried out with pure joy. This, then, was love.

They settled into a pattern of happiness. She lived for the times they could be together. Her skin took on a new glow, her eyes shone, her figure began to fill out again.

Jonathan said she was beautiful and Sybil believed him. She wanted life to go on like this. Sometimes she even imagined that it could and she suppressed her feelings of guilt at not having told Jonathan the truth. She didn't want to think of the truth. She wanted to believe that there had never been any other life for her. Jonathan was her life now.

Sometimes she'd wake in the night and turn to look at him in the semi-darkness. He slept like a small boy, his arm flung across his forehead, ruffling his hair. Then she'd move to kiss him and he'd wake and reach for her, delighted to be awakened and aware of her. She'd feel his strength and his love. She wanted to be his wife, to belong to him fully, to give him children.

She allowed herself to dream that this could be. Time was what was needed. Time! In time perhaps Edward's fury would dissipate, the scandal of her leaving would be minimized. Perhaps then, sometime in the dim future, when Jonathan's years of study were completed, they could face Edward together.

For several months Jonathan said nothing about the efforts he assumed she was making to obtain a divorce. He never questioned her about her marriage or her family.

"I know all I need to know about you," he said. "If you never want to tell me, I won't care. But I'm here, ready to listen, if you need me."

Still, she did nothing, said nothing. There was Ned to consider. She began to follow Marlene's newspapers and movie magazines through which she became very familiar with the pattern of divorce suits. Only when the man left the woman were the children given over to the mother's custody. How easily Edward could prove her an unfit mother! Hadn't she run away? Wasn't she, even now, living with another man? There would be no question of what Edward could do if he wanted to. Ned was his son, the son he so desperately wanted. She had no reason to believe he would give up his son. She had no reason to think he would want to do anything but punish her for what she had done to him.

Neither could she believe that anyone would be convinced of what she knew of Edward's perversion. She'd failed to convince her own sister, who had scornfully turned aside all efforts to describe the horror of life with Edward.

"What rot, Sybil! What rot! There's no one more virile than your Edward. Perhaps he's too virile for you. Admit it. It's the physical side of marriage you don't like. Well, we all have to get used to it, you know. It's the price one pays. What you must learn is how to manage him, that's all. God knows it wasn't easy training Monty, but he learned eventually. They all do."

For the first time Sybil understood the relationship between Monty and her sister. Alicia managed her marriage to suit herself and Monty was too weak to do anything about it. Isn't that what was happening to her and Edward in reverse?

"Marriage is compromise, Sybil. Remember that."

True to his word Edward never again brought any of his young men into their bedroom. He did talk about them, bragging and raging, often berating her for her lack of passion and what he called her prudery.

"Thank God I don't have to depend upon you for sexual gratification," he'd said after Ned was born.

He delighted in describing to her in detail his most recent triumphs until she was sick with disgust.

"I need you for only one thing, or I wouldn't bother at all. Sons!" he thundered. "I expect to have sons. The union of Eldridge and Ashford blood is what I bargained for and what I shall have."

Frightened and unsure of herself, she was unable to stand up to him or fight back. She became more and more nervous and close to collapse after her father's stroke. Finally, even Edward had to agree with her doctor. She needed a change or there would be no question of another pregnancy. She saw her chance and seized it.

She knew exactly what Edward must have felt last fall when he learned that she was not in Washington visiting the Fullers as he believed. She'd outwitted him and the scandal of her running away must have mortified him. He'd been so devoted to the idea of gaining respectability and social position through their marriage. At the time, she hadn't thought of that. She only wanted to be free of him. She thought she had been particularly clever about writing Harriet and carefully confusing the dates. She told Harriet she'd be arriving a week later and suggested to Edward that the time was sooner. That gave her a week or more to disappear. He had seen her off on the train, admonishing her for refusing to take along a nurse. But Sybil could not afford to take along a nurse, especially not one selected by Edward. She'd changed trains at Wilmington and gone on to New York. When Edward realized what she'd done, she knew he must have been as surprised as he was furious. He would not have credited her with such courage. How lucky she'd been! She had not been found and Edward had not been able to take Ned away. But her victory was not complete. Inevitably the time would come when she must take decisive action. Only her love for Jonathan could force her to do that.

In early fall Ned took his first step. He and Jonathan were playing on the floor. They both crawled about on all fours, chasing each other. And then Ned pulled himself onto his feet beside a chair as usual. Jonathan called to him, teasing and growling playfully like a bear. Ned reached out to him and nonchalantly took two steps before sitting down.

Jonathan was delighted. He scooped the baby up and held him high above his head.

"Today you are a man, my son! Sybil, isn't he wonderful? When we're married, I wonder if Ned's real father would allow me to adopt the boy. What do you think?"

She stared at him in consternation. The request was more unnerving because it was so unexpected.

"Well, don't look like that, darling. It's not such a strange request and I do love him. He's part of you and therefore a part of us both. It couldn't hurt to ask. I know you don't want me to interfere with the proceedings, but surely this is not an unreasonable request."

114

"No," she said through tight lips, "of course not."

She went into the kitchen to prepare dinner and knocked one of Ned's bottles onto the floor where it broke and milk spilled out over the linoleum. She stared at it hopelessly, tears stinging her eyes, as she forced herself to face reality. Sooner or later she was going to have to choose between Jonathan and little Ned.

And in November Joey was back. Marlene made the announcement in an offhand way, but Sybil could see she was pleased and excited, no matter what had been said about not taking him back.

"He dropped by about a week ago while you were out with Ned."

"Oh? What did he have to say for himself?"

"Well, he seems to have been through something bad out in Chicago. He sounded different, not so reckless. I told him I didn't know if I wanted to start goin' out again steady like we were. That set him back, I can tell you. He called me three times on Mrs. Philips' phone. So, I figure, why not give him a break? We're goin' out tonight." She looked wistful. "I mean I haven't found anybody new and, well, watching you and Jonathan could make anybody lonesome."

Sybil was surprised. She hadn't realized her friend felt that way. She'd been so wrapped up in her love for Jonathan, she hardly noticed what was going on around her.

Joey made a big change in Marlene. She laughed and joked again and began to be interested in clothes. She'd breeze in and out of the apartment always on her way to somewhere, though she still made time to do her share of the sewing for Mrs. Thorpe.

Several times during that fall Mrs. Thorpe had given Sybil tickets for Broadway shows so that dresses could be copied or adapted for her, or just because she happened to have the tickets. Learning that Sybil had a "special friend" as she put it, she made it a point to send two tickets so they could enjoy the plays together.

Jonathan took such largess philosophically.

"There's nothing like knowing the right people and,

someday, we're going to be the right people and have a box of our own. Then we'll invite Mrs. Thorpe to be our guest in appreciation of past kindnesses. Little does she know that she's piling up good will with the social leaders of tomorrow."

Sybil wished she could be as certain as he of their future. Again and again she promised herself she would tell him the truth. She even planned exactly what she would say and how she would ask his advice. But she couldn't bring herself to speak. She let the days slip by, grasping greedily at the happiness of the moment.

That fall of 1933 they saw Gershwin's *Of Thee I Sing* and came away humming "Love Is Sweeping the Country". When they got home, they found Joey Ferguson keeping Marlene company while sitting with Ned. They looked satisfied with each other and Sybil was pleased that things were working out so nicely for Marlene.

"Well, well, Princess, long time no see." Joey's hearty voice filled the room. "Gorgeous as ever. I still think you oughta be in pictures. Say the word and I'll get you a screen test. Uncle Joey has all kinds of connections."

He was as expansive as ever, but Marlene was right. Some of the reckless spirit had left him and he looked more like a man who was ready to settle down. She would not be in the least surprised if Joey changed Marlene's mind about marriage.

She introduced Jonathan before running in for a quick look at Ned. She never went out now without worrying just a little. When she came back, she found that Joey was holding forth about "the girls", as he called them.

"I mean it, Doc. I think these two have something. All they need is a little capital and I know where to get it for them. Marlene and me have been going over some of the details and I think they can swing it. You can't tell to look at her, but the princess here has got a real marketable item," he said, nodding toward Sybil. "The designs this little girl makes up for their client are really something."

"It's true," put in Marlene enthusiastically. "Sybil just

116

shows sketches to Mrs. Thorpe and she buys them. She likes them better than anything. We're doing O.K. and I'm not complaining, but can you imagine how much better we could be doing with a couple of clients like Mrs. Thorpe?"

Suddenly Sybil wasn't sure if she liked the way the conversation was going at all. She thought she and Marlene had been all through the obvious pitfalls of starting their own business. It was something she was really afraid to venture into. Besides, Joey was forcing them to think about the future and that was the one topic she hoped to avoid.

"What I had in mind was this little shop in the fifties near Madison," Joey was saying, as though he had a right to decide for her. "Nothin' too fancy, you understand. But it could be dressed up to be real high-toned. Why, in a year or two the girls could be raking it in. Ten thousand dollars profit would be peanuts."

Sybil glanced quickly at Jonathan to see what effect this proposal was having on him. He leaned forward, clasping his hands between his legs and asked the question she should have thought to ask.

"Tell me, Mr. Ferguson, what would be your interest in this enterprise?"

"Hey, Doc, everybody calls me Joey. We're all friends here." He leaned back and spread his arms across the top of the sofa.

Are we, thought Sybil. Should she trust Joey just because Marlene did? After all, they both knew he'd been involved in some shady deals and she did resent his interference. What did he want out of this? On her own would she have been sensible and firm enough to question Joey's motives? She hoped she'd grown enough emotionally to be able to do that by now.

"Yes." Jonathan was gazing steadily at Joey. "But what I wondered was, what sort of interest would you have in this business?"

"Well, gee, Doc, naturally I'd expect my cut, a little

117

right off the top, a percentage. After all, I'd be supplying the capital."

"You personally?"

"Well—" Joey shifted his position, crossing his ankles on the already scarred coffee table. "Not exactly. But I got some connections," he finished smugly.

"I see."

Jonathan and Sybil exchanged glances.

"Well, it would only be fair," Marlene said, taking Joey's part and patting his arm. "He'd be goin' out on a limb for us and all. I wouldn't mind agreeing to a little somethin' for Joey. Would you, Sybil?"

She hesitated. She didn't know what to say. She certainly did not want to insult her friends. But she didn't even want to discuss the subject, not now.

Jonathan spoke for her. Only he said so much more than she expected that her heart nearly froze with fear. For she realized at that moment that life for her, for all of them, could never be the same again.

"I really think Sybil's opinion has no bearing on this. You see, we plan to be married. In a few weeks I'll be accepting a position in another city. Naturally she will be going with me. So you see, there's no question of her participating in such a business venture."

Marlene jumped to her feet, a look of consternation on her face.

"Sybil, you didn't tell me! You didn't say one word! You're leaving town?"

Since this was the first Sybil had heard of Jonathan's plans, she was surprised, too.

"I—" she began.

"I meant it for a surprise," Jonathan told them. "Darling!" He caught her hand and pulled her down into the chair beside him. "I just heard today. It's definite. I have an opportunity to study under Dr. Everett Wentworth in Philadelphia. He's one of the most respected men in the field of cardiology. It's an opportunity I can't afford to pass up. It looks like Philadelphia will be our new home."

He slid his arm about her, so pleased with his news he didn't notice her distress.

"Well, that tears it, Joey!" Marlene stood up, trying to keep the resentment from her voice. "Gee, if I had known you two were planning something like this—" She lifted her arms helplessly. "Come on, Joey. Sorry I got you all excited for nothin'. That's the end of Anderson and Grant. It was swell while it lasted. Back to the sweatshop for me. You sure are full of surprises, Sybil."

"Oh, Marlene!" She wanted to reassure her friend somehow, but did not know what to say. Her own world was crumbling about her and she could concentrate on little else. She was painfully aware of Jonathan's possessive arm around her. He was so certain of what would be.

After a brief struggle, Marlene managed a smile.

"Aw, I'm not mad at you, honey," she said and she leaned down and kissed Sybil's cheek. "Just surprised is all and disappointed for me. I hope you'll be very happy. You're a lucky guy, Doc. Come on, Joey."

Sybil blinked back tears of gratitude for Marlene's understanding, but they were tears of frustration, too. Nothing seemed to be going as she expected. Everything was moving fast, too fast, and she was being cut adrift.

"Now, tell me that you're proud of me," Jonathan pulled her close. "There were twenty-five candidates and I was chosen." He could not keep the pride from his voice. "It's what I really want, what I've been working for, hardly daring to hope I'd be so lucky. Wentworth's the best man in the country," he continued more soberly. "In the annals of medicine his name is second only to God."

"Oh, Jonathan, I am pleased for you. It—it's a great honor."

"Yes!" He grinned happily. "More, tell me more. Tell me that I'm brilliant, charming, and that you love me madly."

"I do, Jonathan. All those things are true," she said slowly getting to her feet. Her knees were weak and she felt choked by unshed tears. Now was the time to tell him. Now! But how could she? Philadelphia! It was so unfair! Any other city might have meant the possibility of their being together. Anywhere else she could be anonymous. But Philadelphia! Home! The scandal would ruin Jonathan before he began. Edward would see to that. His need for revenge would be overwhelming.

She was as sure of that as the fact that Jonathan would refuse the appointment if it meant losing her. How could she ask him to do that? How long would it be before he began to blame her for causing him to lose this opportunity? How long would it be before she began to blame him for her losing Ned? And Ned! How could she abandon him to his father?

"Something's wrong."

"Yes."

"What?"

"I— don't know how to tell you."

Jonathan stood and put his hands on her shoulders. All the joy had left his eyes. He was frightened, she saw, as frightened as she. When she thought of telling him the truth, she felt faint.

"Just tell me," he said quietly.

Sybil turned away. She couldn't bear the look in his eyes.

"I don't think it will work," she said softly.

It took all her courage to say that much.

"What? What won't work?" Jonathan's voice had become cold with apprehension.

She took a deep breath. "*We* won't. I can't go to Philadelphia with you, Jonathan. I can't marry you."

Every word burned like a brand on her heart.

"Sybil!" It was a strangled cry of pain and disbelief. "What are you saying?"

"That I can't marry you, Jonathan."

She willed herself not to break down. This had to be done. She must be strong. Dear God, for his sake she must be strong.

"Look at me and say that," he growled from the depth of his pain. "Look at me and say that you don't love me."

She turned slowly to meet his eyes. She loved him more than life itself. If she could have died for him then and there, she would have done it, rather than inflict this pain. How wrong she had been to accept his love! She had no right to those stolen months of happiness. She deserved to die rather than ruin Jonathan's life and prevent him from obtaining the success and happiness that were rightfully his.

"I'm—I'm fond of you, Jonathan. I'll always be fond of you."

"Fond? How can you use such a word after all we've been to one another?" he shouted. His dark eyes flashed their fury. "You're lying! Don't you think I know it?"

He shook her violently and the clasp that held her dark hair in place slipped out and fell to the floor. Sybil felt his fingers biting into the soft flesh of her shoulders, but she did not cry out. She stood before him mute and helpless in the wake of his rage.

"Why? Sybil, why? What have I done? What have you done that you must deny us everything?"

His voice thundered around them. His thin face had grown pale and strained. She wanted to throw herself into his arms and tell him everything. She wanted to comfort him and be comforted. She wanted to hear him say he would give up his plans to study with Dr. Wentworth. She wanted to hear him swear he would live with her always, no matter what. It was what he would say if he knew. Jonathan, dearest Jonathan! No sacrifice would be too great and she could not, must not allow him to do this.

She shook her head. "No one is to blame, Jonathan. It's simply over," she said firmly. "For awhile we had something very beautiful together. Let's leave it at that."

He could not accept anything she said and he refused to leave. He carried on until morning, casting accusations, demanding explanations, pleading with her. She bore it all as stoically as she could. At dawn he left for the hospital, vowing that this could not be the end. He'd be back that night and the next and the next until he had the truth from her.

The moment he left, her strength seemed to melt away. She was overcome with a sudden wave of nausea and rushed to the bathroom, where she was painfully ill. Afterwards she lay down on her bed only to stare wide-eyed at the ceiling. Without Jonathan life would not be worth living. She groaned and turned her face to the pillow and wept. Why had they ever met? How cruel life was!

Weak and shaken, she rose with Ned, who awoke cheerful and energetic as ever. She cooked his cereal and found the odor made her nauseous, but managed somehow to overcome it. She didn't try to eat anything herself.

Marlene came in to work later that morning and was amazed at the change in her.

"My God, kid! What's happened?"

It was all she needed. She burst into tears. All her pent-up emotions poured forth and with it the story of how she was sending Jonathan away, but not why.

Marlene wept, too.

"You sure you know what you're doing? You're sure?" she asked finally.

"It's what I have to do."

"Yeah." Marlene shook her head. "I guess you know what you're doing. Me? I wouldn't do it. A guy like young Doc comes along once in a lifetime." Her voice was tinged with awe. "O.K. O.K.," she said quickly when she saw that tears threatened to overwhelm them both again. "What we need is something to eat. Soup and toast for you and then we'll get to work. I don't for the life of me see how you're going to work the flare in this skirt. It looks like it starts below the knee. How's she gonna walk in something like that?"

Marlene kept her so busy there was little time to think. But the pain of losing Jonathan was constant. He arrived that evening as he promised, but he behaved as though nothing had happened. They all had dinner and he played with Ned, roughhousing about the floor as usual. He joked with Marlene and was tender and solicitous toward Sybil. When they were alone, he told her that he knew what was wrong. She'd suddenly become frightened, over-

122

whelmed by the idea of a second marriage, of making a second mistake. She denied this, but he refused to believe her.

"I'm very patient. Not to mention persistent. We have three weeks. You'll change your mind. You'll come with me. We belong together."

She was grateful for the change in him. False hope had made him easier to deal with. But what would it be like on that last day?

He insisted on taking her to dinner his last night in New York. He seemed to have accepted the fact that she would not be coming with him at first.

"I won't give up hope," he told her. "No, don't argue. I know all the arguments, all of them. They're engraved on my heart. But we won't talk of that. We'll just be two people who have met for a pleasant evening."

He chose a small uptown restaurant. It was not particularly expensive by most standards, but she knew he had sacrificed to take her there and she was as determined as he to make their last night memorable. She never expected to see him again.

She wore the Dresden blue wool dress she'd worn on Christmas Eve. Marlene had done her hair for her. It shone in rich black waves around her head.

Jonathan, too, looked his best. He'd rented a dinner jacket and the stiff white collar of his shirt and his neat black tie made him look suddenly older, more sophisticated. She gazed across the small candlelit table at him, hungrily trying to memorize the lines of his face, his kind eyes, his generous mouth, the faint cleft in his chin.

"I'll always love you, Sybil," he said, reaching out and taking her hand. His voice was husky and he suddenly looked down, pressing her fingertips to his lips. He seemed unable to say anything else.

They spoke very little at dinner. They had, after all, said all that could be said. It was a pleasant autumn night and afterwards they walked over to Fifth Avenue and on past the park.

"I don't think I'll ever want to be in New York on an autumn night like this again without you, Sybil."

He stopped abruptly beneath the light of a street lamp and tipped her face towards his. He traced her lips with his finger.

"You're sorry for me. That's why you don't smile. Don't be sorry, Sybil. You can't love me the way I love you. That's not unforgivable. I think I understand now at last. I was too cocky, too sure of myself. Because I love you, I thought you had to love me. You were very kind and generous. I'll never, never forget you."

"Jonathan—"

"No, it's all right. I know it's over. I didn't until a little while ago, but I can see it's over now. I imagine it will be something of a relief for you not to have me around. Thank you, my darling. Thank you for the best days and nights of my life."

He kissed her then, long and tenderly and she thought her heart would cry out in anguish. Around them a light wind lifted and scattered the dried leaves. Overhead a half moon sailed in and out of clouds in the November sky.

I love you, Jonathan, with all my heart. You, only you, Jonathan. She didn't think she would ever love again.

Her silent thoughts reached out to him as she gave herself to his embrace, feeling the depths of his passion. She felt the strength of his desire as he held her close.

"Good-bye, Sybil. Good-bye," he whispered as he pressed his cheek against hers.

And then he was hailing a cab. He settled her in it and paid the driver.

"I can't bear to go back with you," he said, leaning in the window, his eyes searching hers. "Not and have you shut me out. Tell Ned—" he began in a choked voice and then shook his head and waved the driver on.

He stood under the street lamp looking after her. She turned in her seat to watch him, a tall, graceful figure in the lamplight, growing small and indistinct. His voice came to her through time and she heard it as she had that first day.

124

"All! You're taking them all?"

And, "My word you're beautiful! Will you marry me?"

And on Christmas Eve, "All I ask is loyalty and devotion in return. That's not too much to ask, is it?"

Oh, Jonathan! Then the traffic moved in between them and he was gone.

She turned around to look ahead. Tears streamed down her cheeks, blurring the tall buildings and the bright lights and she found she was the exact center of a world filled with pain and longing.

VI

There was no way to relieve the pain of her loss. She thought of nothing else. Where was he? What was he doing? Did he ever think of her? Of course he did! She knew he did.

She listlessly went through the motions of living. She cared for Ned because he needed her. She worked for Mrs. Thorpe because she had to. Somehow she managed to go on.

She was sick much of the time, too, especially in the morning. She set this down to nerves. Two weeks later she knew she was pregnant and the realization almost made her change her mind. Jonathan's child! She'd wanted to give him children, but not like this. They'd been so careful. It was hard to believe it had happened. What should she do now? If she went to Jonathan, he'd never leave her. He'd give up everything for her. She couldn't let him do that. But if she didn't, was she being fair to him? To the child?

Marlene guessed her predicament.

"This kinda puts everything in a new light," she said. "I mean, you'll have to tell him."

"No," Sybil said quietly. "He must not know. It's very important. He must not know." Her voice cracked with desperation.

"O.K.! O.K.! Take it easy, kid. But what are you gonna do? I mean, you already got one kid. I mean, gee!" she finished helplessly and then looked thoughtful.

"You could get rid of it."

"No!" She was horrified. "No, Marlene," she repeated more quietly.

As the days went by, she became more calm. Jonathan had left her with something. His child. It was more than she had hoped to have, more than she deserved. The thought of managing alone with two children frightened her enough to bring up the subject of the shop Marlene was so anxious to establish. They couldn't depend forever on Mrs. Thorpe. At any time she might give in to one of her whims and leave them for someone else. A shop might represent security.

"Do you think Joey would still be interested?"

Marlene was delighted and sure there would be no problem. "I'll talk to him," she promised.

He was enthusiastic and full of ideas.

"The way I see it, you girls have got to put out the word. Ya know what I mean? Let this Mrs. Thorpe know what you're doing. She must have friends. Let her bring 'em around. She's a walking advertisement for you both."

"I don't know how Mrs. Thorpe will take to that," Sybil said doubtfully. "Part of our charm is working exclusively for her. She might resent the whole idea."

"Yeah? Well, she'll have to get used to it one way or another, if she wants you to go on making her dresses," he said.

"She does, I know she does," Marlene put in. "She gets better work from us at half the cost. She's not going to give that up. And she likes you, honey. She says your designs are really her. I bet she brags about you to her friends."

"All to the good! All to the good!" Joey nodded. "You gotta capitalize on that. Now, I'm gonna start movin' ahead on this. The place is available and so is the dough. You kids gotta do your part and drum up the business. What say we have a little drink to seal the bargain?" he suggested, rubbing his hands together. "As long as the princess here doesn't try to take hers straight."

He grinned up at Sybil, who dutifully went to get

127

glasses, real highball glasses instead of the water tumblers she'd been forced to use before. She was still uncertain about their prospects, but the others were so optimistic. Shouldn't she be too? By the time the baby arrived, the shop might be a going concern.

"You know, kid, you're getting to be quite the looker," Joey said when she returned with the glasses, one filled with ice for herself. "You was a little too thin there for awhile for my tastes anyway. But now—" He made a curving motion with his hands. "Well, you're fillin' out more up front, if you know what I mean."

He poured the drinks, careful not to put too much in her glass.

"I hope you don't mind me saying it, but you really ought to think about goin' out and having good times for yourself. I don't know what happened between you and Doc, but there are plenty of guys I know who could go for you in a big way. Just say the word and old Uncle Joey can fix you up."

He winked at Marlene. "Right, kid?"

"Oh, sure, Joey, sure!" She gave Sybil a reassuring glance. "When she's ready, she'll let you know."

She kept her tone light and smoothed the situation over nicely, but Sybil felt herself blushing furiously with embarrassment. She had, as Joey put it, begun to fill out. Her breasts were full, but as yet there was no other sign of her pregnancy. The doctor Marlene helped her choose determined she was three months pregnant. By next month she'd begin to show. She'd been thinking about moving to another apartment in another building where no one knew her and she'd discussed the idea with Marlene.

"What about a bigger place for both of us? It would be cheaper if we shared expenses and more comfortable, too," Marlene suggested.

It seemed like a practical plan, but she lacked the energy to follow through. Joey's comments made her realize she should do something soon. It was January already and she'd want to move by spring.

"Mama! Mama!"

The loud, urgent cries from the bedroom meant Ned was awake. He'd been sleeping badly the past few weeks. Ever since Jonathan left, he'd become extremely possessive, wanting all of Sybil's attention, demanding that she be with him as much as possible. At night he fought and cried to be allowed to sleep in his mother's bed. Sybil had given in once and regretted it ever since. Ned was never satisfied with only some of her attention.

"Mama! Mama!" The bars of the crib rattled loudly and Sybil excused herself.

It took her longer than she expected to quiet him. When she came back, Joey was gone.

He had to go. One of his *business* meetings. There was a resentful edge to Marlene's voice. Then she seemed to shrug it off.

"He thinks you should go over and look at the shop with him. Do you feel up to it?" She had taken his place on the sofa and poured herself a second healthy drink. Sybil's had already been poured and the ice was nearly melted. "He says you should meet him over there tomorrow afternoon, three o'clock. He wants to talk to you about decorating before he signs the lease and calls in anybody to do the work. Joey has a lot of respect for your ideas, honey. We want the place to look classy, right? What do you think?"

"I'd like to go." She thought it would give her something else to think about, anything to displace her own aching thoughts of Jonathan.

"Great! It'll do you good. You'll see. Joey's right about one thing. You should get out more. When we start decorating and buying stock— Well, all that will help."

She raised her glass.

"Here's to us, Anderson and Grant. We're gonna go places. I have this feeling in my bones."

Sybil managed to smile and sip her drink. No matter how she tried to shake it, she could not rid herself of a nagging feeling of foreboding that plagued her about the new business venture.

First, there was the mysterious source of Joey's capital and his business associates. Even Marlene had shown some concern about that. Evidently, Joey was very close-mouthed about his enterprises.

"What you don't know won't hurt you, kid! Remember that," was his stock answer to all questions.

Then there was the fact that nowhere could Sybil's name appear on the legal papers involved. When Joey found she was not twenty-one, he was frankly astonished.

"A babe in the woods! A babe in the woods!" he repeated over and over again. "Don't you worry, kid. Uncle Joey's gonna take care of you. Don't you worry."

Sybil did worry constantly. She had no real idea of what being in business would mean. They'd have to keep records, of course. And there'd be expenses, the loan to pay off for one thing, but Marlene and Joey spoke only of the profits. There was the matter of cultivating clients, too. Just as Sybil thought, Mrs. Thorpe had been cool towards their plans of expanding their clientele. She'd been polite enough and even murmured something about sending some of her friends to them, but never did, though she continued to give them orders for herself. Sybil wondered how long that would continue once their shop opened its doors.

She had seen the small shop only once. It was sandwiched in between two brick buildings. Only one small display window faced the street. It had been empty for several months before Joey began making arrangements and there was a lot of cleaning up to do and remodeling, as well. The former tenant had been a jeweler. The work area in back could be divided into a small dressing room and a work room. The actual fitting could be done in the front of the shop. This would have to be simple, but tastefully furnished. Remembering her days at Arnaud's, Sybil already had some plans in mind.

The next afternoon Joey was waiting for her across the street from the store. It was just past one. The day was crisp and cold. Snow had fallen earlier, then melted and frozen again, making the streets treacherous. The few cars

130

that were out moved slowly along the slick surface of the street.

She waved to Joey and quickened her steps. She thought he had seen her, but he didn't wave back. He seemed to be watching something beyond her. She turned to see what it was. There was no one directly behind her and only a few cars cruising along slowly. There was one dark sedan parked near the intersection. When she reached the store front, she called to him and started to cross the street. What was he waiting for? Why didn't he join her?

She was halfway across when he went into frantic action, waving his arms and shouting.

"Go back, kid! Go back!"

Why? She saw no reason not to join him. What was wrong? In the second that she hesitated Joey turned, ducked into an alley and disappeared. Behind her, brakes squealed and tires screeched. She was hit by the front bumper of the dark sedan and thrown forward, hitting her head on the curb as she went down.

She awoke in a hospital ward. Her head was bandaged and a nurse was bending over her.

"My baby! My baby!"

She stared up at the nurse with terrified eyes.

"It's all right. The doctor says it will be all right. You just have to rest and stay off your feet for awhile. Your baby will be all right."

Tears of relief streamed down her cheeks. She asked nothing else. Where Joey was? If Marlene knew? How she had gotten there? None of this seemed important.

The next day Marlene came with a small bunch of flowers which the nurse put in a vase for her.

"From me and Ned. He's O.K. Don't worry about him." She did not smile. Her bright red mouth looked bitter. "This is all Joey's fault. That bastard! They were after him. He should be here, not you. At least he called the police and got you some help. You coulda bled to death. He calls Mrs. Philips and tells her to tell me you got into a little trouble at the shop. He got into a tangle

131

with some guys who were looking for him and you got hurt. He says he's awful sorry, but he's gotta get out of town for awhile. That's all! He hangs up."

Sybil turned compassionate eyes to her friend.

"I'm sorry, Marlene. Maybe he'll come back."

"Oh, honey!" Marlene stood up and took Sybil's hand. "It's me who should be sorry. Who the hell wants him back? You're the one who got hurt. You poor kid! You poor kid!" she said over and over again. "But don't worry. It's gonna be all right. You'll see. Everything's gonna be all right. I should have known that bastard would get himself into real trouble someday. I told you he'd been different since he came back from Chicago. Him and his big deals. Big shady deals. He'll be running all his life, if somebody don't shoot him. And I was ready to trust him!"

Most of what Marlene said made little sense to her except for the fact that their plans for the new shop were ruined. She'd be in the hospital for she didn't know how long. The little bit of money she'd been saving would have to go now for medical expenses. If Mrs. Thorpe ever deserted them, what could they do?

Marlene came to the hospital every day. She told her about Ned and brought some of the sewing for her to do to keep busy.

"When can I go home?" Sybil asked over and over again. "I can't get an answer from the doctor."

Dr. Nevins, a physician with an excellent reputation as a gynecologist, had been called in by Sybil's own doctor. He was a gentle, white-haired gentleman who displayed infinite patience and never appeared to be hurried.

"Please, doctor, I haven't much money," Sybil told him. "I have a son at home and there's my work. When can I go home?"

Dr. Nevins gave her a stern look.

"Not until I say you can, young lady. And right now I would not want to be responsible for your losing this baby. You need to be off your feet and here where I can observe you. Of course, if you prefer, I could recommend a good rest home."

"A rest home! Oh, doctor, I could not afford a rest home." She had told him her husband was dead and she had to support herself.

"What about your family? Surely you or your husband have family who would want to help?" The doctor could not seem to understand that she was completely on her own.

"The rest home would really be best," he said. "Think it over, my dear, if you really do want this baby."

If she wanted this baby. *If!* She wanted nothing more. What else did she have left of Jonathan? She turned her face to the pillow and wept. Marlene found her like that.

"Oh, honey, don't! You'll only make yourself sick and that can't help."

Marlene looked unusually pale herself. Sybil wondered why and then realized that her friend was not wearing make-up. Her hair, usually carefully waved, was pulled back from her face revealing dark roots that contrasted sharply with the platinum she was so fussy about keeping touched up.

"But everything's so impossible!" Sybil caught her breath, willing herself to overcome the despair and the tears of weakness that threatened to overwhelm her again.

"You could—you could go to Jonathan. You know the name of the doctor he's working with. It wouldn't be hard to find him." Marlene ventured the suggestion timidly.

"I—I— No! No! That's impossible. I've caused him enough pain. Marlene, how is Ned? I miss him so."

"Oh, Ned," Marlene said. "He's an angel. I brought his crib into my place. He's getting too big for that crib, you know. He's so cute now. He calls me Marly. And strong! I think sometimes he'll break right out of that playpen. Honey, I'm gonna go now. I bet there's a way to swing this rest home deal. There's a couple of people I have to see." Marlene stood abruptly. She had been talking rapidly, trying to keep Sybil from breaking down again or asking any questions. "Don't you worry. Don't you worry about a thing. This is gonna turn out fine, better than you think."

She didn't even say good-bye, but hurried down the aisle between the beds and out the door. Sybil lay back against the pillows and closed her eyes. If only she didn't feel so weak and helpless! If only there were something she could do! She closed her eyes and thought of Ned standing in his crib, rattling the bars and demanding attention. Yes, he was outgrowing the crib. Another expense! She'd have to get him a bed, but a larger bed would never fit in that bedroom. And then, when the new baby came— Tears of frustration slid down her cheeks. It all seemed to be too much. The pungent, antiseptic odors of the hospital depressed her. Dr. Nevins was right. Someplace else, any place else would be better. All around her the sounds of other women complaining about pain and discomfort of one kind or another bore in upon her the knowledge that hers were not the only difficult problems. There were eight beds in this ward and seven of them were occupied by women with more serious trouble than hers. One woman kept all of them awake each night by moaning and crying for her child which had been born dead. The very idea horrified Sybil and her heart went out to the woman, who suffered so terrible a loss. But without the proper rest and care, she knew her own child would not survive. What had Marlene meant about a rest home not being impossible? She wished she could believe it.

Two days later there was no need to believe. The rest home was a reality. She was transported to the country in a cab and greeted at the wide double doors of what must have once been an estate in a quiet community thirty miles north of the city. The home itself was a huge, rambling, three-story house on beautifully landscaped hills overlooking the Hudson River. She was taken to her own room in a wheel chair. Any exertion, even walking, brought on the bleeding again. She was relieved to rest in the comfortable bed in the privacy of her own room whose walls, unlike hospital rooms, were painted a soft blue.

"There!" said Marlene, when she was settled. "This ought to do the trick, honey. You look better already. Do you feel O.K.?" she asked anxiously. "The trip wasn't too much for you, was it?"

"No, no," Sybil assured her sleepily. A nurse had given her something to calm her and she felt perfectly relaxed except for the nagging question that Marlene refused to answer.

"How can I afford all this? Marlene, it must cost a fortune!"

She was almost too sleepy to care and when Marlene gave her the same reply she'd been reciting all morning, Sybil had not the strength to protest.

"Don't you worry! It's all being taken care of. Don't you worry about a thing."

Marlene's pale lips were set in a grim, straight line. "You can stay here as long as you have to, so don't worry about a thing."

How? She knew Marlene would not have gone to Jonathan. But had she gone to Mrs. Thorpe? That must be it. The stay at the rest home was somehow being subsidized by Mrs. Thorpe. The thought of taking such charity made her uneasy. What reason would Mrs. Thorpe have to assume her medical expenses? It was a debt she'd never be able to repay. But the pleasure and comfort of being in her own quiet room at that moment overcame any qualms she had and she pressed her friend's hand gratefully, unable to express her feelings.

Marlene seemed to understand and left promising to visit on the weekend.

"I'll have to find out about trains and maybe I can bring Ned. He misses you something awful."

The enforced rest, the endless, boring days left her with nothing to do but brood and think about Jonathan and feel sorry for herself.

Each day at the rest home was exactly like the others. The patients were on a strict schedule and the nurses were there to see that they followed it. Sybil found that she was not the only woman who was being confined to a wheel chair.

"But I'm perfectly capable of walking," she told Dr. Nevins petulantly.

"Thank God for that," he told her. "Count your blessings, my dear. But don't forget, you're here to stay off your feet. The sooner you get used to that idea, the sooner you'll be well enough to walk around again. This next month is the most crucial in a pregnancy like yours. If you can get beyond that—" He spread his hands. "Well, then we'll see."

See? See what? After this month what could she expect? She wondered if all doctors were so secretive. Surely Jonathan would be more open with his patients. Or would he? Perhaps she was being unreasonable. She was acting like a cranky invalid and Dr. Nevins had been extremely patient with her. Probably the poor man was doing his best. He couldn't tell her what he didn't know himself. She'd been allowing herself to give in to self-pity and was taking it out on her doctor.

"They don't really care what you think. All they want is control. The less you know, the more power they have." The bitter words came from a woman Sybil had not noticed before.

Dr. Nevins had come to talk to Sybil in the solarium. The nurse wheeled her out here for an hour every morning and another in the afternoon. The long room might once have been a gallery, but now was open to the hills and sky and gleaming waters of the Hudson below by means of floor to ceiling windows along the west wall. The woman was reclining in her chair in the corner of the room.

Spoken aloud, the accusation sounded so unfair that Sybil was amazed she'd been letting herself think that way and she was ashamed, too.

"I imagine their intention is to protect the patient by saving her from worry," she replied, realizing that this was more likely the truth.

She looked curiously at her companion who she judged

136

was a woman in her thirties, though it was difficult to tell because she was so very heavy. Her arms were like thighs and the rest of her large body was covered by a blanket.

"You're staring," the woman told her sharply.

Sybil flushed with embarrassment.

"I'm terribly sorry."

"Oh, don't be. Everyone does. I'm an oddity like the side show in the circus."

"Oh, no!"

"Oh, yes. Don't think I don't know it. It's the only reason my husband and my family come to see me. 'How much has Anne gained since the last time we were here? And how does she do it on the rigid diet there?' I know what they say and I don't care. What do they know or care about how I actually *feel*? My husband has his women and I—" She paused and reached under her blanket from which she withdrew a large box of chocolates.

"I have this."

Sybil gasped in surprise as she viewed the obviously forbidden candy.

"Oh, it's easy," said her companion. "You just have to know the right people and cross their palms with silver. Are you shocked? Don't be. Have one?"

She threw off her blanket and lumbered over. If anything, she looked heavier standing up, and the rolls of flesh beneath her shapeless robe seemed to be a tremendous burden, judging from the slow way she moved.

Sybil accepted one of the chocolates and the young woman lowered herself onto the nearby sofa, sighing heavily as she did so. She might have been extremely pretty if her features were not so badly puffed and distorted by overweight. She had rich auburn hair which she wore brushed smoothly on top like a shiny copper cap and twisted into a heavy knot at the back fastened tightly with pins. She had deep blue intelligent eyes that seemed to be ever wary as she appraised Sybil.

"I'm Anne Ward Halburton. I've been living here on and off for three years and I can tell you there are worse

137

places. Prisons, for instance. Insane asylums, leper colonies. I haven't ever had a child. Is this your first?"

Sybil was a little confused by the rapid fire delivery of disjointed thoughts. She introduced herself and described her condition in general terms.

"Oh." Anne did not bother to offer any words of comfort. "Where is your husband? What is he like?"

"He's dead," Sybil said quickly.

"You're better off," Anne said and crammed two chocolates into her mouth.

"Have you—have you been ill?" Sybil ventured. She didn't really know what to say.

"Ill? Well, yes, I suppose you could say I've been ill if you call obesity an illness. My doctor thinks I'm dangerously depressed and he may be right. He thinks I need a change periodically and my husband agrees with him and so I come here. It's as good a place to be as any and I don't have to listen to Malcolm or his sister Beatrice or my mother or any of the rest of them. They don't care about me. They never have cared about me and they never will care about me. I've been alone since the day I was born."

Suddenly Anne burst into tears. She turned her heavy body and leaned her head on her arm against the back of the sofa. She sobbed noisily. Her whole body shook with distress. Sybil could think of nothing to say or do and simply waited for the storm to pass. She was relieved when an efficient, white-haired nurse bustled in and briskly insisted that Mrs. Halburton get up and go to her room. When she discovered the box of chocolates she simply shook her head and pressed her lips together in disapproval but said nothing.

Even after Anne left, Sybil imagined she could hear those pitiful sobs. How awful to appear to have everything and yet know you had nothing! Once she had been like that. But she had forced herself to fight. What had happened to her own desire to survive? The past few weeks she'd all but given up hope herself. She mustn't do that, she wouldn't permit herself to despair.

That evening she inquired about Mrs. Halburton from the white-haired nurse.

"There isn't much hope for someone like that, Mrs. Anderson. She's so sure that she's unworthy of love or friendship. None of the nurses has been able to get close to her."

"Do you think she might like some company?"

The nurse paused thoughtfully. "It's hard to say. Do you mean you want to visit her?"

Sybil nodded.

"I don't know, Mrs. Anderson. Dr. Nevins doesn't want you to upset yourself." She looked doubtful. "Mrs. Halburton is a very difficult woman. We wouldn't want you to be depressed."

"I think it would help to take my mind off myself," Sybil told her frankly. "I think we can help each other."

Anne was lying on her bed, staring at the ceiling. A dim light burned on the bedside table. When the nurse wheeled Sybil in, Anne simply stared at her without speaking.

"I was just looking through this magazine I found in the solarium and I came across these new hair styles. You have beautiful hair. Have you ever thought of wearing it like this?"

She wasn't at all sure if this were the right approach, but she was convinced that every woman was interested in her appearance, no matter how she denied it.

"Hair?" Anne raised herself onto her elbow and stared at Sybil. "You noticed my hair?"

"Oh, yes," Sybil said, realizing she'd scored a kind of victory. "It's a beautiful shade and so rich and thick. It would look lovely styled like this." She held up the picture.

The older woman sat up and reached for the magazine.

"You actually were looking at this magazine and thought of me?" She seemed astonished and there was a hint of pleasure in her voice.

"Why, yes." Sybil smiled encouragingly.

Anne swung her legs around and got off the bed. She

went over to the dresser and switched on the twin lamps as she peered into the mirror. She began unpinning her hair and the bun unwound leaving the long tresses falling about her face in thick waves.

"I never thought about cutting my hair," she said, meeting Sybil's eyes in the mirror.

"Neither did I, but once I did it, I loved it."

Anne gave Sybil's short, dark hair an appraising glance.

"Yes, it does look nice," she said. "Smart." She smoothed her own long hair. "I've always worn my hair like this."

"Change can be fun, now and then."

"Why?"

"Why?" Sybil was at a loss. "Oh, I don't know. I suppose it gives you a lift."

"No, I mean, why me? Why should you care about me?" Anne stood with her hands behind her back and stared down at her.

Sybil knew she must choose her words carefully.

"I guess because I saw something of me in you," she said finally. "Once I was so miserable I didn't care whether I lived or died."

"Really?" Anne drew up a chair and sat beside Sybil. "What made you change?"

"I suppose it was my son. I wanted life for him. And now I want it for this new baby."

"I see. It makes a difference when you have someone. I don't have anyone."

"What about your husband?"

Anne gave a long sigh. "He doesn't love me. I don't think he ever did. For years we haven't—well, you know, been intimate. He gets what he wants someplace else. He doesn't need or want me."

"Do you want him?"

A sob escaped Anne's lips and she covered her face with her hands. "Oh, Lord, yes. I want him. I do. Only—only why should he want me? Look at me."

Sybil looked. She saw a bitterly unhappy woman who was completely unsure of herself.

"I've never, never been attractive. Oh, I wasn't always this—this heavy, of course, I don't know why Malcolm married me. He could have married anyone."

"But he chose you."

Anne looked up and blinked away her tears. For a moment she said nothing.

"I have no friends," she said. "Not one close friend who really cares. I have no one to talk to at home. That's why it's a relief to come here. I keep coming back, you know. I don't suppose I really have to come. But I want to. I ask to come. The nurses are so pleasant. They talk to me. Not the way we're talking, but they talk to me and I need that. I'd rather have them than be shut out at home. Even the servants have little respect for me at home."

She grasped Sybil's hand urgently.

"Do you think we could be friends?"

Sybil smiled. Since she'd met Anne that afternoon, she'd given only fleeting thought to her own problems. It amazed her that this woman was so much like what she had once been and she realized how far she had come. She had to rely on herself and what she could make of her own life. Anne needed to make that decision, too. Perhaps Sybil could help.

Anne's husband dutifully appeared every Sunday. He came in a chauffeur driven Rolls. When the weather was pleasant he and Anne walked about the grounds. When it was not, they sat in the large, communal drawing room where tea was served. Sometimes they played backgammon. They seemed to speak hardly at all. Sybil wondered how they communicated, for Anne remained almost painfully silent. She wanted to introduce her new friend to her husband, but that first Sunday Sybil refused.

"This is your time together. You shouldn't share it."

Anne had taken Sybil's advice and had her hair cut and styled. The soft waves were very becoming. If she would give more attention to her clothes and lose a good deal of weight, she'd be very attractive.

"You're right," Anne admitted. "I don't like to share

141

this time with Malcolm. At home he never has time for me. He comes here because he has to, but he comes."

Sybil thought there was more to it than duty. Malcolm Halburton was an attractive man in his mid-forties. He was tall and well-built with classic features and a receding hairline which somehow seemed to add to his charm. Observing him, she thought him to be gentle and patient. When she mentioned this, Anne's reply was bitter.

"Guilt. It's all guilt. He thinks he has to make up to me for what he's done, for what he is doing. If he ever found me attractive at all, he doesn't any more."

"Then you must make yourself attractive."

"How? I'm anything but."

"Nonsense. Any woman can be attractive. It's a matter of the right clothes, the proper hair style, and a strong inner belief in herself."

"I don't have any sense of style. I never had. And as to believing in myself—How can I?"

That night Sybil sat up late sketching. Anne's figure would be definitely hard to fit, but not impossible. With some clever use of deep pleating, flowing lines, and wide cape sleeves, even now she could look well. Color would help immeasurably and with the lift an attractive appearance would give her, the confidence might follow.

"Why these are beautiful!" Anne was particularly taken with the dressing gown. Sybil could imagine it made up in emerald green satin. "Could your friend— What was her name? Marlene! Could Marlene make this up for me?"

Marlene could and did. The bright green brought out golden tones in Anne's skin and highlights in her hair. When she looked at herself in her full-length mirror, she was astonished at the change the gown made in her. She held her head higher and stood straighter.

"I was once as slim as you, Sybil," she said wistfully. "I thought I'd never look good in anything again. This design works miracles!"

Sybil, whose body had begun now to swell with her pregnancy, was struck by the thought that appropriate designs could hide her own condition and that pregnant women could look as handsome then as at any other time. She worked on a number of sketches that Anne was most enthusiastic about.

"Sybil, you're amazing! You have a wonderful idea here. Any woman would be proud to wear these. And they'd be especially designed for her. Until I lose some weight, I'm going to need all the help I can get myself. Won't you adapt some of these for me?"

Marlene was kept busy the next few weeks fitting and sewing the dresses Sybil designed. It was a long, tedious trip from the city, but Marlene made it several times a week. The money that was paid for the gowns was more than worth the trouble.

Hungry for news of Ned, Sybil was glad to have Marlene come, so glad that she hardly noticed how cool her old friend was toward Anne, how elaborately polite.

"I've been thinking," Marlene said, "about what to do when you get out of here. I think we should go ahead with that plan about moving in together in one big place. You're going to need room for the new baby, so I found something over on Eighth Street. This place has two big bedrooms. We could share one and the kids could have the other one. If we figure the rent we're paying now separately, it won't cost us much more. What do you say?"

Marlene didn't look well. She never seemed to bother with make-up these days and her hair was streaked and straight where it had once been so carefully bleached and waved. Assuming the responsibility for Ned and all the sewing as well was a terrible burden. While she was here resting, Marlene was working for both of them. And now she was offering to share the work and responsibility of life with the new baby as well. It seemed like too great a sacrifice.

Marlene completely misunderstood her hesitation. She frowned and went to stand at the window.

"I wouldn't blame you if you wanted to be rid of me. I mean, I know I'm not your kind, not like Mrs. Halburton. She's a lady like you. And if it hadn't been for me, you never would've known Joey. And all this—"

143

She couldn't go on. Her voice was choked and her shoulders trembled. Seeing her friend suffering so, Sybil rose from her wheel chair and, though her legs felt weak, she crossed the room quickly and embraced her.

"How can you even think such a thing? You mustn't ever blame yourself. I don't. And as for wanting to be rid of you— Why, that's utter nonsense! I don't know what I'd do without you. Really! It's you I'm thinking of. Why should you have to be saddled with my problems? Like finding the money for this rest home. I don't know how you did it—but what would I have done if you hadn't found a way?"

"That was no trick," Marlene said bitterly. "Joey paid every penny. I got to him through one of his friends. Guys like Joey always know how to get their hands on money. He'd gotten the loan for the shop, so he sent most of that. He was real fond of you and I suppose he even loved me in his own way. I shouldn't have gone to him about the money for the shop in the first place. I knew what he was and where he'd get the money. It was just that I wanted to hang onto him. He started to drift away again. Joey's always been a drifter. I thought if he had an interest in the shop, he'd have to stick around. So there you are, honey. That's the truth. I was using you."

Marlene turned to face her. "Now you know the whole thing. I wanted you to know the truth. You can decide what you want to do. If you tell me to get out of your life, I'll go."

"Oh, Marlene!" Her eyes filled with tears.

"Say!" Marlene glanced from her to the empty wheel chair. "What are you doing on your feet?"

She steered her firmly back to the chair.

"You don't have to make up your mind today," she said. "I don't want to push you on this."

"But I want to, Marlene." She caught her friend's hand. It was rough and red from the washing she must be doing for Ned. "Take the new apartment. If you like it, I'm sure I will."

Marlene blinked rapidly and turned away.

144

"Gee! I never thought I'd hear you say that. Gee!"

She found a handkerchief in her handbag.

"Nothing like a good cry," she said afterwards. "Any sign of Doc Nevins letting you out of here?"

"He'll let me know the end of the week."

"O.K. then. I'm going to go ahead with the new apartment right away. You'll have a nice new place to move into."

And there'd be no embarrassing questions to answer from well-meaning, but nosey neighbors who did not know she was pregnant. She would be particularly grateful for that, but she'd miss Mrs. Philips. She promised herself she'd go back to see Mrs. Philips after the baby was born.

Dr. Nevins's good news on Friday was exactly what she expected.

"You're doing very well, my dear. Very well. I think you might give up the chair for the next week or so and if everything remains as it is—well, I see no reason why you can't go home. As long as you don't overdo it. You've passed the danger point. I'm very pleased with you. Of course, there's always the danger of a relapse—"

But she was certain there would be no relapse. She was going home, home to Ned.

Anne looked stricken when she learned the news. She tried to be happy for Sybil's sake, but her old uncertainties arose.

"You can't think how lonely I'll be without you."

"But you should be going home soon, too."

Anne let the book she was reading slide to the floor unnoticed.

"I'm afraid to go home. Afraid of what it's like out there. Afraid to face Malcolm and not be able to hold him. Afraid to hear Beatrice's malicious, 'well-meaning' gossip about Malcolm's women. She hates me, you know. She'd like it if I never went back. Then she'd have Malcolm all to herself. That's what she wants. She wants to take my place with Malcolm. She's always wanted that.

145

Sometimes I think I can win him back and then I think of Beatrice."

Anne's eyes glistened with tears. If it had not been for the tears, it would have been difficult to see the drab, hopeless woman Sybil had befriended several weeks ago. She was wearing a lavender chiffon dressing gown with a deep scalloped neck and long, loose sleeves that Sybil had designed especially for her. Anne had begun to use make-up skillfully. She had lost sixteen pounds and planned to lose more. She moved now with confidence, aware that the clothes she wore were stunning. But the frightened woman hovered just beneath the surface.

"You mustn't let Beatrice intimidate you," Sybil said.

"I know and I try, but it's difficult. If you knew her—"

She broke off and quickly changed the subject, speaking excitedly. "This—this doesn't have to be good-bye, Sybil, you know. I've been thinking. No one has ever done as much for me as you. I want you to go on designing my clothes. Will you?"

"If you like." She was pleased that this bond would help them to continue their friendship.

"And then—and then—I'd like to do something for you, if you'll let me."

Anne smiled shyly. She was older than Sybil, nearly fifteen years older, and yet she seemed so much younger, so much more sheltered from life.

"You've been very kind already. You've helped me more than you know."

It was hard to put into words what Anne's friendship had done for her. It had focused her attention on something other than her own despair. She thought she would never be free of the pain of losing Jonathan, but it was less pronounced. She could see that she had something to give. Dressing women like Anne, helping them to be as attractive as they could, seemed a worthwhile and fulfilling pursuit. It could be much more than simply earning a living.

"Oh, no! I've done nothing, while you—you've given me— Oh, Sybil, you can't imagine! But what I had in mind was your shop. You said once that you and Marlene hoped to establish a shop of your own. I'd like to help. I could make the initial investment—"

"Oh, no! I couldn't let you do that."

"It would be a loan," Anne said quickly, "a business arrangement. I've already talked it over with Malcolm. You'd pay us back with interest."

"Oh, Anne!" She was not sure how she felt. The possibility of having their own shop after all was tempting, but she was doubtful. "What if we failed?"

Anne laughed. "You won't fail. Malcolm and I know dozens of people, not that they were really friends of mine in the past. I don't think I've known how to be a friend until now. I plan to change all that, too, thanks to you. When they see what you've done for me, why they'll come to you, too. Please, say you will think about it at least. Promise me that. It would mean so much to me. Please Sybil."

She could not refuse. The promise of a substantial loan plus the customers to patronize the shop seemed almost too good to be true. If Marlene agreed, and she saw no reason why she would not, they might be well on their way to success.

The excitement of Anne's proposal was completely eclipsed by Sybil's anticipation of seeing Ned again. Children had been completely forbidden at the rest home and she'd had to rely on Marlene's descriptions of Ned's development, seeing in her mind's eye Ned walking about and climbing onto everything.

"One day I found him sitting in the middle of the table trying to drink my leftover coffee. How he got up there, I'll never know," Marlene said.

"And he's talking a blue streak, mostly about you. It's not always too clear, but I get the idea.

" 'Mummy, come home. Mummy hurry, hurry!' And like that. Of course, when he's hungry, well, he leaves nothing to your imagination. 'Eat! Eat! Eat!' he yells. He's always hungry. Wait'll you see how big he is!"

She could hardly wait. She counted the minutes. When

at last she stood in the doorway of the new apartment and Ned came running out of the kitchen to throw himself into her arms, she could hardly believe the change in him.

It was April. She had been away three months. In that time, Ned had become a person. He looked twice as big as she remembered. The rooms of the new apartment hardly seemed big enough to contain him. Ned filled them with the exuberant energy of childhood.

"Mummy! Mummy! Mummy!" he shouted, hugging her, then breaking away to leap up onto the couch and jump vigorously up and down on the cushions.

Marlene grabbed him and set him down on the floor.

"Here, none of that. What did I say about jumping on the sofa?"

Ned completely ignored her and tried to climb back up again, his eyes flashing with indignation when she tried to stop him. He sat down in the middle of the floor and howled.

"Welcome home," Marlene said, grinning wryly. "He's developed into quite a handful and he sure has got a mind of his own."

"Yes," she said, sinking down onto the floor beside him. She knew it would be difficult in her condition to get up again. But this way she could take him into her arms again.

Ned stopped howling, looked up into her face with an angelic smile and planted a wet kiss on her cheek.

"Mummy. Love Mummy," he said and she burst into tears of joy, rocking him in her arms.

"Oh, Ned! Ned! My Ned!" she whispered.

It was heaven to be home again.

She did not have time to be sentimental about not returning to Mrs. Philips' apartment house. She was glad she didn't have to go back where there were so many reminders of Jonathan.

She kept busy all that spring and early summer decorating the apartment which she was pleased to find had more light. There were many more windows and the living room was much bigger. The two bedrooms adjoined one another and there was no door between them. She hung colorful drapes on a rod to separate them.

Then there was the work on the shop. They would open in August in time for the fall season. Marlene found that the very shop they'd been planning to rent that winter was still available. Sybil did what she could to supervise the decorating, but as July drew near she could do little more than make suggestions.

Born on July 17, 1934, Joanna was a healthy baby, seven pounds, two ounces. Sybil searched the new-born face all pink and wrinkled for signs of Jonathan. Would she have his eyes, his chin, his generous mouth? Jonathan! Dear Jonathan! How proud he would have been of his daughter! Holding Joanna in her arms, she allowed herself to think of him. Did he ever think of her now? How did he remember her? Bitterly? Fondly? Was he well? Was he successful?

He was doing what he longed to do, following the great passion of his life. He must have found some sort of contentment and perhaps actual happiness. He'd marry, of course, eventually and forget he'd ever known her.

She didn't think then that Joanna and Ned, too, would one day have some very insistent questions for her about their fathers. Her world was made up of her children, her work, and her friends, without whom she might not have survived.

On June 6, 1934, she had reached her twenty-first birthday. She felt that she'd already experienced the best and the worst that this life had to offer.

PART TWO

I

Sybil replaced the receiver and stared at the phone, wishing she had not accepted the dinner invitation. The last minute call meant only one thing. Anne Halburton had found another eligible man. Her efforts at matchmaking were tireless, if not successful.

Any other time Sybil might have been pleased. Anne's parties were always stimulating and they seldom failed to provide her with new contacts, new customers or, at the very least, good publicity. But today, coming on the heels of the news that Ned was having trouble at school again, she would be much too worried to enjoy herself.

At Anne's suggestion she had enrolled her son in the Parkhurst School in upper New York State last month when it became obvious he wasn't doing well in the public school his sister attended. Now the headmaster had sent word that Ned was to be suspended. An eleven-year-old child suspended! What on earth could be the reason for that? She planned to take the train up tomorrow even though things were quite hectic at the shop. They were planning an important fashion show at the Waldorf, a benefit for Anne's war orphans, in fact. It would also introduce their spring line.

Anne had come a long way since they met nine years ago. At forty-four she was glowing with energy and purpose. She'd solved her marital problems beautifully. She served on half a dozen charitable committees and directed a home for British war orphans. Everywhere she went, she was photographed and her pictures appeared in newspapers and society magazines. She was a much sought after guest and a celebrated hostess. Her wardrobe was the talk of the city. As a result, the fashion establishment of Anderson and Grant was, in 1943, one of the successful custom shops in New York.

Sybil had changed, too. She was a business woman engaged in work she loved. From the beginning the shop flourished. Anne supplied the capital and the customers. Sybil supplied the smart feminine designs, custom made for each client and suited to her needs and personality. Even Mrs. Thorpe did not desert them, though she was perturbed at first.

"She doesn't want to be left out," Marlene observed gleefully. "I knew it was gonna be like this."

Sybil enjoyed their success and she was especially happy for Marlene, who had made so many sacrifices for them both. They moved within two years to larger quarters. It was nearly impossible to handle all the orders that were coming in. Now they had two floors: the mauve carpeted salon, dressing rooms, and Sybil's studio on one floor and the workrooms on the other.

It was a big step upward. Their quarters nearly rivaled those of the House of Arnaud. In fact, Marlene had been able to convince two of Arnaud's seamstresses to join them. Their entire staff consisted of seven people including themselves. And then war came to Europe and the Parisian houses closed down. Americans turned to American designers and Anderson and Grant were there to fill the need.

Sybil gave Marlene credit for the fact that their enterprise ran smoothly. It was she who managed the sewing and cutting rooms. The girls in the workroom called her Miss Grant respectfully and she ruled them with almost as much of an iron hand as Miss Levere ever had. The result was a well-disciplined staff and excellent workmanship.

Heavier and more tastefully dressed than she'd been in the past, Marlene still retained a voluptuous figure. She wore her platinum hair in a smooth chignon and her make-up was far less flamboyant. She had a number of male admirers, none of whom she was particularly serious about. She never forgave Joey Ferguson and seemed reluctant to put her faith in any one man again. She was fond of Joanna and Ned and seemed content with her life as it was.

Sybil, too, would have been content if only there were not these new and disturbing problems with Ned. She rubbed her fingers in a circular motion against her temples. She was getting another bad headache. They'd become more frequent lately.

Nerves, she told herself. Nerves and guilt! There was always the oppressive knowledge that many of Ned's problems stemmed from uncertainties about himself and the lack of a strong male influence in their home, both of which she had done nothing to alleviate.

"My God! You won't believe what's happened!"

Marlene threw open the door of Sybil's studio which they'd paneled and insulated against any disturbing sounds that might emanate from the salon itself. She looked actually white and badly shaken. "You won't believe it! When I get my hands on Jules, I'll kill him."

Jules was their new cutter. Sybil half rose from her chair, thinking to get some water or something stronger. Marlene looked as though she needed it.

"Don't get up! Don't get up. You should be sitting down for this one."

"But what's wrong, Marlene?"

"Government regulation L-85."

Because of shortages in fabrics, the government had limited the amount of material that could be used in clothing. Skirts could be no more than seventy-two inches around. Hems and belts could be no more than two inches wide. Hoods, shawls, and cuffs on coats were forbidden. But they both knew all this and accepted the regulations as a challenge.

"What about L-85?"

"We've got seventy-six inch skirts. And some seventy-eight inches."

155

"What?"

"That's it. Jules! I'll kill him. He says he didn't understand me. That crazy Frenchman! Maybe the girls are right. Maybe he is working for the other side. The girls talk behind his back. They say his family are collaborationists."

Many of the girls who worked for them were, like Jules, French refugees, having gotten out before the Vichy government took over.

"Marlene, that's foolish. He just made a mistake, that's all. We'll have to correct it."

"Oh, sure! Just like that." She snapped her fingers impatiently. "That's twenty-five dresses, half of them are gowns and we only have until Thursday."

"That's two whole days. We'll just have to get it done."

"How? How? That's what I want to know. We'll have to work day and night. And then, I don't know. This show's the biggest thing we've ever done. You know what this business is like. The competition is fierce. There'll be newspaper and magazine people all over the place. We can't afford mistakes like this."

The success of Anderson-Grant Custom Dresses was due, not only to Sybil's considerable talent but to Marlene's drive. Anne's original investment had long since been repaid and Marlene was talking about taking some of their profit and enlarging operations after the war, of course. "The war can't go on forever," she was fond of saying. "Those lousy Nazis are gonna get theirs and then—well, then the sky's the limit for us, honey. We won't need a loan from any of your rich friends. We'll make it on our own. You'll see."

Sybil sometimes thought the idea of expanding their operations and opening branches in other cities appealed to Marlene mainly because it would take them away from such close contact with Anne. Marlene had been antagonistic towards her from the beginning.

"She gives too much. It's not normal. There's no way to repay her, don't you see?"

Sybil did not see, but was careful to avoid speaking of Anne or her many kindnesses.

"I suppose we can do it," Marlene said, now beginning to pace the floor of the studio. "I'll have the girls work in shifts. We'll work all night if we have to. But after this is over I think we'd better consider replacing Jules. A lot of the girls don't like him and we don't want to lose them. But I hate to lose Jules. He's a damn good cutter. What do you think?"

Sybil didn't know what to say. The crisis coming on top of the problem with Ned and Anne's insistent invitation was too much. Her head ached terribly. Marlene usually made the decisions concerning personnel. She knew whom to hire and when. Her judgment was always sound.

"I really don't know, Marlene. I'd rather leave the decision to you," she said, passing a weary hand over her eyes. "I can't seem to think about anything but Ned today."

"Oh, gee! What's the matter with me? I forgot all about that. Hey! You've got one of those awful headaches again. I can see it in your eyes."

She reached across the desk and took Sybil's hand. "Honey, you shouldn't worry. I told you that snooty school was no place for a real boy like Ned. Everything's going to work out O.K. Sometimes I get too excited. Listen, I have an idea. You look tired, It's almost three o'clock. You go on home and take two aspirin and lie down. I'll handle things around here. When I get home, we'll have a nice relaxing dinner just you, me, and little Joanna. And don't you worry about Jules or anything else. We'll have those skirts ready for the show no matter what."

She went to the closet and took out Sybil's coat, and all but forced her into it.

"But what about the alterations? I could help. You'll need me here," Sybil protested.

Marlene wouldn't hear of it.

"That's my department and I'll take care of it. Every-

157

thing's gonna work out fine. It always has. You go home and get some rest."

It didn't take much persuasion. Sybil was used to Marlene's taking over and making decisions for her. She allowed herself to be convinced and was in the taxi, heading for their Tudor City apartment before she realized she had not told Marlene about her dinner engagement. Perhaps she could call Anne and cancel after all. An hour later there seemed no reason not to go.

While she was resting, Marlene called, leaving word with their housekeeper that she wouldn't be back until late. Then Joanna called after school.

"I'm at Regina's house, Mommy," the childish voice came to Sybil over the white phone in the bedroom she and Marlene shared. "She wants me to stay for dinner, but I'll come right home if you want me to."

She smiled. Joanna was an extremely affectionate child, so different from Ned, who kept his feelings carefully hidden.

"No, that's all right, darling. You stay and have fun with Regina."

"Well—" Joanna was reluctant. "All right, Mommy. I love you."

"And I love you, angel," she said, adding silently, "more than you'll ever know."

What would Jonathan think of his daughter now? She looked very much like her mother, the same dark hair, the same creamy complexion and high cheekbones. But the brown eyes were Jonathan's. Sometimes when Sybil looked deep into those gentle eyes she felt herself transported across every barrier of time and space and she'd be looking into Jonathan's eyes again. In spite of everything she could still be moved by that look. Sometimes she'd be walking along the street and she'd see a man who strode in Jonathan's particular jaunty way or she'd be in a store and hear a voice with his familiar timbre.

It was probably Geoffrey Kempton's voice that first

drew Sybil to him. She heard it before she actually saw him.

Anne, radiant in a rose satin gown Sybil had designed for her now lovely figure, greeted her friend warmly.

"You look wonderful. You'll positively dazzle Geoffrey."

There it was! The eligible man, she thought. She wore a dramatic gown of prewar scarlet silk with borders of black at the hem and sleeves. The deep V neckline showed her perfectly smooth, milk-white skin. She wore her shoulder-length hair in a pageboy, parted on the left with a deep wave that dipped above her right brow. Her only jewelry was the single strand of pearls she'd cherished all these years as her link with the past.

Anne led her over and introduced her to Major Geoffrey Kempton, who was entertaining two enthralled women. She was struck immediately by the deep, resonant tone of his voice, so reminiscent of Jonathan's.

"Hello," he said, looking into her eyes. "Have we met somewhere before or are you simply a dream come true?"

He was blond and blue-eyed, Nordic looking, and he was handsome in the polished manner of the New York sophisticate, but he had the rugged tanned look of the athlete as well. She could easily imagine him on a tennis court vanquishing all challengers.

"Now you know why Geoffrey is such a successful lawyer. He simply charms all the opposition 'round to his way of thinking. Heaven knows what would happen if he unleashed that charm against the enemy," Anne said. She smiled and kissed him lightly on the cheek. "Be nice to him, Sybil. Geoffrey may be the army's secret weapon. With him on our side, how can we lose?"

She left to mingle with her other guests.

"I must say, Mrs. Anderson, that the reports of your beauty have not been exaggerated."

Sybil returned his steady look and smiled. She could not help being flattered. She felt she should return the compliment. Major Kempton was a particularly dashing figure in his uniform. The deep olive-green jacket and beige trousers had obviously been custom cut. She noted the gold Oak leaf on each shoulder and the romantically designed insignia on the sleeve, a naked sword bursting through flames on a black shield which denoted his attachment to Eisenhower's Supreme Allied Headquarters in London.

"How long have you been in the service, Major?"

"Since the day after Pearl Harbor. The idea of simply sitting around waiting for the other shoe to fall never appealed to me. May I get you a drink?"

"Champagne would be nice," she said, catching sight of a maid carrying a tray full of glasses.

Anne's dinner parties were lavish affairs. Even here in her New York apartment she managed easily to entertain a dozen people at dinner. The huge living room seemed hardly crowded.

Major Kempton's slick, light banter, the confident tilt of his head, and his knowing smile made her think he was used to flirtations that in wartime meant nothing. Probably he saw her as another one of these amusing interludes. He brought her the champagne and his fingers brushed hers lightly as he handed her the glass. Their eyes met and the unspoken communication in the long, significant look that passed between them surprised them both.

"Well," he said softly. "Well! Come sit down, Mrs. Anderson. I want to know all about you."

"Sybil, please. If we're going to exchange confidences, I think we should be less formal."

She skillfully managed to encourage him to confide in her. He was the second son of an evidently very wealthy family whose sons just naturally gravitated toward the law. Even she was acquainted with the prestigious firm of Kempton, Chalmers, Bolton and Lee. Some member of the family had been in the firm for generations, he told her.

"I'm not sure that I am suited to the law, however. It's something I'm afraid I just drifted into. Now you take my brother, Arthur, ten years my senior and totally dedi-

160

cated. He knows who he is and where he belongs. Which brings me to an interesting question. Who are you and where do you belong?"

She was startled. She couldn't imagine what he meant.

"Aha! I recognize the guilty look. I have not served with the Judge Advocate General for over a year for nothing. You are not at all what you appear to be, Sybil Anderson. You are a woman of mystery." He lowered his voice dramatically and took her hand in his.

"I don't think I understand," she said.

"Don't you?"

"No. What do I appear to be, Major?"

She eyed him now with covert alarm. Was it possible that he knew something about her background? She was certain they had never met before. She would surely have remembered. He was, she judged, in his early thirties, a few years older than she. Could he possibly have been around in Philadelphia the year of her debut? Often nowadays she was aware of the possibility of coming in contact with someone from her past. She moved in social circles where such contact would not be impossible and yet so far nothing had happened. She rather thought anyone she might have known years ago as a frightened young woman would be hard pressed to discover her identity in Sybil Anderson. Still, lately, she had begun to worry about what a chance meeting with anyone who had once known her might mean. She had thought of contacting her family now that she was so well established. She had thought of straightening out the legal tangle of her marriage to Edward. She wondered, in fact, if he had ever taken steps to divorce her on grounds of desertion. She had even gone through a period one year of buying Philadelphia newspapers and scanning them for news of Edward or her family and found the usual social notes. Alicia and Monty were mentioned having attended dinner parties, charity balls, and concerts. There was never any news about Edward or her father which could mean anything. Edward could have gone away, back to Colorado, for instance. And her father might have died by now for all she knew, though she'd combed the obituaries in the *Times* for years without learning anything.

Once she came across a picture in *Town and Country* of Alicia looking aloof and very beautiful at the Devon Horse Show. The picture so unnerved her that she gave up any plans she might have had to contact her family. Alicia's cold eyes stared out at her and every terrible memory came rushing back. She chose the safety and the peace of anonymity. It was best to forget the past. And now this stranger was probing dangerously.

She lowered her eyes. There was something too knowing about that intent gaze.

"I think you mistake surprise for guilt," she suggested hopefully.

"No," he said, leaning toward her and lifting her chin with his fingertips. "No, I'm not mistaken. You look terribly innocent and beautifully proper. Quite calm and aloof really. But I suspect you of being a woman of great passion. You are, aren't you, Sybil? I can see it in your lovely eyes."

She was suddenly very much aware of the strength of his masculinity. If passions smoldered behind her eyes, then surely it was desire she saw in his and she did not turn away. All the emotions she had so carefully guarded since Jonathan left seemed to well up within her. She felt, for the first time in years, the uncontrollable need to be held in a man's arms once again, to be loved.

She looked quickly away.

"I think I should like another glass of champagne," she said.

"Yes, I think we both need another drink." He went to get them.

"Sybil, are you enjoying yourself, my dear?"

Malcolm Halburton was standing beside her, gazing fondly into her eyes. Now in his fifties, he was still a very attractive man. He spent several mornings a week at the Athletic Club to keep trim. It was easy to see why his name had been linked with so many women years ago.

Today he was what every woman longed for, a devoted husband.

She found that her senses seemed to be heightened and she could feel his maleness, be pleasantly aware of it as she had not been for years. Geoffrey Kempton had re-awakened something in her, something she thought had died when Jonathan left.

"Now, Malcolm, be a good fellow and shove off. I've staked out this territory. You already have a wife," Geoffrey said, returning with their drinks.

Malcolm laughed.

"All right, old man. I can take a gentle hint. Anything for our men in uniform. But you be careful, my dear," he warned. "This is the most notorious playboy in America. There must be some reason why he never married. Probably no woman would have him." Malcolm moved off to join some men who were spiritedly discussing the campaign in Northern Africa.

"Harsh words," Geoffrey joked. "Try not to take them seriously. I don't."

"Don't you? I wonder—"

"What do you wonder, Sybil?" he asked, becoming serious again.

She hesitated. Her desire to know more about him seemed alarmingly forward. Curiosity overcame her natural reticence.

"I wonder why you never married."

"Will you believe me if I tell you that I've never met a woman like you before, Sybil? I hope you're going to let me see you often. Tomorrow! What shall we do tomorrow? We can have all day tomorrow and the next and the next. This is only the beginning of my two-week furlough."

With anyone else she would simply have turned the suggestion aside. The fact that she was not free to entertain him constantly had not occurred to him. She wondered how much he actually did know about her.

"I have an—an out-of-town commitment tomorrow."

He raised his brows.

"Couldn't you cancel it?"

163

"It involves my son," she replied and watched his reaction. "He goes to a private school. I'm going to take the train up there tomorrow morning."

"Alone?" he asked. Apparently the fact that she had children was not a surprise to him. Anne had done the groundwork well as usual.

"Well, yes," she admitted, realizing now that she wished she did not have to go alone and that she had absolutely no idea how to handle what gave every indication of being a difficult situation.

"Let me come with you. I'll drive you. That will be easier, won't it?"

"Drive? It's over fifty miles. You wouldn't want to expend all that precious gas on my problems. In case you hadn't heard, there's a war on, Major, and gas rationing is a reality." She answered him lightly, but he would not be put off.

"I'd like to meet your son, Sybil. I meant what I said. I want to know everything about you."

She hesitated, but by the end of the evening he had persuaded her to let him go along.

Anne kissed her cheek and whispered words of encouragement when she saw them leaving together.

"This could be so right for you, Sybil," she said.

Anne's words were like a prophecy and Sybil trembled at her own daring. She did not stop to think of consequences. She only knew she found Geoffrey's company stimulating. He wasn't Jonathan. No one could ever replace Jonathan. But Geoffrey did make her feel like a woman again. Like every woman, she needed the excitement of male companionship. As for the difficulty with Ned, there was no doubt that male advice could only help.

It was after midnight when he brought her back to the apartment. She felt she'd been gone for days, not hours.

"Till tomorrow," he said, standing so close to her that she felt the warmth of his body. He unlocked the door and returned the key, closing his hand about hers as he did. Looking deliberately into her eyes, he kissed her fingertips.

"If it were not for tomorrow, I don't think I could leave you tonight. That doesn't surprise you, does it?"

"No," she said truthfully. She felt suddenly that she could not bear this closeness without touching him, but rigidly restrained herself from moving into the dangerous circle of his arms. He seemed to understand her conflict.

He leaned towards her finally, sighing regretfully, and brushed her cheek gently with his lips.

"I'll have to be satisfied with that," he told her. "For someone like you, Sybil, I can wait."

She found Marlene curled up on the sofa. She was wearing her long blue dressing gown and had fallen asleep over a magazine which had slipped to the floor. Poor Marlene! She must be exhausted. Sybil touched her shoulder and Marlene awoke. She glanced at her watch.

"Hey, what's the idea? I thought you were tired," she said accusingly. "That's a two-hour train ride you have tomorrow. Or should I say today?"

"Yes, I know." She moved around to turn out the lamps. "We should both be in bed. You shouldn't have waited up, Marlene, especially with all you had to do today at the shop."

"Shouldn't have waited up! Why not, I'd like to know. You leave your studio looking dead on your feet and worried to death and then I find you're out half the night. Why?"

Marlene's voice had risen considerably. Lately she had been indulging in fits of temperament whenever Sybil did anything unexpected or went anywhere without her. The pressures of business accounted for most of it. But there were times when Sybil thought she detected unmistakable signs of jealousy and possessiveness. She didn't quite know how to handle this. Marlene was her oldest and dearest friend. She certainly did not want to hurt her.

"It was just one of Anne's parties. She didn't know what to do with her extra man," she said, keeping her voice deliberately low. "I'm sorry if you were worried.

165

You really shouldn't have waited up for me. Come. Let's get to sleep. We both need our rest."

Marlene refused to be soothed.

"Sure! Sure, let's both get some sleep. 'Good night, Marlene. Don't ask me any questions. You live your life and I'll live mine'." The words were bitter, but delivered in an undertone that was barely audible.

She stalked stiffly from the room, leaving Sybil to look after her helplessly.

"Marlene, please, don't let's argue," she said, following her into the bedroom.

"Argue? Who's arguing? I just don't know why you want to go running around in the middle of the night when you're all nervous and worried about Ned. It's a free country and you can do what you want, but you'll let that Halburton woman push you around once too often. You don't owe her a thing anymore. You don't seem to realize that. Aw, what's the use! Like you said, let's go to bed."

Sybil found it difficult to fall asleep. She hated to see Marlene disturbed and unhappy.

But in the morning it was as though nothing had happened. They had breakfast with Joanna. The child was in a gay mood, telling knock-knock jokes she had learned at Regina's house. Marlene laughed uproariously at each one and even told some of her own. She and Joanna left together.

"I'll walk you to school first, sweetie. Aunt Marlene needs the exercise."

As they left Marlene couldn't quite meet Sybil's eyes.

"I guess I was a real pill last night, honey. Gee I don't know what gets into me sometimes. It's all this fuss about taking in the dresses. We made good progress yesterday. Don't worry. Everything's going to be all right. Just take care of Ned. Maybe you can straighten the whole thing out."

She leaned forward and embraced Sybil, affectionately kissing her cheek.

"Keep your powder dry, as they say. I'll expect you when I see you."

Sybil didn't consciously think at the time that she had deliberately avoided telling Marlene about Geoffrey. But later she realized she had been reluctant to say anything.

Not long after Joanna was born and Marlene was feeling particularly sensitive about Anne, Sybil confided everything to her friend. She told her about her family in Philadelphia, her marriage to Edward, and her reasons for giving up Jonathan. Her confession seemed to form a strong bond between them. Marlene was vastly flattered that she was chosen for this confidence and seemed thereafter to accept Anne more freely, knowing that Anne knew nothing of Sybil's past. But sometimes the old uncertainties arose and Sybil learned to be patient. She valued Marlene as her dearest friend, but she knew she must not cut herself off from all other relationships. That would not be fair to either of them. That day she wondered what Geoffrey Kempton might come to mean to her.

It was a crisp February morning and she was waiting at the front entrance to the apartment when Geoffrey's black Chrysler drew up. He parked the car illegally and got out to greet her. Sunlight glinted off the gold insignia above the visor on his cap. He wore a heavy olive drab coat over his uniform with the golden oak leaf insignia of his rank on the shoulders. If anything, he appeared more attractive now than he had last night. Two soldiers passing along the sidewalk stopped to salute him smartly. Geoffrey smiled and returned their salute.

"Carry on boys," he told them cheerfully.

She was now a little sorry she had dressed so conservatively for her interview with Ned's headmaster. She wore a taupe wool suit with a long jacket that molded her excellent figure. Her beret was of the same fabric and she wore it to the right side of her smoothly brushed pageboy hairdo. She had thrown a simple camel hair coat over her shoulders. The only touch of color was the pumpkin blouse with scalloped collar that added a touch of femininity to her tailored appearance.

"Sybil, you look lovely, but much too young to be anybody's mother. The headmaster may have a difficult time accepting that fact."

He took her brown-leather-gloved hand in his.

"Do you really have an eleven-year-old son?" he asked, his own blue eyes twinkling.

"Most decidedly! And I must confess I'm terribly nervous about this interview."

"Don't be. The moment the headmaster sees you, he'll probably forget any or all of your son's transgressions. No mere man could keep his mind on anything but you."

She enjoyed the flattery whether she believed it or not and Geoffrey was a past master at flattery. The ride north was very pleasant. She seldom had an opportunity to drive beyond the city these days. With gas rationing making travel so prohibitive, she and Marlene had not bought a car, though they could now afford one.

The countryside seemed bare on this winter's day. There was snow here and there on the hillsides and miles of trees, stark and black, their branches stripped and gleaming where ice covered them.

She was suddenly seized with nostalgia for the woodland around her home outside Philadelphia. She'd loved to ride on a day like this. But it had been years since she'd been near a horse. She wondered if she'd forgotten how to ride. Perhaps not. They say you never forgot something like that.

"What are you thinking? You're awfully quiet. Is my light-hearted humor too frivolous?" he asked. "You inspire it, you know. I feel light-hearted and frivolous with you."

"Do you?" She turned to look at his handsome profile beneath the visored cap. He was smiling and he did look happy. She wished she could feel the same. But she couldn't help thinking of Ned and the interview to come. That really wasn't fair to Geoffrey and she decided to make an effort to overcome her depression. Before she could think of anything light to say, Geoffrey spoke.

"Tell me about Ned. What sort of boy is he?"

It was a difficult question, probably because Ned was at a difficult age. He wasn't the sweet, lovable baby he'd once been. He was moody and unpredictable. And there was in him a kind of smoldering anger that lay just beneath the surface, erupting at unexpected moments. His teachers in the city said he was a discipline problem in the classroom, often picking fights with the other children. Why, she did not know. It was not something Ned cared to discuss with her and, in fact, refused to do so. But he was bright, terribly bright for his age and he could be charming and that's what she told Geoffrey.

"He sounds very like his mother and I imagine there'll be no real problem. You'll find it's all a tempest in a teapot, I'm sure. Don't worry so, little mother," he added, glancing across at her. "Everything's going to be all right."

She wanted to believe that, but when she actually saw Ned, she wasn't sure at all that anything would be right again.

Eleven-year-old Ned stood facing her, his jaw taut and his eyes filled with a fury it was impossible for her to comprehend. He was tall for his age and he had reached that awkward point in his development where his features looked too big for his face. They were beginning to be Edward's features. She could see that now and tried not to let it prejudice her. Ned was her son every bit as much as he was Edward's. The headmaster took Geoffrey on a tour of the grounds so that she could have this time alone in the office with her son. The midday sunlight poured through the angled wooden blinds at the windows making every object in the room stand out distinctly, etched as it was in the clear, cold light of winter.

There were times in her life, she thought, when reality intruded on the illusions she built for herself and swept away all hope. It left her shaken and helpless, having taken her completely by surprise. Her first impulse was to

169

shut out the truth, refuse to believe it until she could assess the situation calmly. With the perspective of time, the harsher edges were blurred and she found she could accept whatever must be accepted. But there was always that first terrible moment when she must face the unexpected.

"Why, Ned? Why did you do it?"

"What do you care? I did it, that's all. He deserved it."

The voice was still childishly high, but the words were delivered with a venom that could hardly be equated with childhood.

"No one deserves to be terrified, Ned."

"Bascomb did. He deserved it. No one wants to see my side."

He spat the words out, then turned away from her toward the headmaster's desk. He picked up a pen and began playing with it. Standing it on end and allowing it to drop, over and over again.

"Stop that," she ordered in a tone that was more sharp than she meant it to be.

He looked up at her, a gleam of wicked amusement in his dark eyes and continued to play with the pen, deliberately defying her. She caught her breath. This was one of the moments when she saw Edward in Ned and she wanted desperately to wipe the resemblance away. She snatched the pen from his hands and put it back in its place.

"Sit down," she ordered and would have pushed him forcibly into one of the two leather chairs that stood before the desk.

He seemed to sense this and he smiled faintly, shrugging his shoulders lazily.

"I want you to tell me just what happened," she said, trying to speak more calmly and not succeeding very well. She was intimidated by his eyes. He saw and recognized her discomfort, her helplessness, and he seemed to be taking delight in it. Where, she wondered, was the innocent, lovable boy who used to sit in her lap and recite nursery

170

rhymes by the hour. Almost as if he could read her mind he began to chant.

"Hickory dickory dock
The mouse ran up the clock
The clock struck one—"

"Ned!" Her voice was shrill. "Tell me what happened."

"I am," he insisted, pouting. "It was one o'clock. No classes after one on Saturdays. I took old Bascomb into the woods for a walk, you know. He does almost anything I tell him. Almost—" He broke off and his eyes narrowed as he thought of his roommate, Rodney Bascomb, a too thin, intense boy a few months older than he. She had thought him particularly well-mannered the one time she had met him. She thought he might be a good influence on Ned, who tended to be brash and impulsive with adults.

"He's been spoiled by two doting women and an adoring little sister," Anne had told her. "What can you expect? That's why I think the boys' school is such a good idea. He'll have to stand on his own merit and he'll have the benefit of excellent male discipline."

None of this seemed to have helped at all. Ned was as impudent as ever. Even now, when confronted with suspension, he seemed not in the least contrite.

"Anyway, we went as far as the headmaster's hunting lodge. It's not much more than a three-room shack. We went in to get warm. We got to talking and that's when Bascomb said it."

He paused dramatically.

"Said what?" she prompted finally and was instantly sorry for having fallen into his trap. She should have outwaited him. Everything she did telegraphed her anxiety.

His full lips formed a slow smile.

"He called me a bastard!"

She caught her breath and half rose from her chair. The word startled her most because it came from her child. That it had further implications she did not see at first.

"Ned!" she shook her head in disapproval.

171

"Well, you *asked* me what happened and I'm telling you. We had a fight and he said a lot of things and some of them— Well, you never do talk about my father. I don't even know what he did. Bascomb's father is a doctor. The other kids want to know about mine. Their fathers are always around or in the Army. They have letters. Even Brown keeps all his letters. His father's dead. I have nothing, nothing at all. I began to think about what Bascomb was saying, and it made me mad. I didn't know what to tell him. And he was insulting *you,* after all. So I got him down on the floor and rolled him into the supply closet and locked the door. They let him out the next morning. The headmaster's family goes up there every Sunday. I meant to get there before they did! But they started out earlier than I thought. Nothing happened to old Bascomb. He's in the gym right now horsing around with the others," he added scornfully.

She was speechless. It was obvious Ned saw none of the consequences of his action. He just continued to stare at her defiantly, tapping his fingers on the arm of the chair and whistling softly.

"Well," he said finally, "now you know it all. I couldn't let Bascomb get away with calling me a bastard, could I? Particularly if it was true."

With a little cry of fury she leaped to her feet and slapped him smartly across his smirking face and was instantly sorry. What had she done? The cruel words and the insolent delivery had pushed her too far. Tears came to her eyes and she went to the window to hide them from Ned.

Why had he said it? What did he know or suspect? That his mother had left his father and that his half sister was illegitimate? That was the truth. What he had said was almost the truth, so why had she reacted so violently? There was only one answer. She herself had begun to believe the lie she'd told her children. Her own guilt had driven her to strike Ned just when he needed her love and understanding more than ever. What kind of mother was she? What kind of woman?

172

The physical manifestation of her anger evidently served to astonish Ned into silence.

"Ned, I'm sorry," she said. "I didn't mean to do that." Her voice was choked and she didn't trust herself to look at him. "I told you about your father. There was no reason for you to take anything Rodney said seriously. He was just talking the way boys do, baiting you. You shouldn't have taken this seriously. Do you understand, Ned?"

When there was no reply, she forced herself to turn around. He was sitting now with his face in his hands, shoulders shaking, silently crying. He looked very young, vulnerable, and terribly unhappy.

"Oh, Ned," she cried and knelt before him, enveloping him in her arms. "Oh, Ned! Darling! Forgive me! I was wrong. I do love you. I love you very, very much. It's only because I love you that you can hurt me like this. Don't you see?"

"Did my father love me?"

The question came in a small voice and she saw the frightened, confused child beneath the rough exterior. How could she have been so unsympathetic?

She had told both children their father was dead.

It was a lie that seemed necessary at the time. When Ned entered kindergarten it was obvious to him that his family was unlike the families of other children. When he was even younger, Sybil had tried to placate him with gently suggesting that Daddy was in heaven. But by the time he entered school, the questions became more specific.

She sat both Joanna and Ned down one evening and told the story she and Marlene had agreed upon. She even had an old picture of one of Marlene's brothers that was always kept in a silver frame on the mantel.

"Your father died when you were both very little, too little to remember him," she told them.

Five-year-old Ned and three-year-old Joanna sat side by side on the sofa staring at her with wide eyes.

"Why?" Ned asked. He had folded his arms across his

173

chest like a little old man. Joanna's tiny feet in her white laced shoes stuck out stiffly in front of her. She wasn't at all sure what Mommy was talking about and had several times asked for ice cream which Sybil promised to bring her very soon. "Why did he die?" Ned repeated.

"He was very sick that winter, Ned, and I'm afraid he did not get better. So we've had to go on by ourselves. Aunt Marlene helped, of course. Daddy loved you both very much," she went on and added with sudden inspiration, "and he watches over you from heaven."

It was all Ned wanted to know at the time and Joanna hardly seemed to care. Sybil gave them both bowls of ice cream and the ordeal for the moment was over.

But it was only a temporary respite. Ned began to want to know more than the bare essentials.

"What was his father's name? What did he do for a living? What was he really like?"

She tried to satisfy him with her memories of Jonathan. She hardly ever thought of Edward. Her answers were brief and she never volunteered information. Ned absorbed everything she said, sometimes catching her in slight discrepancies which she was hard pressed at times to explain away. The lies she told began to worry her, but not until now did she realize what they might be doing to Ned. He always asked the same question. Did his father love him?

"Of course, he did, Ned. Of course your father loved you. He was very, very proud of you."

She ruffled his dark, curly hair and kissed his forehead. She did not know how she was going to explain the situation to the headmaster, but she must not let this incident ruin Ned's educational experience at the school. What he had done was nothing more than a prank really, a prank motivated by his own doubts which she had done little to satisfy, not realizing their importance.

Later, she gratefully watched Geoffrey go off with Ned on a tour of the dormitories. Geoffrey had, she thought, given her good advice on the drive here.

"These headmasters tend to be a trifle rigid. Every-

174

thing's black or white. I remember that from my own days at boarding school. But they can be made to see reason sometimes. And if not, well, I'd simply put the boy in another school."

She hoped that would not be necessary. Now that she knew the whole story, she was far less willing to blame Ned entirely. Rodney Bascomb must bear some of the guilt. he must have recognized Ned's confusion about his father. The child must have goaded him beyond endurance.

She sketched the situation for Mr. Singleton in general terms and added her feeling that the school was an excellent one and how she felt it was so important for Ned to continue living in this male atmosphere.

Mr. Singleton was a gray-haired gentleman of the old school, but when he realized that she was suggesting Ned's behavior was motivated by chivalrous leanings towards his mother, he looked skeptical, though he did not argue the point.

"You must understand, Mrs. Anderson, that we have to maintain discipline. No harm was done this time by what you choose to call a boyish prank, but there might have been more serious consequences. What I would like to suggest is a week's suspension from classes and a probationary period of a month, rather than the more drastic action of sending him home for a time as I mentioned earlier. And then, we'll see."

"You must have said all the right things," Geoffrey told her, as they were driving back. "Sending him back with you would have been awful for Ned. It always is. I should know."

"Should you?" she asked.

Geoffrey laughed. "You can't tell to look at me, but I was in and out of half a dozen schools before I reached the hallowed halls of Harvard." He gave her a quick sidelong glance and then turned his attention to the road. "The first time's the hardest. You tell yourself you don't care, that you won't care, that you hated the place anyway, and then you go home and cry your eyes out. I

175

couldn't have been much older than Ned the first time it happened to me. Do I shock you?"

"A little," she said. "You make antisocial behavior sound like a way of life."

"It was for me for awhile. I couldn't live up to my big brother's image. It was simply too much for me. He was bigger, smarter, more popular, more responsible, and so I was determined to be exactly the opposite."

"What made you change?"

"Have I changed?" he countered. "Sometimes I think the rebellious child is lurking about inside of me just waiting for a chance to get out. Like Ned, I'm two people, the one who tried hard to please and can summon up enormous charm and the reckless, angry spirit that needs to be held in check."

"Is that the way you see Ned?" She was amazed and a little hurt by this analysis. She wondered if she could see Ned objectively, would she be able to recognize these counterparts.

Geoffrey sighed and reached for her hand.

"It's not too soon to be honest, is it Sybil?"

"I—I don't think I understand."

"I mean for us," he said. "It's the war, I suppose. But time seems to be telescoped. Everything I say or do seems to have an unexpected urgency about it, as though there isn't going to be much time left. Do you know what I mean?"

She had not, until this moment, thought very much about time in relation to the war. To her, the war had seemed very remote. It hardly affected her at all, except that there were certain fabrics that could not be had for the gowns she designed. There were the regulations and the rationing. And the war had brought some highly skilled refugees into the shop to work. They had been a godsend, for what she and Marlene were able to pay in the late thirties was not a princely sum. They had done much of the actual sewing themselves, working day and night, seven days a week to make a success of their business. She had little time for anything but her children and the shop. She'd leave one to go to the other and there was no in between. Her world was the children, Marlene, and the shop. The war in Europe was the distant rumbling of a storm that could not concern her. She had no time for it.

And then, as more and more war jobs became available, the seamstresses left Anderson-Grant and went to higher paying positions. When the first wave of French refugees began to arrive, she was not actually certain. Marlene discovered and hired them and things had been running smoothly ever since. The war itself and the atrocities seemed unreal. Just something one saw in the newsreels, almost an extension of the make-believe world of the film.

And now Geoffrey was speaking of the urgency of time and the need to be honest because of it. She looked at him with different eyes. He was not a combat soldier, but he had seen the war, had been in close contact with the fighting. Death was hardly a stranger to him. Death! She never thought of death. She thought of life and the struggle to make it safe and comfortable for her children. And now she wasn't even sure if she knew her own son. She had never thought of his having two personalities struggling within him as Geoffrey suggested. How honest had she really been with Ned, with herself, after all? She was so certain that all she needed for her children was security and a kind of blind faith that grew out of her love for them. Now she saw that this might not be enough at all.

She felt the comforting warmth of Geoffrey's touch as he continued to hold her hand in his.

"No, Geoffrey, I don't think it's too soon to be honest at all," she said slowly. "Is that really how you see my son—an angry, rebellious child?"

"Yes," he admitted. "I see my own frustrated childhood in him. Please don't be offended. I'm only trying to give you a fair appraisal. And what I see is an angry, unhappy boy. Why is he angry?"

Why? She thought. Why is he an angry, unhappy boy?

Was this what Ned had become because of her? Was not knowing his father so important? Wouldn't it have been worse if he had known Edward? Surely Ned would have been consumed in the fire of Edward's domination, of his madness as well.

She was not aware that they had left the main road until the car began climbing a steep hill.

"This can't be a shortcut to the city," she said. "Think of the gas you're using."

"You're forgetting my family's priority rating. Besides, there's someone I want you to meet. Today, of all days, you probably need the sympathy of another mother. I don't seem to be doing a very good job of consoling and advising you."

"Oh, no, Geoffrey. That's not true. You've given me an insight I never would have had. Whose mother are we seeing?"

"Mine," he said simply. "If it's not too soon to be honest, then it isn't too soon for you to meet my mother."

They left the road and passed through enormous stone gates and followed a winding tree-lined road until it widened into a circular drive before an imposing stone and brick mansion.

"Home sweet home," he said. "Mother doesn't go out very much any more. She loves company and she's going to be mad about you."

She hardly knew what to say.

"You look stricken," he teased. "You look hardly eighteen and positively stricken at the thought of coming home to meet my mother."

He laughed heartily as a guilty flush touched her cheeks.

"Well, I feel like an awkward girl. Geoffrey, she's not even expecting us," she protested.

"That's where you're wrong. I called her early this morning. I told her I'd finally met a woman I wanted her to meet," he said, coming around to her side and helping her from the car. He slipped his arm easily around her and for a moment held her close. Her senses responded

178

immediately and she felt herself sliding rapidly into a relationship she had neither sought nor expected. It was exciting to be with a man again, a man whose attraction for her was so strong. But it was frightening, too. What did she really know of him? Did she want to complicate her life with another emotional entanglement that inevitably could lead nowhere?

"Perhaps if you were not quite so beautiful or only a little less sensuous, you would not find yourself in this predicament, my girl," he whispered against her hair. "I'm moving fast, much too fast for you, I know, and yet I can't help myself. Will you humor me just for today? Well, perhaps tomorrow, too, and the day after that?"

Rose Kempton had been crippled with arthritis for years. She literally lived in a wheel chair, but there was nothing of the martyr about her. She greeted Sybil warmly and insisted upon taking her through the house with a silent attendant pushing her chair.

"This is Cora, my dear," she told Sybil. "Cora's been with me for seventeen years. We have no secrets from one another."

Cora was tall and sparse and wore a grim expression. She nodded her acknowledgment of Sybil's friendly greeting and then seemed to become lost in her own thoughts. She pushed Mrs. Kempton's chair from room to room and was unobtrusive as the air they breathed.

"I had to see you away from Geoffrey," Mrs. Kempton said. "He does have a way of dominating the scene. He was always like that, demanding attention. He'd do anything to get it. I want you to myself for just a little while. You're the first woman Geoffrey has brought home for the express purpose of meeting me. That's rather odd for a man of thirty-three, isn't it? I don't know what to make of it, but I think you must be very important to him."

Mrs. Kempton had dark, lively, beautifully shaped eyes. Her features were strong and classically sculptured. The rich white hair was arranged in long soft curls on top of her head. Sybil judged her to be in her sixties, but her body was so bent and crippled with her disease that she

179

looked much older. Only her voice was young and strong.

"I don't see how I can be important to Geoffrey," Sybil said truthfully. "We only met last night."

Mrs. Kempton laughed and the sound was gay, almost girlish.

"How like Geoffrey! He's terribly impulsive. So unlike his father and older brother. You have a son, too, I believe."

"And a daughter." She supplied the information willingly.

"Ah!" Mrs. Kempton nodded. "It's difficult for a woman to raise two children alone. I know. Geoffrey's father passed on when Geoffrey was only three. I never remarried. I planned to devote myself to my children. It was a mistake. Geoffrey would have been much better off with a second father to guide him. A boy needs a father. So does a girl for that matter. It gives children a kind of balance, don't you think?"

She looked up at Sybil and smiled. "It wasn't enough to have a procession of suitors and interested uncles. Not for Geoffrey anyway. And then there was the problem of his devotion to me. Geoffrey has always been extremely possessive, more like a lover than a son."

She laughed lightly. "I don't shock you, do I? There's a touch of incest in most families, some more than others. I'd like to see Geoffrey securely married to a sensible woman. It's just what he needs."

The frank talk was embarrassing. Mrs. Kempton spoke as if Sybil were a fiancée rather than a new acquaintance.

They went from room to room. Particularly attractive or unusual pieces of furniture were pointed out as they went. The house was exquisitely furnished.

Sybil admired everything from the English glass and ormolu chandelier in the mid-Georgian parlor to the Aubusson rug in the music room. Above the Delft tiles of the mantel in the formal dining room were cut glass candelabra. There were cut glass sconces on either side of the windows. In the entrance hall were Hepplewhite window stools upholstered in yellow brocade.

"Next time I'll show you the second floor, my dear. I do think the bedrooms are a bit intimate for a first visit, but that is where my children grew up. Perhaps we can exchange some stories," she said as they returned to the library.

"Geoffrey, you look positively forlorn! Ah, here is the tea. You'll feel so much better after you've had some."

"Thank you, I already have my refreshment," he said, holding up his glass of Scotch and soda. "Mother, you've kept Sybil from me nearly thirty minutes. I hardly think that was considerate," he added petulantly.

"It's this awful war," Mrs. Kempton confided to Sybil. "They've all become so impatient because of this awful war. No one has time to be gracious any more because of it. When it's all over, Geoffrey, you'll wonder what you were running from. It's never wise to move so quickly from one thing to the next that you have no time to savor the moment. You say you have a sense of time moving too fast and yet you aid and abet the illusion yourself. Poor Geoffrey! I'm afraid you shall somehow manage to wish your entire life away without really enjoying it. Lemon or cream, my dear?" she asked, turning to Sybil with a brilliant smile that belied the serious warning she meant to give her son.

II

It was Sybil who took the warning to heart. Wasn't that exactly what she had been doing, wishing her life away, living in a dream world, hoping against hope that she could keep the truth from invading and shattering the illusions she'd built for herself and her children? She had to be constantly on guard for fear something or someone would penetrate her emotional armor. So far no one had, but now there was Geoffrey. He gave every indication of wanting to do just that. Being with him was like moving back into the real world again.

That evening he met Joanna who adored him on sight. He took them both to dinner. Afterwards, when Joanna reluctantly agreed to go to bed, he begged to be allowed to see Sybil the next day.

"I'll pick you up at ten o'clock. We ought to be able to find something exciting to do."

"I have business commitments, Geoffrey. Right now we're terribly busy with the spring show."

He looked crushed and did not seem to understand how important her work was to her. Nothing mattered except that they be together.

"I'll settle for the evenings and the weekends," he told her grudgingly. "We've so little time."

He took it for granted that she would want to be with him. The truth was she did. She'd forgotten how pleasant it was to be with a man she admired, to enjoy the delightful womanly responses.

182

Even the excitement of the fashion show could not take her mind off him entirely. Was it possible that she could love again? She meant to go slowly, but his sense of urgency was infecting her. In a few weeks he'd be gone and perhaps she'd never know.

On Thursday, Anne's benefit luncheon was sold out. The Grand Ballroom was packed with women anxiously awaiting Anderson-Grant's new spring designs. Sybil did the commentary herself as she'd done on other occasions. As usual, she became so tense with excitement that she felt she would not be able to go on. Only when she was actually in front of the microphone, realizing that everyone was depending on her could she speak. She'd done her best, she told herself. She'd altered each costume until it was exactly what she wanted. She gained strength from the knowledge that the collection was the best she had to offer and smiled encouragingly at the models who waited nervously in the wings to step out onto the runway that had been specially constructed for the occasion. When delighted applause greeted the first suit—a pencil-slim pink skirt and bolero jacket with a soft feminine blouse—she knew the show would be a success.

Marlene stayed with the fitters in the dressing room to see that changes were made smoothly. Afterwards she questioned Sybil closely.

"What about the striped playsuit with the wrap-around skirt? And the red wool? You know how I felt about the shoulders on that one."

Sybil shook her head and smiled at her friend affectionately. There was no doubt in her mind that the collection had been well-received, but she knew Marlene would not be convinced until she saw the reviews in the morning papers. There'd be a party for the staff and their friends at the salon tonight. There'd be drinking, nervous chatter, and self-conscious laughter until the verdict was in. Every one of their employees felt a special responsibility for the success or failure of a show.

Geoffrey came. He was surprised and a little confused by the hectic confusion.

"It took me ten minutes to find you," he complained.

"It gets worse," she told him happily and slipped her arm through his. She introduced Marlene who was too distraught to be impressed.

When the papers arrived in the early hours of the morning, everyone was too deliriously happy to think of anything but the flattering phrases.

" 'Austere elegance!' I like that." One of the models struck a pose. "That was my red gown."

" 'Creative decolletage!' I don't know what it means, but I love it," said another girl.

"I wish someone would translate for me." Geoffrey had been relegated to the sidelines and was feeling left out.

Sybil touched his cheek and laughed at his woeful expression.

"It's just fashion talk and it's all good. Our spring collection is officially a success. Have some champagne."

"I'd rather have you," he told her huskily. "I don't want to disrupt the party, but when can we be alone together? We can do a little celebrating on our own, can't we?"

It seemed to Sybil that they continued to celebrate every night for the duration of Geoffrey's leave.

They spent an inordinate amount of time in the back of cabs, kissing and caressing like children playing at being married and too frightened of the actual intimacy to go any further. They had to be satisfied with what they had though her senses cried out for the union of physical love.

When he tried to speak of the future, of after the war, she silenced him. She lived for today, she insisted. She could make no promises, she said, and he agreed to her terms.

She knew in the back of her mind that what she was asking was unfair. But she was lost in the joy of feeling like a woman and she closed her eyes against every warning. She was strongly attracted to him. She enjoyed the sudden release from the prison of domestic and business chores and she allowed herself this brief respite of pleasure.

184

Vaguely she decided that he would return to London and forget her as she intended to forget him. She didn't think she really loved him. She was caught up in a kind of infatuation. She had loved only one man in her life, Jonathan. Geoffrey was fun and exciting and terribly attractive. But he lacked Jonathan's stability and strength. Jonathan went about everything he did purposefully. Geoffrey seemed to act on impulse and with abandon. No, Sybil did not think she loved him and was quite certain she would forget him easily the moment he was gone.

But she was wrong. She found that when he left she missed him very much or, at the very least, the side of New York life to which he'd introduced her. His New York was the posh supper club, socialite set. He moved among them easily.

The people he knew were bright, wealthy, and outwardly happy. They managed to keep up their spirits despite the war or perhaps because of it. Many of the otherwise idle, pampered women had thrown themselves enthusiastically into volunteer work in hospitals and canteens. Almost all the men, of course, were in uniform and, if not actually fighting the war, were making some contribution.

Her name began to appear in society columns as "Geoffrey Kempton's new flame, Sybil Anderson, the designer". It brought even wider publicity for the shop.

During those two weeks of Geoffrey's furlough she gave little thought to the more difficult responsibilities of her life. But she was pleased to receive a letter of apology from Ned—rather lengthy for him, a full page. Joanna became so busy with her new friend, Regina, she hardly was aware of Mommy's sudden flurry of social activity. Marlene was silent on the subject of Sybil's interest in Geoffrey. There were no more midnight confrontations and matters ran smoothly enough at the shop.

Not even on his last night did Geoffrey talk seriously of the future, perhaps because he knew how much she disapproved of such talk. He must have known she would have stopped him if he tried. But his first letter from London arrived ten days after he left. It was a lengthy, beautiful, emotional letter in which he asked her to marry him.

"You're the one, good, real thing to come into my life, Sybil. I want you to come home to. You don't have to answer right away. Think about it. Take all the time you want, but say yes. I love you more than I can say."

She was deeply moved. And the feelings of guilt that had been building for weeks since Ned's difficulty at school seemed to engulf her. She had been neither honest nor fair with Geoffrey. He was in love with her, he said. But what did he really know about her?

"You can't be considering this seriously." Marlene's face was bare of make-up and she was sitting up in bed reading a movie magazine when Sybil told her about the letter. Her plucked eyebrows without the aid of the dark pencil left her face almost without expression except for the deep angry furrow between her eyes.

"I've been thinking these past days," Sybil said slowly, "even before I got his letter."

She paused, finding it difficult to say exactly what she meant.

"Thinking about what?" Marlene prompted.

"About Ned and Joanna. About the deception. My life seems to be one long deception, Marlene. Can I go on like this forever? Is it fair to the children? What am I doing to them? To myself? To everyone I meet? Perhaps it's time I ended this lie!"

Marlene put down her magazine.

"How?"

The one word was a challenge. "How are you going to end this lie? You'd have to start by telling Ned. You really want to do that?" Her tone was almost sarcastic.

"It's not so much what I want, but what is right for Ned. That whole incident up at the school might never have happened if he were not forced to live the lie I've built for him. Perhaps—perhaps he has the right to know about his father. Perhaps it's time I straightened out my personal life."

Marlene was speechless. She stared in open-mouthed amazement.

"When I came to the city, I was a—a child-mother myself. Ned was helpless, completely dependent on me. I thought he was my life. I thought he was all I would ever need or want. But then there was Jonathan and Joanna. And Ned is growing up now. He's thinking for himself. He's curious. He's asking specific questions. He won't be a schoolboy forever. He'll grow away from me. So will Joanna. I have no right to make either of them my life. They'll want to live lives of their own. And what will be left for me?"

She sat down on the side of her bed, feeling lost and alone already.

Marlene threw off her covers and came to sit beside her. She slipped her arm around Sybil's tense shoulders.

"Hey, you sure have got a case of the blues tonight. You make everything sound so sad. Maybe you went for the Major in a big way. It's not unusual. It's wartime, honey, and these big romances crop up. They don't mean anything and they don't last. For every one guy like the Major there are a hundred others. Nobody takes them seriously."

"I do. I believe Geoffrey means what he says."

She got up and went to the dresser where she picked up her hairbrush, but didn't use it.

Marlene shook her head. "Then you're heading for a big disappointment, I'm afraid. The Major's going to be gone a long, long time. Who knows how he'll feel when he comes back? You're living in a dream world. What man is going to want to take on you and two kids when he's thinking clearly, answer me that?"

"You think Geoffrey hasn't considered Ned and Joanna?"

"Not exactly. But you said yourself, you've been living a lie. What would he think if he knew the truth? What would that classy mother of his think?"

Sybil caught her breath. This was something she had

187

been thinking, but afraid to explore fully. Would he feel the same if he knew the truth?

"That was cruel, Marlene," she said, her voice heavy with reproach.

"Yeah, I know and I'm sorry, honest I am, but it's the facts, right? It's the facts. Now look, honey, what do you want to put yourself through all this for?" She scratched her head wearily and got back into bed. Clearly she thought she'd won her point. "Look, it'll all work out for the best with Ned. He'll get over whatever is bothering him, you'll see. And, I wouldn't worry about making your kids your whole life. Look what you've done for yourself. Look at the business we've built up. And don't forget, this is only the beginning. We're going places, you and me. After the war, we're really going places. Forget this guy. He'll bring you grief. The only way to deal with men is to use them when you need them. I learned that from Joey Ferguson. Make sure you're in control all the time. That's the way to come out on top. The only person you can depend upon is yourself."

Marlene quickly became absorbed again in her magazine. She seemed to feel that the discussion had ended quite satisfactorily and that Sybil would recover from her moment of weakness.

But more and more, she began to think of the life she was leading. She looked at Joanna and knew that someday the same questions that puzzled Ned would plague her daughter. Would she have to go on lying forever? And Geoffrey! What had she done to him? Perhaps Marlene was right and his interest in her was nothing more than a romantic interlude, heightened by the war. But if it were not, if he sincerely believed all that he had said in his letters, wasn't she being cruel to deceive him further?

She did not answer his letter at once. Then one Sunday morning she had the apartment entirely to herself. Marlene had taken Joanna to Central Park. It was a warm March day, making them all feel that spring could not be far away. Spring! New life! New opportunities! A new start!

She sat down to write two letters. In the first to Geoffrey she confessed everything. She told him who she was and what she had done, giving details she might never have been able to confide in person. But a letter was an inanimate intermediary and she found that she could say these things on paper. When she reread what she had written, she was shaken by the life of confusion she had wrought for herself and for her children. She begged him to forgive her for any pain she had caused him. She did not expect to hear from him again.

The second letter grew out of the first and was far more difficult to write.

"Dear Alicia," she began.

She made several false starts and in the end, the letter was very short. She simply asked for a meeting alone. The reply was not long in coming. It was difficult to tell if her sister had been surprised or not at hearing from her. She agreed to the meeting at the Plaza, where she intended to be staying the following week.

Sybil said nothing to Marlene about the meeting, though as the time drew near, she grew quite obviously upset and nervous.

"You coming down with something?" Marlene asked. "Maybe you need a vacation. You and the kids should go somewhere for Easter. We can afford it. I can handle things at the shop," she offered.

She thanked her and said perhaps a vacation would be a good idea. She was feeling tired. And then on the day of her meeting with Alicia, she did not go into the shop at all.

All morning she was bothered by terrible misgivings. It was not too late to change her mind. She had used a post office box for her address. Alicia really did not know where to find her. She had told her very little except that she was living in New York and that Ned was fine and doing well in school.

She had no reply from Geoffrey, but then hadn't she convinced herself that she did not expect one? She wasn't doing this for Geoffrey, was she? It was for herself and for Ned and Joanna. What terrible chain of events she might unleash by her actions, she did not know. But she had to come to terms with the truth at last.

What could she expect Edward to do? It was difficult to say. Eleven years had seen tremendous changes in her life. She was well-established financially. She had friends and was not without resources. She was a mature woman and yet she felt suddenly like a terrified child. What had she done to Alicia, Edward, to all of them by her wild, hysterical flight? What else could she have done at the time, she wondered.

This last, she knew, would have little effect on Alicia. That Sybil had left, stolen away with Edward's child, would be enough to warrant the anger of the gods and she trembled to meet her fate. But it had to be done if she were ever to leave this web of lies with which she had insulated herself against the realities of life.

Alicia was already seated at a table in a secluded corner of the Palm Court. As she promised in her letter, she was alone. Sybil was a little surprised to find that her sister had changed so little. She wore a pale blue linen suit and a broad-brimmed, highly flattering straw hat, Her hair seemed redder, but her features were as cool and beautiful as ever. No one would have taken her for a woman of forty-seven. She held her head at a particularly attractive angle and waited calmly for Sybil to make her appearance.

Watching her now from the entrance, half hidden by the profusion of plants, Sybil wondered what could be going on in Alicia's mind. But then, it had always been difficult to tell that, even when she felt closest to her sister during those weeks before her debut.

And now it seemed as though the time between had never been. She was suddenly struck by a feeling of nostalgia for her innocent childhood. Alicia was part of that and the emotion she felt for her now was unexpected affection.

"Madame?" asked the maître d' and leaned toward her

confidentially, as though he expected to be able to offer her a great service.

She smiled at him a bit wryly. He'd never know what his escorting her to Alicia's table would mean.

"Well, Sybil, is it really you?"

She smiled a bit uncertainly. She leaned forward thinking to kiss her sister and stopped, cooled by Alicia's unnatural calm and her languid glance.

The languid look was deceptive. Alicia was taking in the details of the smart linen dress and coat with white trim at collar and cuffs. It was one of Sybil's own designs and the color contrasted well with her rich dark hair.

"What have you done to yourself, Sybil?"

"Hello, Alicia." The moment of nostalgia had passed. Faced with the reality of Alicia, she found she was nearly tongue-tied. It really didn't matter. Alicia did most of the talking, asking pointed questions.

"I must confess I never thought to see you again, not alive anyway, and not looking so well. I used to think we'd eventually find you in a hospital for the hopelessly insane. And here you are, alive and doing very well from the look of you. How did you manage it?"

"I've been very fortunate." She told her something about the shop.

"Alone? Surely you were not able to do all this alone? Who helped you, Sybil? It was a man, wasn't it? I told Edward that was the only explanation. He didn't believe me. He simply could not accept the idea. In many ways Edward is rather naive, poor dear. You made a terrible mistake in leaving him. He was willing to give you everything. He is wealthy and clever. He's tripled his fortune. But then you don't really care about that, do you? Edward's fortune, or Edward, or Monty and me? Poor Monty! He took the first opportunity to leave the scandal behind. He's been in Washington since 1941, a desk job at the Pentagon. How much has happened, Sybil! How very, very much has happened! Have you any idea at all what we suffered when you disappeared? Edward was beside himself! He moved heaven and earth to get you back! You and Neddy! He was desperate to find his son. How could you have done it, Sybil?

How could she answer that question? She remembered those early days when she worked at Arnaud's by day and came home to a restless, crying baby whose needs were endless.

"It wasn't easy," she said evenly, though she felt suddenly angry. The only thought Alicia had was that Sybil must have had the help of some man. Someone who encouraged and protected her. It would be nearly impossible for Alicia to understand that she had worked and suffered to achieve what she now had.

"You haven't mentioned Papa, Alicia. Is he—?"

Alicia sighed and her long eyes narrowed.

"I'm surprised you bothered to ask. He is just as he was, more or less. He's still partially paralyzed, but he can get about more. He needs constant care which I see to, I might add. He'll never recover completely, of course. He still doesn't remember you. Thank God for that. What you did destroyed him."

She didn't try to reply to the accusation and so they sat for a time in uncomfortable silence. The news that her father was still alive brought tears to Sybil's eyes. How she longed to see him again! Perhaps now she could.

"What is it you want, Sybil?" Alicia asked after they had given their order to the waiter. "Surely you don't plan to come back!"

"I don't think I know what you mean by 'come back', Alicia."

"Why, to Edward, of course."

She almost laughed aloud. "I have no intention of going back to Edward."

"Then what is it you want?"

"A divorce, for one thing," she said slowly. "And I suppose Edward has a right to know his son."

"Oh, you think that?" Alicia asked.

"Perhaps I should put it the other way around. Ned has a right to know his father."

"Ah." Alicia sat back and eyed her curiously. "What have you told Ned about his father?"

"Nothing."

"Nothing? I can hardly believe nothing. The boy must have questions. How old is he, ten? Eleven? He must have questions."

"He does. And I want him to meet Edward." She said the words with difficulty. It was hard to believe she'd said them at all. But there they were.

"Well, then you should not be surprised to learn that Edward wants to see Ned."

"You told him of our meeting?" she asked, feeling alarmed and looking about as though she expected to see him.

"That worries you, doesn't it? Edward, I mean. You're still afraid of him. You always were. I told you that was no way to begin a marriage. You have to learn to handle a man like Edward. You could have managed once you had Ned. Edward wanted children badly. Tell me," she said, leaning forward, "where is Neddy? I'd like to see the dear child myself."

She drew back. "He's not in the city at the moment."

"Oh?" Alicia raised her perfectly arched brows. "Away at school, is he?"

"Yes."

"Where?"

"He'll be home shortly for the Easter vacation. You can see him then."

Any vague idea she had of reasoning with her sister was gone. She had thought to try to explain her position, to seek Alicia's advice. They were sisters after all. To whom could she turn but her sister? She felt threatened, something she hadn't expected, not after all this time. Had she even been wise seeing Alicia like this all on her own? Perhaps she should have sought legal advice first. The fear of losing Ned to his father had become remote over the years. Edward would certainly not try to take her son away from her at this late date, would he? If she was willing to arrange visiting privileges for him, surely he would be satisfied. She convinced herself that this was all true before she wrote Alicia. Now, she was not so certain.

"Well, Sybil," Alicia took a small pad and gold pen from her purse, "at least give me your address in the city so I can be in touch with you."

She hesitated. She met her sister's eyes and was chilled by what she saw there.

"Oh, come now, Sybil, there's no further reason for secrecy, is there? You want everything settled and so do we."

Sybil took the pen and wrote her address.

Alicia lifted her teacup and sighed as though she'd just completed a difficult task.

"I suppose you already have a lawyer?"

"Oh, of course," she lied and wondered where she should go for advice.

"Well, then he can be in touch with us. In touch with us," she repeated to herself. The word "us" had such an ominous sound.

In the cab going downtown she went over and over their interview. She could not decide if it had been satisfactory or not. It was what she might have expected. In a way she was relieved. She'd taken the first small step, but an irrevocable one. That's what frightened her.

That night she told Marlene what she had done and that she planned to tell Ned the next day.

Marlene couldn't believe it at first and she was angry, terribly angry.

"What the hell are you trying to do? Have you gone nuts? We're going along good and you have to rock the boat? I thought you gave that idea up."

"Marlene, this is between my children and me. This is something I have to do."

"Oh, sure! Sure it is. Between your kids and you. That's what you think now. Just you wait. This could ruin us. What if it gets into the papers? Those 'holier-than-thou' society women who come into the shop, how do you think they're going to take this?"

"It doesn't concern them."

"Oh, no? Think again. They got a picture of you as a poor, innocent widow. I'm telling you they don't go for illegitimate kids."

"Marlene, please." She was shocked by the very sound of the word.

"Please! Please what! Don't bring out the truth? That *is* the truth, isn't it? And how do people react to that kind of truth? Even divorce sends rich society dames into a tailspin. They're solid American stock, apple pie and motherhood. That's the kind of clientele you've built up. What do you think they'll do when your story hits them? What do you think your friend, Mrs. Anne Ward Halburton, will think?"

"She *is* my friend. She'll understand." She wished Marlene would lower her voice.

"Will she? Well, maybe now you'll find out what kind of friend she is. What about the others, though?"

"My personal life has nothing to do with the dresses I design." She was angry, too, now. Or was she simply afraid? "And you're assuming the story will be in the papers. It doesn't have to be. It can be settled out of court."

"You better pray it will be or we're going to be fresh out of luck. Why? Why are you doing this? That's what I don't get?" Marlene paced about the living room frantically. "We got a good thing going and you want to ruin it."

"Marlene, you're getting upset unnecessarily."

She was close to tears herself. She'd gone over and over all the possibilities. But the answer always seemed clear. There were risks involved, she knew that. With luck and if Edward would agree to be reasonable, they'd be all right. If!

"Mommy! I can't sleep."

Joanna stood in the doorway rubbing her eyes. She was wearing her yellow nightgown with Snow White and the seven dwarfs printed on the fabric. Her dark hair was tousled and she blinked owlishly up at them.

Sybil lifted the little girl in her arms and hugged her. Joanna smelled sweet, like baby powder and Ivory soap.

She was small for eight and Sybil could still hold her comfortably on her lap. What would the word "illegitimate" mean to Joanna?

"I'll bet you can sleep if Mommy tells you a story," she said.

Joanna smiled. "A long story," she said.

Glad to have a reason to escape the painful argument with Marlene, she carried the child back to the bedroom.

The story she told was a long involved tale, a combination of all the fairy tales she'd ever heard. Joanna loved it. Soon the child's eyes grew heavy and she slept. There was a faint smile of contentment on her lips.

She kissed her daughter's forehead. How easy it was to satisfy her! She was still such an innocent baby. If only Ned could be that easily satisfied. If only the children never had to grow up. Then she would not have to do what she knew she must do.

Reluctantly, she went back to the living room where Marlene was waiting for her. She'd poured herself a drink and was staring sullenly at the dark liquid in the bottom of her glass.

"I know why you're doing this," she said at last, her voice carefully restrained. "You want to marry the Major. That's it, isn't it?"

"I don't honestly know."

"Don't! Don't do it, honey. Don't marry him."

Her tone became pleading. She leaned toward Sybil, who sat in the chair opposite her.

"You don't need him. What for? Tell me that. All these guys give you is a lot of grief. Now, you can't deny that. Look at your husband and all you went through with the Doc. We don't need them, do we? We got a family right here, don't we? You, me, and the kids. You want a guy now and then? Well, go ahead. But you don't need to marry any of them. They take over then. They think they own you. That's not for you, honey. You had enough of that. Am I right?"

Sybil looked at her as though she'd never seen her before. Had they grown so far apart that one didn't know what the other was thinking? She knew Marlene's attitude toward men had changed after Joey. But she enjoyed male companionship. She did volunteer work at the canteen regularly. She dated buyers and salesmen. It wasn't as though she had cut herself off entirely from men. And yet she was advising Sybil to avoid any lasting, normal relationship with a man. Marrying Geoffrey wasn't the point. Ned was. Being honest was. She wanted to make Marlene understand that, but her head had begun to ache. It might be better if they talked in the morning.

"Marlene, I'm awfully tired—" she began.

"What about me? Shouldn't I be tired?" Marlene demanded angrily, though she was careful to keep her voice low. "I've been working in the shop all day, the shop that keeps us all going around here, in case you forgot. The shop that might just fall on its face if it gets hit hard enough by bad publicity. Don't kid yourself. It could all go right down the drain. We could lose everything. I just hope you realize that. Everything! And one more thing. You owe me. Do you ever think of that? You owe me."

There wasn't anything she could say to that. It should not have been said at all. The silence that followed was awkward. Marlene's eyes wavered and she picked up her glass, draining it in one gulp. Finally she left the room. Sybil could hear her in the other room getting ready for bed.

It was impossible to sleep. Sybil lay awake for hours, staring into the darkness. She was very much aware of Marlene's presence in the other bed. The apartment was large, as New York apartments went. There were three bedrooms, but tonight it did not seem large enough and she felt she desperately needed privacy. After a time she got up and went into Ned's room. There at last she slept, but not well for she awoke in the morning with a stiffness in her limbs and an oppressive sense of weariness as though she had not slept at all. The thought of facing Ned with the truth was almost too much, but she knew it had to be done.

"What's the idea?" Marlene asked when Sybil came

into the kitchen the next morning. "You scared me half to death last night."

"I did? How?"

"How? When I found your bed was empty, I didn't know what to think. I thought— Well, I thought you'd gone."

Marlene shook her head and her voice grew suspiciously husky. All her anger of last night had dissipated. "Gee, honey, don't you know I worry about you? I do, you know. You're all I got. You and the kids. I'm sorry if I said anything to upset you last night. I was tired. You know how it is." She laughed nervously. "I've been thinking. Maybe we both need a vacation. We should take the kids and go off somewhere for a rest. Yeah, that's what we should do. When I get tired like that, I don't know what I'm saying. Don't pay any attention to anything I said last night, will you? I mean, well, we're going to make out all right any way you want it. O.K.? And that includes marrying the Major, if that's what you really want. You gotta do what you think is right. I know that. I'm—I'm sorry. I shouldn't have sounded off like I did." She laughed shakily. "You're not mad at me, are you?"

Tears stung Sybil's eyes. Marlene was the most resilient person she'd ever known. Emotional and volatile at times, she was basically practical and fair. Her warmth and generosity are what kept Sybil going.

"I don't know what I'd do without you, Marlene," she said, brushing the tears away.

"Yeah, right," Marlene replied gruffly and patted her shoulder. "You still going to see Ned today?"

She nodded as she began making cereal for Joanna's breakfast and glanced at the clock. It was still early. The housekeeper wouldn't arrive for another hour.

"O.K. If that's what you have to do, you do it. I just hope for your sake Ned is going to understand."

She thought of Marlene's warning all the way up on the train. It took an hour and a half and another twenty minutes in the cab to the school. She had plenty of time to think, but it all came back to the necessity for truth.

Emotionally drained when she reached the school, she was hardly prepared for the hostility of the headmaster.

"I've been extremely patient, Mrs. Anderson, extremely patient. But as it happens your coming is most opportune. We've decided that Parkhurst is not the place for Ned. He's obviously not happy and he makes others unhappy."

"Makes others unhappy?" she asked.

Mr. Singleton launched into a recital of Ned's transgressions. To her it all sounded like childish gossip, horribly snobbish and unfair. If he picked fights with other boys, it must have been with good reason.

"Where is Ned now?" she interrupted Mr. Singleton to ask.

The headmaster glanced out the window. From here they could see the baseball diamond crowded with upperclass boys. Beyond that was the duck pond.

"As it happens, I think I can see Ned down there." He indicated the pond. "I'll have someone escort you."

"Thank you," she said stiffly. "That won't be necessary."

She didn't want anything further from this man or the school or anyone connected with it. She made her way past the noisy boys at the ball field and on toward the pond where she could see Ned. He was a solitary figure in gray slacks and an open-necked white shirt, skipping stones across the water. When he saw her, he dropped the handful of pebbles he'd collected and ran to throw his arms about her.

"Oh, Mother, I was hoping you'd come," he cried with such sincerity that Sybil's heart swelled with joy. "I want to go home, Mother. I don't ever want to come back to this awful place again."

He cried. She hadn't seen Ned cry in years and she hugged him to her, crying herself.

"Oh, Ned! Ned!" she said. "It's all right, Ned. It's all right now. We are going home."

She told him nothing of what she'd come to say. They packed his clothes and made arrangements to have them sent on. When they were at last on the train to New

199

York, she saw no reason to burden his already burdened mind with the truth.

He talked all the way to the city. He was full of ideas about what they'd do that summer.

"You said this year you would take a vacation in June. Can we go to the seashore? I've never been. The other kids talk about the seashore all the time. Joanna will like it, too. Say we can go, Mother. Just you and Joanna, Aunt Marlene, and me."

His dark eyes were bright with excitement and love, she thought. He needs his family, wants to be with us, with me. It made her happy to think this.

He had grown during the months he'd been away. But he was much too thin. His face looked boney and his eyes enormous. Perhaps he was growing too fast. What sort of food had he been getting at school? He never complained about it, but he needed pampering now. She would see to it that Mrs. Norris prepared his favorite dishes.

In the back of her mind she buried the fear that had been growing since her frank discussion with Marlene. Perhaps she was doing this for very selfish reasons. Perhaps she did want to marry Geoffrey, if he still wanted her. But even that seemed unlikely since she hadn't heard from him. Was she gambling everything on the chance that he would marry her? And what would she have when it was over? She might not even have Ned.

And so she put off telling him.

Joanna was beside herself with the joy of seeing her brother. She hugged and kissed him, then danced around the room only to throw herself into his arms again.

"Oh, Neddy, Neddy! Come see my fish! Wait till you see. They had babies. I'll give you some. Any ones you choose. And I have an extra tank, too. Come see."

"All right, Joanna. Will you excuse me, Mother?" he asked politely.

She was overwhelmed. He would never have thought to ask to be excused before. Perhaps the school had been good for something.

"How did he take it?"

She and Marlene had after-dinner coffee in the living room while the children went to Ned's room to listen to the radio serials.

"I—I didn't tell him yet. There was—there was some trouble at school."

She explained what happened and was relieved when Marlene agreed she'd been wise.

"Well, I guess it can wait awhile," she said. "He's changed," she added thoughtfully. "He's growing up, I guess, but there's something I can't put my finger on. He just seems different to me. Maybe he was unhappy up there and was ashamed to say it. If I were you, I'd take it slow with him."

She decided to wait before enrolling Ned in the local school again, mainly because he asked her to. She did think he needed a rest. He seemed to find plenty to do, though he was alone most of the day. He was mad about model planes. He liked building them and he knew the names of all the Air Force planes, as well as their function. She could listen to him hold forth for hours on the subject. Joanna's admiration knew no bounds. Ned even let her take two of his models to school. Marlene and the children spent endless hours exchanging "knock knock" jokes.

The best part of those two weeks for Sybil was having him home when she got in at night. If she were tired, she was completely revived the minute she saw him. It was a kind of fool's paradise for her because, of course, it could not last.

Only Mrs. Norris seemed to see this. Ned's behavior was cheerful, polite, and loving when his mother was around. The housekeeper saw another side of him.

"A boy his age should not be spending so much time alone. Gives them funny ideas. You have to keep them busy," she added, but refused to elaborate.

And then Sybil found out by sheer accident. She went into Ned's room one evening without knocking to show him an article on Messerschmitts she'd found in a magazine. She came in so quietly he did not hear her. He was lying on the bed, the lower portion of his body unclothed. His eyes were closed and, at first, she thought he was asleep.

Then she saw his hands moving rhythmically as he stroked himself. He was lost to her in a fantasy of self-induced pleasure.

She spoke his name sharply.

He sat up and his eyes flashed with such venom she felt she'd been struck.

"What do you want?" he demanded furiously.

"Why—I— Ned, what were you doing?"

The moment the words left her lips she knew she should not have said them.

He laughed at her then, a low guttural sound.

"We all did it at school," he said. "What did you think we did when there was nothing to do, Mother? You don't die from it. You don't even get sick."

The many complaints the headmaster had about Ned came back to her. One of them involved molesting younger boys. Molesting!

Before the word had an entirely different meaning. She thought of it as teasing or fighting. Now she thought of Edward. Was Ned going to be like his father? Ned was not, after all, growing up.

She snapped on the light.

"Get dressed and come into the living room. I want to talk to you."

"We can talk here," he said, casually drawing a sheet over his body.

His look of disdain astonished her. She wanted to handle this well and yet was not sure how to go about it. He seemed so strange, so much older suddenly.

"I'd rather talk in the living room," she said, finding it difficult to meet his eyes.

"All right, Mother, but I already know the facts of life, so you don't have to get worked up about that."

"Come inside when you're ready, Ned."

She didn't trust herself to say anything else. Fortunately, Joanna had gone to bed and Marlene was out at a movie so they had the apartment to themselves.

Ned sat in the blue velvet chair opposite the sofa and fixed his cold eyes on her. He waited and when she could not seem to find the words to begin, he started for her.

"It's perfectly normal, you know. Everybody does it." He sounded mater-of-fact and confident, as if he were the parent and she the child.

"Ned!"

"It's true! We all did it at school, even the teachers, I'll bet you."

"Ned!"

"Mother, I don't know what you want me to say. This is the way things are. If my father were alive, he'd tell you himself what it's like. He'd understand."

Suddenly he smiled at her fondly and a little indulgently.

"Let's talk about my father. We haven't in a long time."

Startled and confused by the sudden change in conversation, she hardly knew what to say. But she knew the time had certainly come.

"All right, Ned. There is something I want to tell you."

She began the story slowly, haltingly with her own lonely childhood, remembering as she did her own first faint stirrings of sexual interest. As delicately as she could, she told him about this, too. She wanted him to know she understood.

How much better it would have been if that part could have been handled by a man. She knew so little about young boys growing up. Briefly and with the same sharp pain of loss thoughts of him always aroused, she thought of Jonathan. How different things would have been if Jonathan were here! How he had loved Ned! He would have been just what Ned needed.

As she went on with her story, telling of her marriage, she tried hard to be fair to Edward. It was difficult to bear the look of utter disbelief on Ned's face as he began to understand what it was she was telling him. He listened with a kind of horrified awe. When she was finished, she was not particularly surprised by his reaction. He was angry.

"You were wrong to lie to me, Mother. That was very wrong. I want to meet him. I want to know my father," he said and his tone was defiant as though he expected her to refuse him.

"Yes, he wants to meet you, Ned. I told you he was very proud of you."

"Tomorrow," Ned said insistently. "Can I meet him tomorrow?"

She hesitated. She had not mentioned the legal problems involved. She simply told him that she and his father could not live together and so she had left him. She tried not to think what Edward would tell the boy. She had to go on believing that whatever it was, Ned would not lose faith in her. He'd continue to love her.

"Arrangements have to be made, Ned. Perhaps not tomorrow."

"What sort of arrangements? Don't try to put me off."

He rose and began to pace up and down the room, his hands behind his back.

"All these years! You had no right to do this to me, Mother. No right at all."

"Oh, Ned! You don't understand, darling."

"No, I don't." He stopped abruptly before her.

"Are you divorced?"

"Well—no."

"You mean you're still married to my father?"

"Yes."

"Then how can you possibly marry Major Kempton?" he demanded.

"Marry Major Kempton?"

"That's right. I know that's what you're planning. He told me in his letter."

"He wrote to you?" She hadn't expected this.

"Yes, as soon as he got back to London."

She realized Geoffrey must have written both her letter and Ned's at the same time.

"He had no right to do that," she said, her cheeks flushing.

"Didn't he?"

"No."

"Mother, I don't know what to believe any more. Maybe— maybe—"

"Maybe what, Ned?"

She was alarmed by the look on his face.

"You said Bascomb was wrong when he called me a bastard. Maybe—" Ned's eyes narrowed. "Maybe he was right. And you're—you're nothing but a—tramp."

Sybil caught her breath, but before she could say anything Ned left the room. She heard him slam his door shut and turn the key in the lock.

What had she done? How could she have bungled matters so? She went to his room, but he refused to speak to her. Later she thought she heard him crying.

She walked aimlessly from room to room, mentally berating herself for her stupidity. It was a long night, but in the morning she determined what must be done. Ned wanted to see his father. That had to be arranged. She could give him no further excuses.

"Neddy won't get up," complained Joanna at breakfast. "His door is locked and he told me to go away. He sounded mad. What did I do anyway? I'm not mad at him."

"Ned is just tired, darling. He was up late last night. You must let him sleep."

Joanna pouted over her orange juice.

"Was Ned up with you last night, Mommy?"

Sybil nodded.

"I never get to stay up late with you. Never!" complained the child. "I think you love Ned more than you love me."

"Joanna, that's not true and you know it. Ned had a problem. We needed to talk."

Joanna continued to scowl grumpily, but drank her orange juice and said nothing more.

"Well, what happened?" asked Marlene after Joanna left.

Sybil almost broke down then.

"It was awful. Just awful. He wants to see his father."

For a moment Marlene said nothing. "Well, that was what you wanted, wasn't it? You'd better get a lawyer, though," she said finally. "A good one. Didn't you say the Major's family had one of the best firms in the city?"

"I couldn't go to Geoffrey's brother!"

"Why not? He's the best and you need the best, especially if you're going to keep this as quiet as possible. Go to him. What do you think your sister and your husband have been doing all this time? You can bet they're not sitting around. You need some good legal advice. I think you may have waited too long already," she added grimly.

Too long! Alarmed, she called the offices of Kempton, Chalmers, Bolton and Lee that morning. When Arthur Kempton realized who she was, he made time to see her and insisted upon taking her to lunch. They went to a small, exclusive restaurant where the headwaiter immediately ushered them to a quiet corner. She wondered how many clients were brought here to unburden themselves of difficult problems in these comfortable surroundings.

Arthur Kempton was not at all like Geoffrey. In his early forties, he was a thin, ascetic-looking man whose intense manner was at first disturbing. Everything he said seemed to carry great import. Even ordering eggs Benedict took on new meaning.

"You've done something to my brother," he said as soon as they'd taken care of the amenities.

"Have I?" This was not the direction she thought their interview would take.

"He's never sounded so sane and sensible in his letters, I mean. In fact, Mother and I seldom heard from him before this. A post card here and there was all we could expect. And now here he is taking life seriously because he's taking you seriously."

Suddenly, unexpectedly, Arthur Kempton smiled and

his entire face changed. The burden of responsibility was temporarily gone and he looked younger, more relaxed, and genuinely pleased to be with her. Like Geoffrey he was fair-haired. His features were sharp, almost gaunt, but when he smiled, his face softened. She could see the resemblance to Geoffrey then.

"If there is anything at all that I can do for you, well, it will be my pleasure, Mrs. Anderson."

She wondered how long the desire to help her would last once Arthur Kempton realized how tangled the affairs of her private world had become. Perhaps it was a mistake to come to Geoffrey's brother especially since she had not heard from Geoffrey himself since she'd written him the truth.

"I don't know how— That is—"

She stumbled over her words. There seemed no delicate way to put her position. Arthur Kempton continued to smile encouragingly.

"Suppose we eat first and talk over coffee. That way we'll both feel better."

He was right. The good food, expertly prepared, seemed to calm her.

"Mr. Kempton," she began when coffee was served, "I do not want to lose my son. Can you help me? I haven't been honest, I'm afraid, with your brother or your mother, whom I met only briefly. I haven't been honest with anyone. I've lived this lie so long, I've begun to believe it myself."

It took her nearly two hours to tell her story in halting, anguished words. He asked a number of personal, painful questions, but he asked them gently and when he was through she felt ravaged, but in a way grateful. He knew more about her now than any man she'd ever known, even Jonathan.

She came back to the reality of the present as if from a long distance. She became aware again of the sounds of the restaurant and the muted voices of other customers and the quiet, unobtrusive movements of the waiters. Looking into Arthur Kempton's compassionate eyes, she was vastly relieved to see that he seemed to think no less of her after having heard her story.

"The possibility of surviving a court battle is almost nonexistent," he said. "But it needn't come to that, of course," he added hastily. "A settlement out of court, a compromise—"

"I know," she whispered, interrupting him. "I know."

She stared down at her hands. When she was a child, she would sit for hours simply staring at her hands. They were small, childlike hands then, well-formed and very white with small crescent-shaped pale pink nails. She could trace the blue veins beneath the skin with her eyes even then and imagined how the hands would look when she was old, all wrinkled and gnarled like the ladies who came to tea with Mama and sat for hours, fingers curled around teacup handles. Old hands she thought were for teacups. She wondered when she was seven years old if, when she grew old, she'd be able to remember her smooth, white child hands lying idly in her lap as though they belonged to someone else.

The hands she saw now were lady-like hands, not terribly old or terribly young. But she could still remember her seven-year-old hands and her innocence. How simple life was when growing up meant nothing more than wrinkled hands on a teacup and nothing in between. She'd come so far from those early, lonely days of innocence.

"Mr. Kempton," she said, still staring at her hands, "if I lose my son, I will have lost everything."

"Then we must see that you don't lose him," he said gently.

"You believe that there is a possibility?" she asked, desperate for any ray of hope.

"There is always a possibility," he told her, signing the check left by the waiter.

It was late afternoon when she returned to the apartment. Joanna must be home from school. Her books were on the hall table. The moment she stepped inside, Sybil heard raised voices. Ned was shouting.

"Get out of here and leave me alone, you little witch!"

Witch! Had he said witch or—

She went back to Ned's room without taking off her coat. Joanna was standing near the fish tank, her small face red with anger.

"You're mean, Neddy Anderson. All I wanted to do was feed these fish. You haven't fed them in days. They'll die!"

"What do I care if they die? Get out of here, I said," Ned retorted furiously. "You have no right to come sneaking in on me like this when I'm busy."

"I wasn't sneaking in and you weren't busy," Joanna yelled.

Ned was lying in bed. He hadn't even bothered to dress. Had he been lying there all day?

"Ned! Joanna! Stop this at once!"

"Oh, Mommy!" Joanna rushed over and threw her arms around her mother. "Ned's mean! He's so mean."

She firmly disengaged herself from the child's embrace. "Go to your room, Joanna. I want to talk to Ned."

Joanna turned to her brother and stuck out her tongue.

"Now you're going to get it, smarty."

"Joanna, go to your room at once."

"Oh, all right!" Joanna stalked out managing to look extremely hurt.

Sybil sighed helplessly and turned her attention to Ned.

"Why aren't you dressed, Ned? Are you ill? It's four o'clock in the afternoon."

"I know how to tell time, Mother," he said in an insolent tone.

She bit her lip. She did not want to be angry. She wanted to be calm and reasonable.

"Ned, sit up and look at me."

"I don't want to look at you. I don't even know if I ever want to see you again. I want to see my father. You said he wanted to see me. When can I go to Philadelphia and see him?"

She tried to understand. Ned was upset and confused. He was a sensitive, unpredictable preadolescent. He didn't realize how he was hurting her.

"Ned," she said, coming into the room and picking up the clothes he'd tossed on the floor last night. "I'm making arrangements for you to see your father. I went to a lawyer today."

"A lawyer? Why did you have to see a lawyer?" He glared at her. "Why can't you just call him up and say I want to see him?"

"It's not that easy."

"It's not easy because you don't want it to be," he snarled.

"I don't know what you mean by that, Ned." Her patience had worn dangerously thin. "Please get up, shower, and dress so that you can be presentable at dinner."

"Presentable at dinner? What do I care about dinner? I want to see my father."

She looked at his dark, tousled hair and his rumpled pajamas. He looked wild-eyed and almost feverish. The air in the room was close and stagnant. Probably he hadn't opened a window all day. There were comic books with lurid covers strewn about the floor and parts of model planes everywhere.

"I will not discuss anything with you until you have made yourself presentable and cleaned up this room. And I do not care for your tone of voice. It is disrespectful. Now, get up at once."

She started to leave.

"Disrespectful! Disrespectful! Do you think you deserve *my* respect?" he screamed. "I don't respect you and I don't have to do anything you say."

She was badly shaken by the angry words, but she kept her voice steady. "As long as you live in my house, you will obey me. Get out of that bed at once."

She did not wait for a reply, but left the room and hurried to her own, where she leaned on the dresser trembling violently. How had she let this happen? She told herself that all she ever wanted was the love and happiness of her children. And now, it seemed, she'd lost Ned.

"Mommy, Mommy! Don't cry. I still love you."

She hadn't realized she was crying until Joanna came in quietly and slipped her arms around her mother.

"Oh, Joanna!" she whispered and rocked the child in her arms.

The meeting between Ned and his father was to take place in Arthur's office a week later. All the arrangements had been made for Marlene to go with him, but at the last minute she knew she had to be there. Against Arthur's advice and over Marlene's protests, she brought Ned to Arthur's office herself. They all met in the law library where row upon row of leather-bound volumes reminded Sybil that hers was only one small drama in the long history of cases the courts had seen. The meeting, however, was no less traumatic.

In ten years Edward had aged little. He had put on some weight and there were new lines in his face which simply served to accent his strong features. There was gray in his hair and gray in the heavy brows that hooded his dark eyes.

She felt his presence in the room like an omniscient, oppressive spirit and nearly bolted at the last moment. She had dressed carefully for this meeting, choosing a dark blue shantung suit trimmed with white piping. She wore a small blue and white hat of the same fabric. Her gloves and blouse were white eyelet. She wanted to look cool and composed. She must betray no tremor of fear. Edward's strength fed on fear. She knew that now and that's why she had decided to come herself. She did not want him to think she was afraid.

On the trip over in the cab Ned betrayed some of his own misgivings. It was obvious he did not know what to expect. Being a child he was more reluctant to leave the safety of what he already knew for the unknown. Halfway uptown he broke his silence of days and kissed Sybil's cheek impulsively.

"Don't worry, Mother," he said. "I suppose I'll always love you."

She could have cried. She hugged him to her and blinked back her tears as she caught blurred glimpses of

211

buildings along Park Avenue. She recalled her first trip through the city streets in a cab with Ned in her arms. She was just as frightened then, she thought. And yet how far they'd come!

"Well, Sybil, you've changed," was Edward's first remark. He and Alicia were seated at the long table. "When you left you were hardly more than a child. I must say maturity becomes you."

Holding her head high, she spoke clearly. Determination and a sense of her own worth had given her strength. She could meet his gaze without wavering.

"Thank you, Edward." She looked down at her son, who was staring at his father with open admiration. "This, of course, is Ned."

Arthur stood beside them and she was acutely aware of his strong disapproval. Still, she was glad she had come. In her mind she had built an image of Edward that was hardly realistic. He was, after all, a man, not a monster. His pleasure at seeing Ned was genuine enough. Even Alicia looked pleased.

"How well he's turned out, Sybil!" she said and introduced herself.

The boy did not seem to know what to do next. He looked hesitantly from her to his father.

"Well, Ned, come here and let me look at you," Edward said.

He smiled and Ned responded, moving slowly away from his mother, but purposefully toward his father. It was obvious he was not frightened nor reluctant and she felt as though something of herself was being torn away.

"How do you do, Father? It seems so odd that we've never met."

The two figures seemed frozen in time, Edward's large handsome head was inclined toward the boy's thin, upturned face. In profile the resemblance between the two was very strong.

"This," Edward said at last, "is one of the happier moments of my life, Ned. Sybil, he's everything I had hoped," he added without taking his eyes from Ned's face. "Everything!"

The meeting with Edward and Alicia discouraged even Arthur. He had hoped to avoid a court battle. Now it seemed inevitable. Edward was insisting on complete custody. As she might have known, his need for revenge was rekindled and he appeared to be driven by it.

"Don't give up, Sybil. There's always the unexpected," Arthur told her kindly.

And there was! Two days later he called her and she went to see him.

"All that money, Sybil. Think of it. For years Edward's been in control of your father's money. Evidently your brother-in-law and sister agreed to the arrangement. You were not there, so you could not object. Edward has used your father's money freely, making investments and consulting no one. But the divorce would change this position drastically. He can threaten to take Ned away in a court battle, but you can threaten his financial position. Which would he choose, I wonder. You could offer *him* visiting privileges in exchange for the right to continue to manage your father's money. I don't think he'll want to give that up. How would you like me to handle this?"

Handle it? She couldn't answer him at once. It seemed to her that they were now bartering for Ned and the idea horrified her. It was Ned who was important and what was best for him. Once he had been her life. Now they were talking about him as if he were a commodity and not a person at all.

She walked part of the way home. On Park Avenue she found herself behind a family, a man in uniform, a young, well-dressed mother, and twin boys who clung to their father's hands and looked up at him, admiration shining on their young faces as they chattered excitedly. They all stopped at a corner for a light and Sybil saw pass between the husband and wife a look of the greatest satisfaction. She felt suddenly unbearably envious and this only served to depress her more.

What joy parents must experience together watching

213

their children grow! What satisfaction there must be in sharing this experience! She'd never had that. Ned had never known the comfort of a real family. She felt the loss deeply for them both.

She could not decide what to do or how she should answer Arthur. But when she got home and Ned asked anxiously about his father, she knew that some sort of shared custody was the only answer and she told Arthur to go ahead with his idea.

"It's what Ned wants. He wants to live with his father. I've—I've failed him, I'm afraid," she admitted to herself. She was dry-eyed. There were no more tears to shed.

III

In the last weeks of the summer, just before he left, Sybil nearly despaired of Ned. She could only hope that when the legal proceedings were over, when Ned grew a little emotionally, he'd develop a more magnanimous attitude toward her. His behavior was rude and insufferable. He spent much of his time baiting Joanna, letting her know that *his* father wanted him.

"And yours, Joanna? You don't even know yours," she heard him say once.

Joanna rushed to her mother in tears. Confused, she still could not take in the situation.

"Why doesn't my daddy want to see me?"

She tried to explain, telling her everything she remembered about Jonathan and their love for one another. Perversely Joanna would not be consoled. She didn't want her daddy, she asserted. She didn't need him.

"I only want you, Mommy."

It was a terrible time for all of them. Sybil was constantly on the verge of tears. Tension and exhaustion showed in her face, in the deep hollows of her cheeks and the strained look around her eyes.

When, at last, the time came for Ned to go, the parting was anticlimactic.

"Think of it as though I'm going back to school," he told them all from the wisdom of his eleven years. "I'll be gone approximately the same amount of time really. And I'll be back for vacations."

Once everything was settled she thought of returning to Philadelphia to see her father.

Alicia argued vehemently against it.

"He won't know you. You'll only upset him. God knows what further damage you might cause."

She refused to believe this until she'd actually spoken to her father's doctor on the phone.

"I can't say what effect your visit might have. He's getting along quite well and he's content with the world as he knows it. He could go on for years like this. In my opinion it would be better if you did not come."

Reluctantly she gave up the idea. Perhaps it was better to remember him as he had been on her wedding day, happy for her, loving her.

Late in July she heard from Geoffrey. The letter was written from an Army hospital. He'd been injured in an accident and had not been able to write. How badly he'd been hurt, he did not say.

"I've been thinking about your letter. I told you the first time we met that you were a woman with a secret. I'm glad you told me your secrets, Sybil, honored really, because I know now how much you trust me. How you must have suffered! I've seen a lot of suffering here at the hospital. It changes you, just being aware of the suffering. Life is short at best. And to spend so much of the early part suffering seems inexcusable. I thought at first that I'd be disappointed if I never saw any real action in this war and yet I was afraid of it, though I never admitted it. I was glad to get the desk job in JAG. I was close to the war, never a real part of it. Most Army lawyers aren't. Now I wonder if I could have been a part of the real action. Or would I have broken down like so many of the fellows I see here?"

He talked a good deal about fear and courage in his letters. Once he started to write again, she received a letter every week. He did not mention marriage. He did not talk about his own condition or the accident, though she asked repeatedly.

It was Arthur who told her.

"He was badly burned, his legs especially. They've done a lot with skin grafting and it seems he'll have to learn to walk all over again. That I got, by the way, not from Geoffrey, but from his doctor. I wrote finally and asked. Mother, of course, was frantic to know. She hopes you'll visit her and bring Joanna. Would you? I think she needs to talk about Geoffrey, not to me, but to someone he loves."

She was surprised by the request. Mrs. Kempton was taking a lot for granted.

"Of course, I'd like to visit your mother, Arthur. But as for Geoffrey's feelings toward me—I'm afraid— That is, I think they have changed." She wanted to add, "And your mother's will, too, when she knows the truth."

But the words were too difficult to say.

That fall there had been a noticeable drop in business. Marlene was right. Once the story was out, the women who had been eager for her designs shunned her. Their views of morality were rigid and there was little room for understanding. It had taken only the smallest comment in a Philadelphia society column about Edward Ashford at last finding his wife and child. The story spread rapidly by word of mouth through the upper echelons of Philadelphia and New York society.

Anne Halburton apologized for her narrow-minded friends. She and her husband would be spending the year on the West Coast so there would not even be the solace of her old friend.

"I only wish that I were going to be here," Anne said. "I'd at least be able to stop some of this gossip in my own home. But they'll come around eventually. The moment a new, more interesting story turns up to occupy their minds, they're sure to forget this. You have to remember that they don't really know you as I do, dear Sybil. I wish there were something I could do." Her eyes lit with sudden inspiration. "Why don't you come out to the coast with us? You can start over again out there. San Francisco, they say, is a beautiful city. It's the perfect solution."

But she could not imagine herself so far away from Ned. It was Marlene who understood this better than anyone else. She never again spoke of the problems the divorce had created. She worked hard to salvage what was left of the business and she inspired Sybil with her strength and optimism.

"If you can't open one door, you find another," Marlene said philosophically. "Who says we have to be a custom house? Maybe we can sell to department stores. We've got contacts, don't forget. We can still make out."

It seemed like a good idea and Sybil was enthusiastic at first. She prepared a portfolio of sketches. But the only booming industry in the country was the war industry and nothing came of their plans. She was often depressed and worried. Little seemed to have been gained from her impulse to be honest. She'd even lost Geoffrey, or so she thought.

Her thoughts turned now more and more often not to him, but to Jonathan. Where was he now? Perhaps he was in the service. Many doctors were. Had he married? Was he happy? She dreamed of him, long, confused dreams filled with happy memories of the past which always ended in the frustration of them being kept apart by unexpected barriers. Doors wouldn't open. Trains left without her. She began to think she was losing her sanity and should seek help.

Then Geoffrey came home. She wasn't expecting him. He swore Arthur and his mother to secrecy. And so when he came into the studio, she, who had been working at her desk, listlessly sketching dresses that in all probability would never be made up, was astonished to see him.

"You haven't changed a bit!" he said, standing in the doorway and smiling down at her. "Thank God!" he added.

"Geoffrey!" She dropped her pad and pencil, too surprised at first to move.

He looked the same, perhaps a little thinner. His face was tanned, probably from the shipboard journey home. The laugh lines around his eyes had deepened and his expression had a bittersweet quality. He stood erect, though she noted he carried a silver-headed cane.

"I hardly need it at all now," he said, hastily, noting the direction of her glance. "It adds dignity, don't you think?"

He held his head to one side, gazing at her inquiringly.

"I thought perhaps a warmer welcome——," he began slowly.

She was in his arms. Their lips met hungrily and he held her close, enveloping her in the warmth of his desire.

"Darling, I've waited so long for this," he whispered against her lips, "dreamed of it. Do you know how often I've dreamed of you? Sybil, darling, darling!"

She gave herself up to the joy of being held and kissed. All the worry and turmoil of the past months which she'd kept carefully in check welled up suddenly and she was overcome with her need for his strength and support. He had come back to her. She was not alone any more. The fantasy world she'd built about Jonathan was just that, an unsatisfying, make-believe world that could never be. Geoffrey was real and he wanted her.

"What's this? Tears?" He caught them on his fingertips as he gently touched her cheek.

There was a flurry of activity in the hall behind him as a model and one of the seamstresses tried to hide the fact that they'd been watching. He reached around and pushed the door shut, grinning as he did so.

"This probably looks like a John Wayne movie," he said laughing and then grew sober again. "But it isn't, is it? It's all very real. My love for you is real. Darling, darling, Sybil. What you must have suffered over Ned. You had to go through it all alone. If only I had been here."

"Arthur was wonderful."

"Not as wonderful as I would have been," he said, his eyes tender. "Do you think we could sit down? I wouldn't want this to get around, but I haven't quite got my land legs back."

She led him to the settee beneath the windows. Its narrow back, thin curved legs, and delicate mauve brocade

219

covering were hardly appropriate for a man and something less than comfortable, but that did not bother him. He threw aside his cane and held her quietly in his arms.

"You'll never have to be alone again, Sybil. I promise you that. We'll be together now and always."

His kisses rekindled a long-suppressed desire in her. She had felt abandoned by her sister and even her son. And now Geoffrey was here and it felt safe and comfortable to lean on him, to know that he cared for her, that he wanted her. Willingly she settled into the pleasant role of one who is cherished.

Outwardly he had changed little, but it was a different Geoffrey who returned from the war. He still enjoyed the theater and the supper clubs. He still loved music, though he found it difficult to dance. They sat the dances out, holding hands, content simply to be in each other's company. But there was another side to this new Geoffrey. He no longer seemed to delight in the small talk and the chic banter of his socialite friends. In a way, she was glad. She found the knowing glances of the men and the cautious acceptance of the women difficult to bear.

"Nothing they say or do or think has any meaning. They don't allow themselves to think. They're shallow or afraid or both," he told her. "And I was one of them. Was! I say was and yet I wonder if we ever really change. I want to. After—after the accident I began to think about my life and what it had been. I wasn't very proud of it. Selfish and useless really. That's what I was."

"That's not true!" she protested.

He shook his head grimly. "I know what I was," he said with such vehemence she did not dare argue. His blue eyes became dark as he seemed to be looking inward, remembering an experience she could not share.

"What was it like, in London?" she asked. "It looks awful in the newsreels. All bombs and destruction, fires and homeless people everywhere. The reports are heavy with doom. I've been afraid to listen to them, they're so depressing. It must have been terrible for you."

She tried repeatedly, but without success to get him to

talk of his experiences, of the accident that injured him, but he refused to say anything. Then one night he did want to talk. He described his experiences so vividly that she could nearly feel his pain.

"They're a very brave people, the British. Stoic and strong," he said. "In the face of the most horrible disaster, they carry on."

He began to pace the room, limping slightly. After the first month, he refused to carry the cane. They spent a good deal of time in his apartment. It was uncomfortable for them to go to hers with Marlene or Joanna apt to interrupt at any time and so they invariably returned to his place for a nightcap or just to talk. Much of the time they didn't talk at all. They simply lay in each other's arms on the huge sofa, kissing and caressing. It never went beyond that. He seemed to be in full control, though there were times she thought he wanted her and certainly she wanted him. He seemed to be operating under a strict code of ethics. They planned to be married the moment her divorce became final. They were not children, after all, and yet he behaved as properly as if they were both still innocent.

"You can't come away from the war without learning something about yourself," he was saying now.

"Tell me about it," she prompted, holding out her hand to him.

He sat beside her and began to talk as though he were reliving a nightmare.

"It's worse, a hundred times worse than you can imagine. Homes are destroyed every day. A man never knows when he leaves in the morning what he'll find at night. Hundreds of families are sheltering in the Underground. Believe it or not, they've had to turn their subways into dormitories. Really! There's no other way to accommodate the homeless. They have canteens down there, lavatories, everything, and new people joining their ranks every day. With all the destruction going on over there, America seems like Utopia."

For a moment he was silent, remembering, and she sat

watching his tense features. She said nothing, thinking it best to let him tell it all in his own way.

"I was coming back from a music hall one night. Oh, yes, it's life as usual over there. The people are amazing. If there's an alert, it's announced and everyone goes out to seek shelter. They've learned to live with disaster, you see. Well, that's what happened. We'd all gone and huddled in the Underground, and when we came out one whole row of houses had been completely destroyed, houses I'd seen every day on my way to and from Headquarters.

"And there was a woman standing before the front of one of those houses screaming. Just screaming. Well, there were plenty of people around to help, but I suppose I got to her first. Her child, a ten-year-old, no bigger than Joanna, was lost. She insisted the child was beyond the burning doorway. There was nothing else I could do. Someone had to find out."

His hands had begun to tremble and he clasped them together.

"The child was there all right and she was alive. She was pinned down by a beam. You should have seen her face! That pitiful little face lit by the flames. She reached out her arms to me. I think she yelled 'Yank'. I tried to get to her, but the flames were all around me. I didn't know whether to plunge in and try to snatch her free or step back. I wanted to go forward. My mind told me to go forward, but I couldn't move. Then the door frame went. It hit me on the head. People were yelling all around. The mother was screaming and the last thing I heard was the child calling 'Yank!' I didn't save her. She died in the fire and I would have died, too, if someone hadn't pulled me out. I failed, don't you see? Someone saved my useless life and the child died."

"Not useless, Geoffrey. Not useless! You came back to Joanna and me. We need you, darling. I could spend the rest of my life proving that to you."

Not since the night Jonathan left had she been so profoundly moved. She thought then she could never love

222

again, but she was wrong. She saw in Geoffrey tenderness and compassion she knew were rare in any man.

There was still some of the old spirit of fun, but he was sober and thoughtful, too. He was gentle and indulgent with Joanna and kind to Marlene, who did not in the least appreciate his efforts.

Joanna was delighted to have him back. She openly adored him. They spent endless hours at the parchessi board.

"Get out the game, J.A.," he would say the minute he saw her. "And no cheating!"

"I don't cheat, G.K.," protested Joanna virtuously, "but I'm not so sure about you," she added, wickedly, laughing and tapping an accusing finger on the middle button of his military jacket. They used initials constantly instead of names, a practice inspired by the fact that Joanna had not recognized her own initials on the Irish lace handkerchiefs he brought back for her along with the gold locket and pink rosebud compact Sybil had quickly confiscated.

"She's too young, Geoffrey. I'll save it for her."

"Typical mother," he teased. "Hate to see them grow up, eh? Another baby or two will make all the difference," he told her complacently.

She should have expected it. Of course, Geoffrey would want children of his own. He was generously willing to take on Joanna and even Ned part-time, but he'd want children of his own, of course. She wasn't sure she wanted any more children—could hardly bear the thought of three children by three different fathers. Wouldn't that simply complicate already existing problems?

But she wanted to marry him. She thought she loved him, though not in the way she'd loved Jonathan. She thought she could make a good marriage and she wanted to be married. She wanted Joanna to have a normal home. They'd work out the problem of other children in time.

The shop was her immediate problem. There were still a few faithful customers, but they brought in little profit.

223

Anderson-Grant received hardly any notice in the papers that fall. No one was particularly interested. Sybil felt discouraged and frustrated.

"Close the place," Geoffrey urged her. "I can see what these woman are doing to you. Judging you! Why should you go on taking it?"

It was hard to explain what her work had come to mean to her, how proud she was of what she and Marlene had built. Closing the shop would be like giving up a part of herself. But Geoffrey was persistent.

"Besides, I need a full-time wife," he added, kissing her. "We'll both have full-time jobs. After the first of the year, Arthur's going to take me back into my quiet niche at the family firm. He thinks he's doing me a favor, but I plan to surprise him. I'm afraid I wasn't much of an asset to him before."

He looked rueful and then laughed.

"Geoffrey Kempton, private citizen has a new life plan. Think positively, act positively, and make yourself worthy of the life that was so undeservedly spared."

"Don't talk that way, Geoffrey."

This new desperate desire to atone frightened her. She was sometimes lonesome for the old, carefree Geoffrey who found life a joy. Once she confided this to him.

"That Geoffrey is dead. He died in the fire as he was meant to."

She never mentioned this again. The experience in London had a devastating psychological effect on him, one she could not begin to fathom. She knew when they spoke of it they were treading on dangerous ground.

He received his medical discharge in January, 1944, and once again the pressure of fleeting time seemed to consume him.

"I don't want to wait," he said one evening. "We've lost so much time already. Your divorce won't be final for another year, but if you went to Reno—Reno would take only six weeks. Sybil, I want and need you now."

She had been hoping he'd say something like that and agreed at once. It meant closing the shop right away. She thought of this as a temporary measure, just until she was settled in her new life. It wasn't as if she were giving up her career entirely. She didn't want to do that and knew she would miss her work. She thought Marlene would understand, but she didn't.

"When? When would you be planning to marry?"

It was the only thing she said to the news. Not, I wish you every happiness, or how wonderful for Joanna to have a real home at last!

"When?"

It wasn't as if the news were unexpected. And yet Marlene had not accepted the fact that Sybil might be planning to be married soon, though Joanna had been expecting it weekly. She'd even told Regina she was going to have a new daddy and Regina's mother had actually called to congratulate Sybil two weeks ago.

She looked now at Marlene's closed face and wished her closest friend could be happy for her. Marlene did not seem to be able to accept Geoffrey. Sybil sensed a feeling of hostility between the two which she could not explain satisfactorily. She recalled how much Marlene liked Jonathan. Was that it? Did she feel Geoffrey did not compare favorably? Or was she simply feeling left out? The loss of the business was a terrific blow and Sybil knew she was guilty of causing that and destroying all of her friend's grand dreams. She would do anything to make that up to her. Someday she hoped she could. As Marlene suggested, they'd find another door, perhaps in retail houses.

"I thought we could be married in April, the end of April. It will take time to find and decorate an apartment. Ned has vacation then and can be at the wedding, too."

"O.K. I can manage by April, I guess."

"Manage what?"

"Well, I gotta have some place to go, don't I? We're gonna close the shop. Well, I have to relocate, as they say. I have to find a place to live."

"But, Marlene, you'll always have a place in our home. We're going to find an apartment big enough for all of us. Geoffrey and I want you to stay with us."

Marlene put her glass down.

"Now wait a minute! Let me get this straight. You're going to marry the Major and you want me to come live with you? What, as a charity case?"

Her dark eyes looked like cold glass. She was not in a mood to be reasonable and Sybil was almost afraid to continue explaining the plan she and Geoffrey had hit upon. She owed so much to Marlene. It was impossible to imagine life without her.

"Marlene, you know better than that!"

"Do I?"

"I hope you do. I thought you did."

Sybil's voice was soft, but her tone was urgent.

"Please say you'll stay on with us. Help me run the household and look after Joanna. And then after the war we'll make plans about opening the shop again. The war can't last forever. You're always saying that. I'll miss the business as much as you and I'll want to get back in."

She hadn't discussed this with Geoffrey, but she knew she'd miss the exciting, creative life she'd led. When the time came, she'd make him understand.

"Marlene, please say you'll come. I need you. Joanna needs you. It wouldn't be home without you."

Marlene burst into tears. Sybil embraced her and together they had a good cry.

It was Marlene who made Sybil's wedding suit, a pale blue silk with a long jacket. It was Marlene who helped handle the many details of planning the small reception at Mrs. Kempton's home and who took over the burden of closing the shop.

The actual ceremony was lovely. It was a small wedding. Only family members and very close friends attended. Ned was there, subdued and correctly polite. He actually seemed to like Geoffrey, had liked him since they'd first met that day at Ned's school. Since the boy had been living with his father, he'd become calmer and more reasonable. Knowing who he was did that for him and Sybil was relieved and grateful to find that he was happy.

They spent their honeymoon in the hills of Virginia.

"You'll like the lodge. It's comfortable, but far enough away from town to give you the feeling of being totally immersed in nature. I learned to hunt and fish there and I learned something of self-reliance, too. I used to camp out by myself with only the stars and the unseen creatures of the woods for company. It's a peaceful place full of happy, carefree memories. I love it and I hope you will, too," he told her.

They left New York by train and picked up a car outside Washington. It was early evening when they began driving through the winding mountain roads. He talked as he drove and Sybil settled back comfortably and thought that at last he was beginning to relax. The strain of the past few weeks had been difficult for them both. He wore a soft, brown casual suit with an open-necked sports shirt that gave him a boyish look. She, too, was casually dressed in a beige cashmere sweater and skirt with a bright orange scarf about her neck.

They stopped once and got out to watch the sunset, a glorious glowing sphere enveloped in rose and lavender. She leaned against him as he slipped his arm about her. A deep sense of contentment came over her and she looked up at him.

"I love you, Geoffrey," she said.

"Darling!"

He held and kissed her tenderly.

"My Sybil. My darling wife," he said. "Now I feel we're really married. Here alone before God I feel you are mine."

He touched her new wide gold band.

"With this ring I thee wed. There! I can say it now and mean it."

"Didn't you mean it before?" She laughed softly and kissed him. "You sounded as though you did. You even fooled me."

He lifted her chin and made her look into his eyes. She was surprised to find them so serious.

—"I was distracted before. We had too much of an audience. I was always conscious of performing. I want to make my promises to you alone. Why must wedding ceremonies be such public affairs? All I really wanted was to hold you in my arms like this and tell you that I love you, that I'll always love you and that I want to make you happy."

"You have made me happy, darling, very, very happy," she told him fervently.

Her first view of the lodge was at twilight. It was nestled among tall trees and the faint glow of lights within made it look warm and welcoming. The low structure was built of logs and stones and might have begun as a pioneer cabin with a loft, but had grown over the years to a rambling ten rooms.

"This is never-never land for me," he said. "I feel I'll always be happy here, always be young and always in love."

He held her hard to his lips. In the dim light from the dashboard the longing in his eyes was unmistakable.

"Come. I'll introduce you to the housekeeper, Mrs. Colby. If I'm not mistaken, she is even now at the door watching our every move through the small windows at the top. You'd better hope she approves of you," he teased. "She's mad about me, you know."

"I think I'm going to like Mrs. Colby. She has very good taste," she told him.

The housekeeper welcomed them both warmly. She was a small capable-looking woman with an over abundance of snow-white hair. She spoke with the soft accent of a born southerner. After serving them a light supper and satisfying herself that there was nothing else they needed, she discreetly reitred to her room.

"None too soon," Geoffrey said, taking her into his arms the moment they were alone. "Darling, darling, Sybil. I've waited all my life for you, only you."

Their room was spacious and furnished with a large canopied double bed. Deep dormer windows looked out onto the moonlit mountains. Sybil was aware of very little but her husband. Her every sense seemed to be stirred and awakened by his physical closeness. She reveled in it, but was suddenly seized with doubt. This was his first marriage, but he was not inexperienced.

"Oh, Geoffrey, I want to be a good wife. I—I hope I won't disappoint you."

"Disappoint me? Oh, my dear!"

He slipped the peignoir from her shoulders. Her low-cut gown revealed her smooth, full breasts and he bent to kiss them. She trembled with delight at the touch of his warm lips.

"You are everything I have always wanted."

He pulled her close and her body arched to meet his. He slid his arms down, caressing her and lifted her onto the bed, pressing his lips to hers, exploring her mouth with his tongue. His hands were tender and gentle. She gave herself to the joy of love-making. Gradually she began to realize that something was very wrong. She was ready, but he was not. Patiently she kissed and caressed him, but she'd had little experience in arousing a man.

With a groan he turned finally, released her, and sat up.

"It's no good," he said.

"Geoffrey!" She touched his broad stiff back, but he pushed her hand roughly away.

"It's no good, no good at all."

He reached for his cigarettes and lit one. "I'm so sorry, Sybil. God, you don't know how sorry I am!"

Her heart filled with compassion for him. His doctor had warned her of this, but she hadn't taken him too seriously.

"There might be a problem," he'd said. "Nothing that your love and understanding can't overcome. But he sees his failure to save that child in the London fire as a blow to his manhood, his virility. You must be patient with him."

She looked at him now and she could feel his suffering.

"It's all right, darling." She tried to move closer to him, but he got up and began to walk about the room.

"No, it isn't all right."

He bit the words off angrily. "Don't you think I know it isn't all right?"

"You're tired. You're tense. Let's try to get some sleep. Perhaps in the morning—"

"In the morning," he repeated. "Do you think you'll even want to look at me in the morning? Do you think I could bear to have you look at me? What must you think of me? No worse than what I think of myself, I can assure you."

"Geoffrey, that's nonsense. Come to bed, please. It really is all right. Please."

He crushed out his cigarette and came to stand beside her. She could see only the outline of his powerful body, but she could feel his eyes on her and she was suddenly frightened for him, for what he might do in his despair. She wasn't prepared for anything like this and did not know what to do next.

"Come to bed," she repeated.

"No! I—I need to be alone for awhile."

She grasped his hand.

"That's just what you don't need. Come to sleep. I want you here beside me. I love you, Geoffrey."

He pulled away.

"I can't."

She didn't know how to persuade him. She could understand his embarrassment and frustration at his failure, but why did he feel he must leave her? She didn't want to let him go and yet nothing she said seemed to make any difference. She heard him moving about, gathering up his clothes in the dark. She reached toward the bedside lamp.

"Don't!" he commanded and his voice had an hysterical ring. "I don't want you to look at me. I don't want you to see me like this. Don't worry about me, Sybil. I just have to be alone for awhile. Please try to understand. This is something I have to work out alone."

"But we can work it out together. Don't go!" she pleaded.

And then the tears came. She couldn't hold them back. She loved him. She needed him, but he would not allow himself to need her. He adhered rigidly to his masculine code. The strength in the marriage must be male strength or there could be no marriage. He'd never said it in so many words, but she knew. It was what he believed. He could tolerate no weakness in himself. He would never agree that his problem was their problem. He would come to her on his own terms or not at all. What if he could not resolve his conflict? What if he never came back?

"Geoffrey! Geoffrey!"

But he left. That night very late she put a call through to his doctor. She needed help. They both did.

Doctor Evans was remarkably calm.

"I'd give him a few days."

"But I don't know where he's gone or what he might do."

She was frantic and had all she could do to keep from breaking down.

"Forgive me, Mrs. Kempton, but I've known him longer than you. He's a very strong person and I've no reason to think he's self-destructive. Give him a few days."

And then what? she thought. Won't it be too late? Oh, Geoffrey! Why can't you let me love you as you are? Why?

There was nothing to do but wait. She spent much of the time walking in the woods. hoping to come upon him. He could be anywhere. He knew the area so well.

She couldn't maintain the myth of the normal, happy honeymoon for the benefit of the housekeeper, but she tried. She said there'd been an emergency in New York and Mrs. Colby pretended to believe her.

Two days! Two long days! In those solitary hours she began to blame herself. Had she been too anxious and insensitive to his needs?

The second evening she found him in their bedroom sitting in front of the long windows when she came back

231

from her walk. She knew he was there before she opened the door.

"I think perhaps I can go on now, Sybil, if you still want me," he said, his eyes narrowed against the cigarette smoke.

He looked terrible, as though he'd slept in his clothes. He hadn't bothered to bathe or shave.

"If I want you! Oh, Geoffrey, I've been so worried."

She was on her knees before him, holding him and sobbing with relief.

"I don't know why you should want me."

His body was rigid and he did not touch her.

"I don't know if I can be a husband to you, Sybil, but I want to try. Believe that. I want to try."

"We'll both try, Geoffrey. And we'll be all right. Oh, darling, look at me, please. Can't you see how much I love you? We will be fine, you'll see."

All that mattered was that he'd come back to her. She wanted to feel his arms about her, to kiss him, but she did not dare.

"I'm so tired. So tired." He closed his eyes wearily.

"Of course, you are. I'll run a hot bath for you and you can get right into bed."

He agreed, but when she came out of the bathroom she found him fast asleep across the spread. She did what she could, taking off his shoes, loosening his belt, and covering him with an extra blanket. She tried to sleep in the chair. but spent much of the night listening to his deep, even breathing and wondering how she could help him, how they could help each other. Towards morning she lay down beside him resting her cheek against his. He stirred, sighed, and pulled her to him. The rough stubble of beard scratched her skin, but she did not complain, responding to his every touch. Wordlessly, tenderly, they began to make love and when it was over he sighed contentedly and slept. The wonder and pleasure of that night made up for all the hours of anguish.

It was mid-morning before she awoke again to find herself happily in his arms.

"Have I told you that I want sons, only sons?" he asked smiling at her. His eyes were clear and untroubled. His demons had left him. "Do you think you can arrange that, my darling Mrs. Kempton?"

PART THREE

I

Joanna was in love and from the very first there was
nothing Sybil could do about it. Her daughter was nineteen and a sophomore at Barnard, where she'd chosen to
go so that she could live at home, refusing acceptance to
Radcliff and Bryn Mawr.

"I don't want to have to cope with those snobbish girls
day and night," she said. "I'd rather live at home and be
able to walk out on that nonsense whenever I choose."

"That nonsense", Sybil came to understand, was what
Joanna considered an inordinate interest in family background, a subject she preferred not to discuss. The fact
that Geoffrey had formally adopted her made very little
difference. As it worked out, she was every bit as involved
with college life as any girl her age.

Since she was seventeen Joanna had been going to parties at Princeton where Ned was showing signs of becoming a perennial student. Sybil was realistic enough to realize that her son planned to go through life along the
easiest possible path. He had charm. He was attractive,
very much as his father was attractive, and he had a
smooth, confidential way of talking that made you forget
what it was he wanted. In Joanna's case, he saw that his
beautiful, very desirable sister added to his image at
school and he had her down quite often, inviting her for
weekends.

At first she'd thought of this as a wonderful opportunity. Joanna was enjoying herself and judging from the

number of suitors she acquired, she was quite popular. But there wasn't anything serious. She never showed any lasting interest in any boy until she'd met and fallen in love with Alfred Skinner.

What a shock it had been when she first heard his name! Of all the odd twists of fate, this seemed to her to be the strangest. Alfred Skinner could only be Jason Skinner's son. How surprised Joanna would be to learn that Alfred's father had once courted her own mother! She wondered, too, if the importance of the Skinner name had made any impression. Probably not, except perhaps on Ned. Joanna was too much in love for that. All she could think about was Alfred himself. But what sort of boy was he?

"He's the sort of man I can love without reservations," Joanna told her when she asked. Her dark eyes became velvety soft and misty. She smiled dreamily. "I've never met anyone like Alfred before. You'll have to see for yourself. I can't begin to describe him."

It was obvious she adored him. During the week, when they were separated, she wrote every day and on Friday evenings she took the train from Penn Station to Princeton, returning home, starry-eyed and happy, but anxious for Friday to come again.

Could it last? What if he began to talk of marriage? What then? The Skinners would have to know about Joanna, would be bound to find out, really. How would they be affected by the truth?

"When are we going to meet this Alfred?" Marlene wanted to know. "And while we're on the subject, this letter writing looks like a one-way street. I don't see any envelopes with his return address in the mailbox. What's he got, two broken arms?"

Sybil did not say that they would not have an opportunity to glimpse such an envelope since Joanna always met the mailman herself. But there were no letters. She concluded that Alfred was not a letter writer. But he must return Joanna's feelings. She always recovered quickly from her disappointment. And there was no doubt that the weekends made the girl terribly happy.

In March, five months after they'd first met, Alfred was finally going to make an appearance. He was coming to lunch on Saturday and taking her to a matinee.

"That way you can all meet him and have plenty of time to visit. Geoffrey could come home for that, couldn't he? And Arthur should be there. I want Alfred to see what a handsome family I have. Oh, and I suppose Aunt Marlene, too," she added as an afterthought, a guilty look crossing her face. Her large clear eyes met Sybil's and then quickly slid away.

"That is— Oh, Mother, I don't mean to sound disrespectful, only—"

She didn't finish. She didn't have to. Marlene, with her too bright hair, too frank, down-to-earth speech was not socially acceptable, not when it came to someone as important as Alfred Skinner. She was glad her daughter had the good grace to blush. Marlene had been a second mother to the girl, nursing her when she was sick, sharing the happy, exciting moments of growing up, and comforting her during the bad times, too.

"I'm sorry, Mother." Joanna lowered her eyes until the long dark lashes touched her cheek. "I know what you're going to say and I deserve it."

"I wasn't going to say anything. I can see I don't have to."

Joanna need not have worried. Marlene would never have intruded on a family lunch even if she'd been asked. She had found a comfortable place in the Kempton household as Sybil's friend, confidante, and official housekeeper. She never joined any of the social activities which involved outside guests, though she'd been asked dozens of times. She had her own social life, her own friends. She still dated several of the salesmen she'd known from the time they'd had the shop. When there were parties, she quietly retired to her room or went out. Sybil came to accept and anticipate this kind of behavior, but Joanna had obviously not, or else her desire to impress Alfred had blocked it from her mind.

Early Saturday morning, Joanna was up supervising flower arrangements and going over the details of the lunch menu with Mrs. Norris.

"Mother, can we use the Wedgwood? Alfred appreciates nice things."

She hovered about in a state of almost hysterical anticipation. When Geoffrey called at eleven to say he could not make it for lunch, she almost burst into tears. Marlene, who had been observing her behavior and managing not to comment, gave up then.

"You're making too much of a fuss. A guy likes a girl to be a little hard to get, you know? He appreciates her more," she added pointedly.

"Aunt Marlene, you don't understand. Fellows today don't want to play games. They want to know where they stand. I love Alfred and I want to show it. We're living in the atomic age. Who knows? Tomorrow someone could touch off a nuclear confrontation and we'd all be wiped off the face of the earth. This war in Korea could do it. We haven't time to play games."

"Don't you believe it! Show me a guy who doesn't like a little mystery about his girl and I'll show you a guy who's dead from the neck up."

Marlene's scorn had little impact on Joanna. As the time for Alfred's arrival approached, she grew even more nervous.

"Mother, are you sure this suit is all right?"

The long line of the jacket and the flattering shade of burgundy were perfect. She'd inherited her mother's lovely figure. Heads turned when she walked down the street. She had a graceful, sinuous walk that inspired whistles.

"It's fine, darling. You look beautiful, as only a young girl can."

She kissed her daughter's cheek impulsively and insisted she sit beside her on the sofa. She could feel the tension in the slim body and wished there were something she could do. She didn't remember love producing such anxiety, but she was more than twice Joanna's age. Perhaps she'd forgotten.

"You always look so great, Mother, calm and poised and so beautiful." She laughed self-consciously. "It will serve me right if Alfred falls in love with you instead."

Sybil wore a yellow wool dress with a scarf that was draped artfully around her neck. At thirty-nine she expected some lines to show and scarves could be so flattering, though perhaps not necessary yet. Most people took her for Joanna's sister rather than her mother.

She still designed her own clothes and many of her daughter's and Marlene's. Anne Halburton's requests were never denied, but she had not, as she'd expected, been able to give much thought to designing and opening her own shop again. There'd been Arthur for one thing.

Of her three children, Sybil found Geoffrey's son the most satisfying. Young Arthur, named for his uncle and grandfather, was mature beyond his years, intelligent, and sensitive. She liked to visit his school for the sheer delight of having the teachers speak in such glowing terms of him. He was meticulous about everything he did: his school work, his clothing, his room at home. He had inherited Sybil's coloring, black hair and deep blue eyes. In many ways, Arthur reminded Sybil of herself at that age because he had to become self-reliant without any other child his age in the house.

She hadn't thought of doing anything about her shop while Arthur was small, but he was almost nine. Soon he'd be as independent as Joanna and Ned.

Her daughter looked far from independent now. Today she needed her family. Sybil did what she could to calm her. When the buzzer rang, signaling Alfred's arrival, she had all she could do to keep the girl from rushing to the door herself.

"Mrs. Norris will get it, darling, or Arthur. You know how he loves to answer the door."

Joanna's smile was weak, but she agreed reluctantly.

241

They could hear Arthur's high clear voice and Alfred's deeper tones.

"You must be Alfred. I'm Joanna's brother, Arthur."

Sybil could imagine her son gravely shaking hands. He was a terribly serious child.

"You don't look at all the way I expected you to look," he said calmly.

"Mother!" groaned Joanna and would have gone to interrupt what she considered an embarrassing discussion if Sybil had not detained her.

"Alfred will understand. Let Arthur be himself."

"Oh? And what were you expecting?" Alfred sounded amused.

"Someone older, I guess."

They came into the living room and Joanna's face lighted up as he smiled at her.

"Here he is, Joanna. He doesn't look at all like Van Johnson."

"Good Lord, why should he look like Van Johnson?" She went to him and linked her arm through his. It was a familiar comfortable gesture. Sybil thought they looked nice together.

"Well, you used to have all those pictures pinned up around your room and I just thought—" Arthur began.

Alfred threw back his head and laughed. "Well, we're going to have to have a very long talk. What else don't I know about Joanna?"

He did not look like Van Johnson. He was dark-haired, brown-eyed, though nearsighted, with square-jawed, clean-cut features, rather enhanced by large, horn-rimmed glasses. He had a perfectly delightful smile.

"Mrs. Kempton, it's so nice of you to have me," he said, taking Sybil's hand and all but clicking his heels.

Her impression was that there was more to Alfred than splendid manners. He was a nice person, warm-hearted and humorous. During lunch he was particularly kind to Arthur, asking his opinions on the upcoming baseball season. He was gentle with Joanna, trying to calm her when she became too intense over world affairs. The war in

Korea was uppermost in her mind these days mainly because she worried about Alfred. There was talk of draft boards refusing to accept college deferments in the future. Alfred would most certainly be called.

He did not seem to be unduly alarmed as she knew Ned would be. She could see Alfred's attitude was entirely different. He looked upon service to his country in the Armed Forces as a sacred duty. How fine of him, she thought. And how sad! How sad for all today's young men! No wonder Joanna was upset. War of any kind seemed so utterly inhuman.

"Eisenhower says he will end the war in Korea and I believe he will," Alfred insisted quietly.

"When?" Joanna demanded. "If it doesn't end soon, you'll have to go."

"I know. But that's no more than others have been asked to do."

"I don't believe in war." Joanna bit her lip and twisted her pink damask napkin into a knot.

"I don't suppose anyone does anymore."

"Then why go?"

Sybil wasn't sure how they had gotten on the subject. She wished they could talk of something else. But what was there? Right now this war was the most important thing in their lives.

"It's a man's duty to do what his country requires of him. Isn't that so, Mrs. Kempton?" There was something in his eyes, some question she could not quite interpret. She liked him, though. She was rather glad Joanna had chosen him. Perhaps with a little luck everything would work out for them. Perhaps Eisenhower might end the war in time for Alfred to be untouched.

"I have always thought that," she said slowly. What else could she say?

"There you are, Joanna. Even your mother agrees with me." She bit her lip and said nothing.

"Me too. I agree with you," Arthur said helpfully.

"Well, thanks, half pint. I appreciate your support."

They talked of other things, school and Ned and the

243

movies they'd seen. But they were all thinking about the war.

Finally Alfred glanced at his watch. "Do you think we should be going? Curtain at two."

When they left, Joanna was clinging to his arm for all the world as though she would tie him to her physically. If he asked her to marry him tomorrow, she would. Seeing them together left little doubt in Sybil's mind that this is what they intended. Whether Alfred meant to plan marriage now or later, was difficult to tell. It seemed that young girls were always ready for marriage sooner than the boys they loved. Alfred might have two or three years of school ahead of him, depending on what he wanted to do. Then there was his Army service. When would he be really free to marry? She felt suddenly terribly depressed.

She saw Arthur off to his party which was on the fourteenth floor of their building. He looked horrified when she suggested riding down on the elevator with him and she realized once again that he, too, was growing in independence.

"But not away. Please, not so far away as the other two," she prayed. "He's all I have now."

She returned to the lonely apartment and sat down in the living room thinking of Joanna. Marriage to Alfred might well be what the girl needed. It would give her stability and a place to which she could believe she belonged. Ever since she'd known Arthur was on the way, she'd seemed to feel displaced. She became withdrawn and secretive, clinging to Ned and looking forward to the times he'd be home for holidays. It was difficult to reach her emotionally most of the time.

She paged through a fashion magazine noting the vogue for the new tapered pants and long shorts. Sports clothes had come into their own. Everyone seemed to be showing separates. She kept up with new trends in the industry. How excited she'd been when Dior's "new look" hit the fashion world after the war! She wished she'd been able to convince Geoffrey to take her to Paris to the showings.

But he was adamant about not returning to war-torn Europe.

"If you had my memories, you'd never want to go back either," he'd said.

She thought she understood. Still, perhaps Paris and the glamour and excitement of the ateliers would help erase those awful memories from his mind. He wouldn't hear of it, though.

"Go," he said, "you go! You and Marlene. You wouldn't need me. That's your world, isn't it? I wouldn't belong there anyway."

He sounded so angry she was disturbed. The way he had said "your world" had the ring of jealousy. He didn't mind the fact that she designed clothes for herself and close friends. In fact, he was proud of her artistic skill as long as it remained a hobby. But when she spoke of opening a shop again, he cut her off.

"You haven't time for that."

When they were first married this was true. She had little time on her hands. She did all the decorating of their first apartment herself. And when that was finally finished, they moved to this larger, more lavish place and she had to start all over again. Then there was Arthur. She refused to allow a nurse to take over. She wanted to enjoy her child, be there whenever he needed her. But now even he was growing independent. And what was there for her to do? How was she to fill the hours of each day? Even the many parties she was called upon to plan for Geoffrey's clients were not enough.

By late afternoon, the bright March day had turned gray and damp. She heard the faint click of the front key and thought at first Marlene was back from her movie, but it was Geoffrey.

"God! I need a drink," he said, loosening his tie as he came in and tossing his briefcase onto a chair. "Actors! They are the most impractical, exasperating creatures—" He paused to kiss her cheek. "—Who ever lived. Shall I make you something, too?"

"All right. What happened?" she asked hopefully,

245

ready to listen and share his problems, but, as usual, he simply shrugged off the question with the certainty that she could never begin to understand.

"It's unbelievably complicated and petty. I think I'll just try to get some rest before we have to leave for the Halburtons'. At the moment I don't feel as though I could put one foot in front of the other." He picked up his martini and started toward their bedroom.

After a moment she followed him. Even if he didn't feel like talking she would have the comfort of being near him. She carried her untouched glass of sherry and came to stand in the doorway of his dressing room. She watched him impatiently unbuttoning his shirt.

"Joanna's friend came today. He seems very nice." She'd never told Geoffrey about her own connection with the Skinners. It was something she preferred to forget.

"Good! I'm glad. She probably needs someone. A girl her age should be married. She's wasting her time in that college. What will she do with all that education anyway? I'm surprised she hasn't given it up. I don't think she enjoys it."

How like him to assume that women had no real place in society except as wives and mothers! She wished she could make him understand that women, too, had the need to achieve outside their homes, that they had minds—very good minds—that cried out for stimulation. Joanna was not a particularly good student at the moment, but she could be. She was very capable.

He threw his shirt over a chair and began unbuckling his trousers. As always his lean, athletic body aroused in her a sense of pride and desire. When she was alone, she became restless for him to return. Today especially she needed the comfort of his arms. She put her glass on the chest and went to him, touching his shoulder lightly with her fingertips.

"Geoffrey, don't take a shower just yet," she said softly.

She glimpsed their reflection in the mirror on the far bedroom wall beyond the open dressing room door. They were two very attractive people. She was slim, dark-haired, and softly curved. Geoffrey was a blond haired, powerfully built man whose sexual attractiveness brought him admiring glances from most women. He looked down at his wife in surprise.

"Now, Sybil?"

"Why not now?" she asked, slipping her arms around his neck.

He caught her wrists and pushed her hands gently, but firmly away.

"Your sense of timing could be better, don't you think?"

She stiffened, feeling hurt and rejected.

"I'm sorry, darling. I thought—"

"Yes, well, please let me do the thinking in that direction, if you don't mind," he said, turning away and moving towards the bathroom.

She stared at the closed door, listening to the sound of the shower and blinking back tears of frustration.

"Geoffrey! Oh, Geoffrey, what's happened to us?" she whispered.

They'd had a difficult time adjusting to marriage, far more difficult than she'd dreamed possible. His repeated failures built up a wall of humiliation and fear. In the evenings, they both grew so tense that love-making was impossible.

It was she who first suggested seeking help.

"Both of us, Geoffrey. Perhaps it's simply a matter of—of some sort of therapy."

The suggestion infuriated him.

"Don't be ridiculous! There's nothing wrong that we can't work out. You want me to confide in some self-righteous, all-knowing psychiatrist? No, thank you very much. We're intelligent people. We'll work this out ourselves."

"But that's just it. I don't think we can. We could find someone—" she hesitated. "Someone acceptable to us both. Someone we liked."

"There's no such animal," he snapped. "Everything would be all right if you'd just unbend a little."

"I?" She was astonished the first time he'd said this. "But, Geoffrey, I'm willing to try anything."

She thought she was. She loved him and wanted to please him. But old fears did rise up to plague her. There were the ugly memories of Edward. And then, when she'd least expect it, thoughts of Jonathan's gentle love-making came to her and she'd compare Geoffrey to him. Realizing guiltily what she was doing, she'd fail to respond and he would become hurt and unable to continue.

Still, they tried, but their efforts were sporadic. Sometimes she was able to initiate their love-making, but was often afraid of being rejected. It wasn't easy to measure his mood. Usually he'd become amorous the moment he'd had too much to drink. He'd be relaxed and affectionate after a party in the cab coming home. Fortified by alcohol this would persist until the effects of the drinks wore off. He was often too quick for her. Anxious for success, he'd be ready before she was and it would be over without her having derived any real pleasure from the act. Still, he blamed her for their failures.

"You make love," he told her once angrily, "like a lady, charitably dispensing favors. Isn't there even a little of the whore in you? I should think there would be, judging from your past. But, no, I'm beginning to think you're frigid. Lord, you remind me of my mother. I expect you to rap me on the knuckles for taking forbidden liberties. This isn't all my fault, you know," he told her bitterly.

The cruel words nearly shattered her. She wept openly and he was immediately sorry.

"Oh, darling, forgive me. It's just that—that I get so damn frustrated. Please, don't cry. Please! I am sorry. I'm a clumsy, selfish fool. Forgive me."

He kissed her eyes, her lips, her neck. Her sobs quieted and she tried desperately to please him a second time, but it was useless.

He was right. Some of the fault did lay with her. At first she'd been terrified of becoming pregnant. She began to use a diaphragm without telling him and when at last he detected it, he wouldn't speak to her for days.

"I want sons. I told you that. You knew I wanted children when you married me. I have a right to have them."

She had to admit this was true and at last gave in, but after Arthur was born there was no need for any protection. It was a difficult birth and an emergency hysterectomy had to be performed.

He was terribly disappointed and he seemed for a time to lose all interest in sex. But gradually he responded to her gentle persuading. He needed affection as much as she did, but seemed unable to show it without a great deal of prompting. She learned to make the overtures and withstand the rebuffs. His real need for reassurance helped her overcome her original qualms and they became for a time at least moderately successful in their love-making.

When he came out of the shower, she was seated at her dressing table doing her nails. He threw aside the spread on the oversized double bed and lay down in his robe glancing at her only briefly and saying nothing.

She meant to say something. She started to. She thought she could explain something of what she felt, her sudden sense of loneliness, of uselessness.

"Geoffrey, I—" she began tentatively.

He groaned and threw his arm across his eyes.

"Not now, Sybil," he said between clenched teeth.

Without another word she picked up her bottle of polish and left the room, her heart still and cold. He sounded as though he hated her. How had she offended him? What could she do to make amends? There was no way of knowing because he refused to discuss his feelings. She lay on the lounge in her dressing room staring into space. She felt suddenly quite exhausted. Her life, she thought, had become one long effort not to offend Geoffrey, to be as unobtrusive as possible when he was not pleased to acknowledge her presence and to be responsive when he did want her. She was his official hostess and the mother of his child. But she was not a wife. Tears slid down her cheeks as she wept silently for the Geoffrey she thought she knew, the Geoffrey who loved and needed her.

By the time they were dressed for dinner, she was quite composed. She wore an ankle-length gown of white wool, beautifully draped. She pinned a diamond clip in her dark hair which she wore upswept in soft waves.

Geoffrey, completely refreshed after his nap, came and stood behind her smiling. He always looked especially handsome in evening clothes. He touched her cheek with the back of his fingers, stroking gently.

"Sorry about before," he said, meeting her eyes in the mirror. He bent and kissed her bare shoulder. "I'm afraid I was a little tense."

"I understand," she said, but she could not return his smile. Had she been hurt once too often? He could forget what happened. It probably wouldn't cross his mind all evening. And then perhaps with enough to drink later they'd—

She couldn't even finish the thought.

"Arthur's very excited about your taking him to the circus in two weeks," she said.

"Good Lord! Is that in two weeks? Not the twenty-eighth! I completely forgot. I'm going to be out of town."

"Oh, no! Oh, Geoffrey. He'll be so disappointed!"

She knew only too well how disappointed. There was something in Arthur's serious, too intense nature that seemed to put Geoffrey off. The child sensed this and was hurt by it. He adored his father, though he hardly knew him. She was constantly trying to find reasons for them to be together. She was convinced that all they needed was to spend more time with one another. Here was the son he'd wanted so badly, but he seemed to prefer Joanna, or even Ned and she couldn't understand why.

"Couldn't you possibly change your plans?"

"Change my plans? Nonsense, Sybil. He's only a child. We can go to the circus another time. It's not a problem. I'll stop around and order something for him from Schwarz's, just to show he's really loved."

"He doesn't need something from Schwarz's. He needs you."

His eyes grew cold.

250

"Damn it, Sybil. I can't be at the child's beck and call and still carry my full share at the firm. Now you know that, and Arthur will just have to learn it, if he doesn't know it already. Come on. I think we're going to be more than fashionably late as it is."

Even so, she managed to stop by Arthur's room on her way out. He was sitting on the floor in his blue pajamas surrounded by tiny toy figures of Indians and soldiers.

"It's Custer's Last Stand," he told her gravely. "I won it at the party. I want to put them all in their proper positions, but I can't read all the words in the directions."

She bent and kissed his cheek. He smelled clean and innocent and faintly of Ivory soap.

"Why don't you just put them where you think they should go?"

"Oh, no, that wouldn't be right. I want them to go exactly where they were in the real battle."

"I see," she said. Arthur's desire for order and accuracy seemed odd in a child his age.

"Aunt Marlene will read it to you. Or Joanna."

Arthur's eyes lighted up. "Is Joanna back?" he asked.

"Well, no, not yet, but she's bound to come in soon. Alfred has to get the early train back."

"Oh, I'd like Joanna to help me, if she has time," he added.

She looked at her son closely. He seemed so anxious for Joanna's approval and attention. He got so little of it. It was hard to be the youngest child, so much younger that you were constantly left behind. She often wished he had been twins. It seemed unfair to bring up one child alone no matter how self-sufficient he seemed.

"Well, ask her when she gets in," she said and stood up, smoothing her dress.

"Have a nice time, Mother. Tell Daddy to have a nice time, too." He looked up at her with large solemn eyes and she wished suddenly they could call the whole thing off and stay home with him.

"No," she said impulsively. "You tell him. Come on."

He looked surprised. He knew his father expected him to be seen and not heard.

"Do you think I could?" he asked.

"Certainly. Come along."

Geoffrey was waiting impatiently in the living room, holding her mink stole. He looked sophisticated and very remote, hardly like a loving father.

"Good heavens, Sybil, they'll be halfway through dinner—" He glanced at Arthur. "Well, what's this?"

He was always in great awe of his own son which came off as impatience. He hardly knew what to say to the boy and seldom tried to say anything.

"I came to wish you a pleasant evening, Father." He held out his hand quite formally.

Geoffrey looked down at the small figure in surprise and then smiled broadly. Arthur was, after all, a very handsome child.

"Why, thank you, Arthur. And you—you have a pleasant time, too. Er—will you be watching television?"

"Yes, I think so."

"Well, good! Then we all have plans. Good night, Arthur."

The boy was a forlorn figure as he waved good-bye. Sybil had all she could do to keep from running back and enveloping him in her arms.

Anne's party was, as usual, a great success. She managed to gather together men and women of diverse social backgrounds and interests who brought something new and stimulating to the discussions because of their varied points of view. Geoffrey's new client, the one who had given him such difficulty that afternoon, was an unexpected guest.

"Good Lord! Claudia Barrett! I suppose she'll want to pick up right where she left off at lunch." Geoffrey muttered. "Sybil, couldn't you distract her some way. I don't think I could go through that again."

"You didn't say your client was Claudia Barrett."

She was impressed. She'd always admired the actress.

"Show people! They're all alike. And that husband of

252

hers is insufferable. Please, Sybil. Talk to her about her last play. They always love that."

He hurried off in the direction of the bar after briefly greeting Miss Barrett. He need not have worried. The actress was not apparently interested in him at the moment. She moved with the graceful art of one born to the stage. She was tall—statuesque, they called her in the columns. Her hair was platinum and her complexion exquisite. When she spoke in the most musical effortless tone, heads turned. Her voice had a deep, throaty quality and even a stage whisper would carry to the last balcony.

"So you're Sybil Kempton," she said, taking Sybil's hand and tucking it firmly beneath her arm. She led her officiously off into the quiet of Malcolm's study and closed the door. "We have to talk," she said, gesturing toward the leather sofa. "That dress is magnificent. It must be one of yours."

She was nearly overpowered by the force of Miss Barrett's personality, but she smiled and nodded.

"Yes, how did you know?"

"Anne, of course. My dear, she's told me everything. And actually I'm grateful. All things considered, it's going to work out beautifully."

She had absolutely no idea what the woman was talking about, but she tried gamely to look bright and intelligent.

"I—I understand you're going to be opening in a new play in the fall. I'm so glad. I'm one of your greatest admirers."

Miss Barrett smiled her most dazzling smile and sat gracefully in a chair opposite Sybil.

"You are? How nice! Yes, we will be opening in the fall. Believe it or not, it's a musical. It should be magnificent. My best effort to date. That's why everything about it has to be perfect. Especially my clothes. Sybil, my dear, you must let me come to you for my costumes."

Miss Barrett sat back comfortably, fitting a cigarette into her jeweled holder and beamed radiantly at Sybil who stared at her in disbelief.

253

"Me? But I no longer— That is, I gave up my shop when I married Geoffrey. Surely Anne told you."

"That's the very reason I want you now. Don't you see? Costumes designed exclusively for Miss Barrett by Sybil Anderson," she said, writing in the air with the tip of her lighted cigarette. "No, why don't you simply call yourself Sybil? It has a certain style."

"But I—I've never done anything like this—a Broadway show. I hadn't thought— That is, I haven't designed clothes commercially for some time."

Her thoughts came out in a confused jumble. She was immensely flattered by Claudia Barrett's suggestion, but it came as such a surprise to her, she simply did not know what to say.

"Nonsense, my dear. I have great confidence in you. And it's not a period play. The designs would be contemporary, the simply stunning things you've always done. And you know," she added, leaning forward and looking directly into her eyes, "I won't take no for an answer. I never do. Ask anyone. I never do."

She smiled dazzlingly and Sybil found herself smiling back, caught up in the excitement of the idea. She felt challenged and stimulated as she hadn't felt in years. What a joy it would be to dress someone as attractive as Claudia Barrett and then to have her designs seen again and again at every performance! Here in Malcolm Halburton's study, cut off from the reality of her everyday life, it seemed to her that such a thing was not only achingly desirable, but possible.

When the door opened and the sounds of the party rushed in, she started guiltily. Was it only a dream made real by the magic of Miss Barrett's persuasive charm? She knew that Geoffrey would resist any such proposal. But, oh, how she longed to accept!

The man standing in the doorway was thin, almost completely bald. He wore an expression of infinite patience on his nondescript face.

"Claudia, they'd like to go in to dinner," he said tentatively.

"Not now, Harry! Not now!"

Miss Barrett waved him imperiously from the room without looking at him and he ducked back quickly, pulling the door to silently.

"Now when can we start? You'll want to read the script first, of course. And then we can get together and pool our ideas, so to speak. Why don't I have a copy of it sent around to you tomorrow? Then we can meet early next week."

"Oh, please, Miss Barrett," she said breathlessly. "Not so fast. There's my family to consider and Geoffrey. I'm afraid he would not react too favorably to this idea."

"Oh, Geoffrey! Between us we can certainly handle Geoffrey. And it's Claudia. Please, call me Claudia. We're going to be very close friends, Sybil."

She did not at first realize how close. Claudia Barrett was a demanding taskmistress. She expected the best and she got it. But she imposed her thoughts, her personality on everyone with whom she came in contact. And her needs were insatiable.

When she rejoined Geoffrey she felt strangely excited, as well as fearful. It must have shown in her face.

"Good lord, she's gotten to you already!" he said. "What you need is a good stiff drink." He placed one in her trembling hand. "Now you know what I went through this afternoon. That woman is the most stubborn, self-willed creature I've ever met. She's determined to invest a large percentage of her own money in this upcoming production just so that she can control every aspect. I told her she was a fool. What woman has any kind of good business sense? She'll be ruined!"

He shook his head in disgust. "If I'd known she was going to be here tonight, I'd have told you to beg off."

Claudia dominated the dinner conversation. Her voice, her rich laughter could be heard above everyone. Once she glanced at Sybil and winked with the utmost certainty of one who knew she'd get exactly what she wanted.

Sybil had to admit that Claudia Barrett frightened her,

but she intrigued her, too. Later, as they were leaving, Anne took her old friend aside.

"She's great fun, if you don't let her intimidate you."

"Oh, Anne, do you know what she wants me to do?"

"I must confess to suggesting it. Are you going to do it?"

"I don't know. She thinks I am."

Anne laughed. "Well, then, it's settled."

Was it? Just like that? Only this afternoon she'd been wondering what direction her life was taking and how she could keep herself from sinking into depression. Now this! Did she dare discuss it with Geoffrey?

He leaned back in the cab and closed his eyes.

"That was one party I thought would never end! If I don't see that woman for the next ten years, it will be too soon. And that husband of hers never let me alone not even at dinner. He's her business manager, agent, and general factotum. He's insidiously persistent. You know the type. Quiet, apologetic, but persistent. God knows what kind of marriage they must have. She treats him like dirt and he takes it. I can't stand either of them. I'm going to speak to Arthur and see if someone else can take over. God save us all from aggressive women."

He sighed and slipped his arm around her shoulders. He leaned toward her brushing his lips against her cheek. This was no time for a serious discussion. Her need for him was every bit as strong now as it had been this afternoon. Her timing had been poor then. Perhaps they could make up for it now.

When they reached their bedroom, he did not even wait for her to undress, but threw off his own jacket and trousers and pulled her down on the bed, roughly pushing aside her beautiful gown. He was particularly forceful that evening and she gasped with surprise at his sudden strength.

"There," he said, leaning over her and smiling proudly. "Wasn't that worth waiting for? I do love you, darling." He kissed her once more and rolled off the bed to go into the shower.

She sat up slowly. Once again he had left her too soon. She would like to have lain in his arms for a time, sharing the pleasant afterglow of their love-making. He always left her so abruptly that she felt used instead of loved. He had absolutely no understanding of this. When she tried to tell him, he became angry, taking everything as a criticism. She felt unfulfilled in their love-making and in the empty life she thought she now was leading. Claudia's offer loomed large in her mind. At least if she went back to work again she'd have the satisfaction of creativity. But how could she ever get Geoffrey to accept the idea?

Slowly she removed her gown, picked up her robe and went into the children's bathroom to bathe and change. When she came out it was nearly three o'clock by the grandfather clock in the hall and still there was a light beneath Joanna's door. Curious, she hesitated, then knocked.

Joanna was sitting up in bed looking bright-eyed and pleased with herself. Recently she'd had her dark hair cropped short in a poodle cut and the curls shone in the lamplight. There were papers strewn about the coverlet and the floor.

"My dear, why aren't you asleep?" she asked.

"Oh, Mother!" She was out of bed and in her mother's arms in seconds. "Mother, the most wonderful, wonderful thing has happened."

She couldn't help smiling at her daughter, who was so obviously, deliciously happy. She's shining, she thought. She's shining because she is in love. How wonderful for her! She hugged the girl to her.

"Well, tell me about it."

They sat down on the edge of the bed. Joanna clasped her mother's hand in hers and laughed aloud.

"Oh, Mother, we've come to an understanding, Alfred and I."

"Have you?"

"Yes! We're going to be married, probably this summer. He's going to tell his parents tomorrow and then— well, then we'll make it official. Do you think we could

257

get something at the Essex House for the reception? I've been making out lists and lists of people to ask and things we'll have to do. Oh, and clothes!"

Joanna stood up and went to the mirror. She pulled her nightgown tightly about her slim body and smiled with satisfaction at her reflection.

"I'll need lots of new clothes, Mother. Your designs!"

She threw her arms around Sybil and kissed her. "I love everybody," she cried, her soft brown eyes aglow.

Sybil laughed from sheer delight to see her so happy. "Darling, darling! You'll never get to sleep tonight if you don't calm down. Time enough to make plans in the morning. I'm sure we can work everything out, but you must sleep."

The thought crossed her mind that Joanna was too happy. She was not in the least concerned about the possibility of any kind of problem. How would Alfred's family feel about marriage just now? How would they feel about Joanna herself?

"Oh, who cares about sleep?" she asked, but she helped pick up the papers and put them on the night table. She climbed into bed and let herself be tucked in.

"You know," she whispered, as her mother was about to turn out the light, "this is like old times, isn't it?"

She looked down at the large eyes in the childish face. She's still a little girl, she thought. Half child and half woman. Was I ever that young?

"Yes, it's like old times." She kissed her daughter's cheek. "I'm so happy for you, darling. Alfred's a wonderful boy."

"We're going to be so happy!" She closed her eyes.

Sybil tiptoed back to her own room where Geoffrey was already asleep sprawled across more than half the bed. She got in quietly beside him and lay for a long time staring into the dark. She told herself she should be happy for Joanna.

Hadn't she decided that Joanna was ready to be married? Her impression of Alfred was very favorable. Why should she expect the worst? But in her heart she knew the answer to that. It lay in her own background and what the Skinners would consider the scandal of Joanna's birth. She was not naive enough to think that Sybil Ashford's story had escaped the notice of the Skinners. Everything depended on Alfred. He seemed more independent than most boys his age. He seemed to be quite confident, but she'd have to see him with his family to be sure. What sort of control did they exercise over the boy and how enmeshed was he in the protocol of Philadelphia society? Society could be cruel. She knew that only too well. But they loved each other. Everything would be all right because they loved each other, wouldn't it?

She listened to Geoffrey's even breathing. She turned so that her body curved to fit his. She needed his warmth and comfort. She wished she could wake him and talk, but she hesitated. They shared many things in their marriage, but Geoffrey did not like to be reminded of her past and she could not blame him. This was something she must face alone.

He stirred then and threw his arm across her, pulling her close in his sleep.

"Oh, Geoffrey," she whispered. "If you only knew how much I need you."

II

"What the devil is this?"

He was standing beside the bed holding a large manila envelope.

She stared up at him sleepily.

"What?"

"This!" He shook the envelope at her. "It just came by special messenger for you from Claudia Barrett. What is it?"

She was instantly awake. She tried to speak calmly. This was no time to talk about Claudia's plans. After Joanna's news last night, the offer had almost completely left her mind. She wasn't at all sure now if she wanted to pursue it further.

"Well?" he demanded. He looked like an angry giant towering over her that way and she felt intimidated. She sat up and held out her hand for the package.

"Why don't we open it and see?" she asked evenly.

"Oh, come now, Sybil. You don't have to open it, do you?" he asked. "You must have some idea what's in it. You two were closeted in Malcolm's study last night. What did you talk about?"

"Her new play," she said quietly. "Geoffrey, there's no need to shout. That's no doubt a copy of her new play."

"A copy of her new play! For God's sake, why would she send you a copy of her new play?"

He was completely perplexed and this finally made her angry. He was treating her as if she were a half-wit child.

"Why not? I do read, you know. I am interested in the theater I'm not illiterate," she snapped.

"Don't be a fool! I didn't mean that." He handed her the envelope. "The woman is devious. I want to know what she's up to. Whatever it is, she has no right to involve you."

"I offered to read the play."

"Offered? Whatever for? Sybil, I really think you might have mentioned this to me last night."

"Why?" Her eyes were wide with amazement. He had never been so intensely interested in what she did or said at parties before.

"Why! Because I would have told you not to become involved, that's why. Now I suppose you'll have to read the thing and send it back with a polite note as soon as possible. What is it she wants? Your opinion?"

Geoffrey began to prowl about the room.

"Why *your* opinion for heaven's sake?"

She felt a rush of fury at what she read as contempt in his voice, contempt really for her abilities and her intelligence. It was this that prompted her to do the one thing she had not meant to do, certainly not yet and certainly not in that way.

"Why not my opinion? Claudia respects it. She knows something of my ability as a designer and she's asked me to do her clothes for her new production. If I like the play, I'll probably do them," she added defiantly.

Still furious, she went on saying what she really felt. "It's high time I did something other than supervise the menus and the cleaning around here. Sometimes, Geoffrey, I feel like nothing more than a very high-priced whore. That's your word not mine," she told him hastily when his mouth literally dropped open in surprise. "It's demeaning to be called to bed whenever you think you need me. And that's all I have to look forward to day after day. We never really talk any more. I hardly know what you're thinking. I'm lonely, Geoffrey, lonely and stagnating. My life is empty. Why shouldn't I accept

261

Claudia's exciting offer? It's the first really interesting one I've had in years," she finished.

She'd gotten out of bed and was standing before him, blue eyes blazing. She was a slim figure in her white nightgown, but she felt forceful and rather daring.

She'd never talked like this to him before. All the pent-up emotions of years of self-control and adaptation to his wishes burst through the walls behind which they'd been so carefully contained. She felt suddenly strong and free. What a relief it was to have it all out in the open!

His jaw was rigid and his cheeks flushed. For the first time in their married life he struck her. He slapped her smartly across the face. She gasped in pain and surprise.

"How dare you? You ungrateful little slut! How dare you speak to me that way? Don't you know what I've given you? Don't you realize it even now? What were you when I married you? Answer me that? Think about your reputation when I married you. A woman, scorned and divorced by a man who easily gained custody of his son from the wayward mother who had borne an illegitimate child. I've put up with the sly looks, the innuendos. Don't think your past was lightly glossed over by my associates. But I put up with it. I gave you respectability and I gave your daughter a name. Yes, your illegitimate daughter. And you stand there and tell me your life is empty, that you find it demeaning to perform your wifely duty. Demeaning! God, you're self-righteous. And why? You have no reason to be anything but grateful to me. Yes, grateful," he shouted when she tried to speak. "You're lonely and stagnating, are you? What the hell do you think you'd be now without me?"

He stamped out of the room, slamming his dressing room door behind him. She heard him turn the key in the lock and still she went to the door and tried it. Absolutely terrified at what she might have done, she shook the knob anxiously.

"Geoffrey! Geoffrey! No! Please come back and talk! Geoffrey!"

There was no reply. It was useless. She sank down on

the floor in front of the door, her head on her knees, sobbing bitterly. Everything he said was probably true and how little thought she had given it over the years. Is that how he really saw her, a fallen woman he had raised from the gutter? He'd never once given any indication of this, not once. And not once had she realized it. Dear God! What had she done? Why couldn't she have waited to tell him about Claudia until they were both calm and reasonable?

Someone was knocking at the door.

"Mother, Mother! Are you awake?"

She wiped her eyes hastily and looked around for her robe. It had slipped onto the floor at the foot of the bed.

"Mother, may I come in and talk?" Joanna's voice was high and as excited as it had been in the early hours of the morning.

"Give me five minutes, darling. See if you can get some eggs and coffee ready for us."

Joanna hesitated briefly. She was disappointed. Her exciting plans couldn't wait comfortably even those few moments. Probably she hadn't thought about breakfast.

"All right. Please hurry."

She swallowed, hoping her voice sounded less husky than she thought.

"Of course."

She did what she could with cold water and make-up, but her eyes looked haunted and her face ravaged. Joanna probably would not notice.

She gave one last look at Geoffrey's closed door. She could hear him moving behind it, gathering his clothes. Probably he'd go golfing. It was a warm day. They would not have another opportunity to talk until tonight. Perhaps that was wise. They were both far too emotional for discussion now. It might be best to wait.

But she ached to go to him, to throw her arms around him, to apologize for the hateful, bitter words. How he must hate to think she found the life he'd built for them was so abhorrent to her! How could she have said those

263

things? And he— Sybil shook her head. She dared not think of his words. They were too painful.

What was it Carl Sandburg had said about "proud words"? They could never, never be taken back, erased. Oh, Lord! But they could be used to understand. She would try to understand. They both would, wouldn't they? But when she left her bedroom she went with a heavy sense of disaster, knowing in her heart that irreparable damage had been done this morning. She did not even stop to pick up Claudia Barrett's play which had fallen to the floor in front of the night table.

He did not come back that night. He called to tell her he was staying at his club. That was all. He simply stated the fact and hung up. She tried not to let this upset her unduly. He had done it before. He was punishing her.

He'd come around, the way he did the time he was certain she'd been paying too much attention to an attractive writer they'd met at a supper club a few years ago. He had been unreasonably jealous about her having a long private conversation with the man at a party afterward. She found Carter Hayes stimulating and had not realized she was flirting, as Geoffrey seemed to think she was. Afterwards she thought perhaps she had been. She'd enjoyed the younger man's company. It was refreshing, but that was all she'd had in mind.

"It wasn't what he had in mind. You can bet on that," Geoffrey told her later grimly. "And people talk. You have to remember who you are. It's important to us both."

She had agreed to be circumspect and there had never been a repetition of this particular problem which had amounted to nothing. But he punished her all the same, staying at his club two nights to reinforce his disapproval. But he'd come around then and he'd come around this time, too, wouldn't he?

It was a long difficult day. She'd tried to be enthusiastic about Joanna's plans and even begun some sketches for the trousseau just to please her. They'd even phoned the Essex House about possible dates in June and Joanna happily continued making and remaking long lists of everything. But by late afternoon she became anxious, hovering about the phone, expecting it to ring at any moment. When Alfred had not called by evening, she called him twice and was unable to speak to him either time.

She called the third time at nine and Sybil could have cried for her.

"Oh, yes, yes, Foster. This is Joanna Kempton again. I—I wondered if Alfred was back yet."

Her voice had become strained. Sybil wished there were something she could do. Was it possible that Alfred had been legitimately detained? Please, God, let it be that.

There was a long pause as Joanna apparently listened to the reply. "I see. Not until late tonight. Well, you know, Foster, it doesn't matter to me how late. Just please tell him to call me. Tell him I'll wait up for his call," she added. "Tell him that, will you, Foster?"

"What's wrong?"

Marlene came in from the hall where she'd openly been listening to the phone conversation. Sybil shook her head and held her finger to her lips. Marlene grunted in disgust.

"I told her she was acting too eager beaver," she said in a low tone. "Where's his highness, by the way?" she asked, meaning Geoffrey.

"Business meeting," Sybil lied. "Come in and keep me company."

Marlene ventured into the living room. She was wearing her late Sunday evening attire, a long pink robe and soft slippers.

"Mother, do you mind awfully if we don't go over that guest list now?"

Joanna came out of the study looking puzzled and vaguely frightened. It was obvious she did not know what to make of her inability to contact Alfred. He should have called that morning after telling his parents of their plans.

"Whatever you like, dear."

Joanna sighed and feigned a yawn. "I guess I'm tired. All the excitement and everything last night. I didn't real-

265

ly sleep well. I think I'll just go to my room and nap until Alfred calls. Evidently they've gone out. Poor thing! He probably hasn't had a minute to talk with his parents." She paused. "Well, I'll say good night."

She moved off slowly as if she were in a kind of daze. Only this morning she had been so happy and self-confident.

Marlene stared after Joanna for a moment and then looked back at Sybil.

"That bastard's not going to marry her!" Her eyes widened with sudden insight. "That's it, isn't it? That's it and you know it. I can see it in your face. That high and mighty family of his probably stepped in. My God! Aren't you going to do anything?"

Sybil swallowed a sob. "Oh, Marlene, what can I do?"

"Geez!" She stood in the middle of the room waving her arms frantically. "Geez, I don't know. Something! Anything!"

"It might not be that. It might be something else. Perhaps they have all gone out. Perhaps he has not had the opportunity to—"

"Opportunity! Don't make me laugh. You know as well as I do what this is all about. And that poor kid—"

"I'll talk to her now." Sybil rose resolutely. She'd been wrong. She saw that now. All day long she'd been pretending with Joanna, pretending that there would be a wedding, that Alfred's family would welcome her eagerly. It was what Joanna wanted to believe, but it would never come to pass. Time, time and a more open and tolerant attitude might have changed people like the Skinners. But it hadn't. She recalled Geoffrey's angry words last night about what he'd had to put up with. Sly looks and innuendos he called them. It was all the same. People were the same, rigid and unforgiving in their morality.

Joanna lay on her bed, her arm across her face. She was not asleep.

"Oh, Mother," she said, sitting up and snapping on the small bedside lamp. "I guess I'm not ready for sleep either. I—I keep thinking about Alfred. He's a wonderful

266

person, Mother. Do you know what he said when he first met me? When Ned introduced us, I mean?" She patted the bed beside her and Sybil sat down. "He said, 'Ned's little sister, eh? Well, we're going to have to take good care of you. You look like Alice in Wonderland. My dear, this Wonderland is full of wolves and lechers. You just stay close to me and I'll see you through safely.' And he did! He's so honorable. He positively reveres women. He's never made an improper advance toward me. And the other boys—well, they can be awful, you know. But not Alfred." She smiled dreamily. "He'll make a wonderful husband. He's so thoughtful. That's why he'll be a good father, too."

She sat up against the pillows, warming to her subject. She talked rapidly, running words and sentences together.

"We'll have to have a baby right away. They won't take him in the Army if he's a father. He's decided to go on to engineering school and he'll be deferred because of that, but we'll need the baby, too, for insurance. Everybody says so. Mother! I can't imagine him in Korea. He's so gentle. He'd never—I mean he couldn't kill anyone. I can't imagine him killing anyone. He'd be killed himself. And he doesn't want to go."

She waved her hand impatiently. "Oh, I know what he said yesterday, but he doesn't want to go. He'd only do it because of honor. He believes in honor. He really does. Mother, why do you suppose he hasn't called?"

The sudden silence in the room was painful. She knew that now was the time to warn her daughter. Now was the time to discuss the possibilities of disappointment. But she couldn't. Perhaps if Alfred was as strong and independent as Joanna thought, he could withstand the disapproval of his family and marry in spite of it. There was always that possibility.

She leaned forward and kissed her daughter's cool cheek. She could not bear the look of fear in the girl's eyes.

"I'm sure he'll call as soon as he can, as soon as he is free to call. Didn't you say Alfred was an only son? Per-

267

haps his plans came as something of a shock to his family. It's difficult to face the prospect of the marriage of an only son. When you're a mother you'll know what that means. Why don't you try to get some sleep, darling? Aunt Marlene and I will wake you if there are any calls."

She stood for some time outside her daughter's closed door. She could think of only one thing to do. She talked it over with Marlene and they decided it was worth a try. Geoffrey had not returned and so she made her plans without him.

She was in Philadelphia by noon the next day. She had not been in the city since she was a girl of nineteen, a desperate young woman with a child she loved very much and a strong instinct for survival. Twenty-one years ago she had risked everything for her own freedom and happiness. She could do no less for Joanna.

The city had changed very little. It was almost as if she had not left at all. William Penn still stood atop the City Hall benignly blessing his people. The cab made its way slowly through midday traffic. The city looked smaller than she remembered it. As they drove beyond the city limits towards the wooded estates along the river, she felt a strong pang of nostalgia for her girlhood. How she'd like to take Joanna here and show her all this. She'd teach her to ride. She had not ridden in years, but she knew instinctively that she still could and that she would enjoy it as she used to.

She wished Joanna could have known her grandfather. If Joanna did marry Alfred, there was every possibility that she might someday meet him, though her identity would never penetrate his clouded mind. She called Alicia from time to time and questioned Ned closely about his grandfather. Confused at first, Woodrow Eldridge had finally come to terms with his grandson's existence. He was Alicia's son. That was how he'd explained it to himself.

"He gets along remarkably well," Ned reported. "We play chess and he talks about his days at Princeton. He's frail, of course, and he can't walk by himself, but he's O.K. Really!"

She had to be content with that. Most of the time she was, but now that she was here, she had the strongest desire to go to her father. Only Joanna's great need kept her from having the cab drive her there at once.

The Skinner estate was every bit as imposing as she remembered it. She was announced at the gate, giving her name clearly to the gateman as Sybil Eldridge Kempton so that there would be no mistake. There were several difficult moments as she waited for the inevitable reply. "Mrs. Skinner is not at home." Her anxiety had reached a terrible pitch, but she simply ignored her dry lips and trembling hands.

After a long delay, the gates were opened and her cab was waved on around the sweeping drive.

Alfred's mother received her in a sitting room on the second floor. Her appearance was regal. She was older than Sybil by perhaps five years and she had let her hair go gray, though attractively so. She wore a simple blue floral print dress. There were tiny seed pearls in her small, aristocratic ears. Sybil's smart, sophisticated black suit looked out of place in this relaxed country setting.

Mrs. Skinner rose and inclined her head as she entered.

"How good of you to come, Mrs. Kempton! I imagine we *should* have a talk under the circumstances." She smiled slightly. "You don't remember me, do you?"

Remember her? She searched her memory. If she knew Mrs. Skinner's maiden name—

"Cynthia Chase," Mrs. Skinner offered helpfully.

The name was familiar, but she still could not place her.

"I'm awfully sorry. I don't remember."

"Oh, well, it doesn't matter. There's no reason why you should. I remember you, though. You were quite the belle that season. I must confess I was rather envious."

"Envious?"

"Yes, of course. Your debut was so—so successful."

"I—I'm afraid it's all a blur to me now."

"What a pity! One would have thought such a success would be, oh, savored, I suppose. What a pity! Well, but

269

here we are about to discuss our children." The expression on her long, thin face was difficult to read. She was terribly calm. She appeared quite ready to be magnanimous. The thought chilled Sybil.

"Mrs. Skinner, it seems to me that we must reach some sort of understanding. My daughter's happiness is at stake. I can tell you quite frankly that she does love your son. There is no doubt in my mind about that. And from what I could tell at our meeting on Saturday he is quite fond of her."

"Oh, yes, Mrs. Kempton, I agree. They are quite fond of each other. But they are very young and I'm sure you will agree that there are many others of whom they could be equally as fond before a marriage partner is selected. So much more is at stake here than the joy of the moment, don't you see? A lifetime, after all. There is, as far as I can determine, no need for unseemly haste, or—" she paused significantly, "or is there?"

Sybil was furious at the suggestion. She tried to calm herself.

"Certainly not," she said evenly, though she felt her cheeks flush with anger. "This is simply a question of two very fine young people being in love."

"Ah, Mrs. Kempton, I cannot agree with you there."

She went to ring for a servant. "May I offer you some coffee?" She did not wait for a reply. "There is the matter of compatability, a lifetime of compatibility. There are serious differences which must be considered. My son is beginning to understand this, I think. It's something he managed to overlook. Oh, I don't blame him, of course; youth can be so impetuous as you doubtless know."

Her thin lips stretched into a smile.

Sybil was beginning to hate this insufferably self-righteous woman. The allusion to her own past was so cunningly but deliberately made.

"Ah, here is our coffee!" She greeted the entrance of the maid with all the relief due a reprieve. "Cream and sugar, Mrs. Kempton?"

Sybil ignored the question.

"Am I to understand then that Alfred has been instructed to renege on his proposal of marriage?" she asked bluntly.

"I'd hardly call it a proposal of marriage, Mrs. Kempton. A possibility is all that was discussed, I can assure you. Alfred would never make a formal proposal without consulting his parents."

She knew she must choose her words carefully. This was difficult to do. Where was the discussion leading? What hope did she have of success? And now, having seen Mrs. Skinner, what sort of success did she really want. Wouldn't Joanna be better off without any of them?

"That 'possibility' as you call it was taken most seriously by my daughter and by me. All yesterday she expected Alfred to call and yet there was no word from him. I find this difficult to understand. Is Joanna to linger indefinitely in some limbo between joy and despair awaiting your son's pleasure? I'm sure even you can see the cruelty of such action. She needs to see your son. She deserves an explanation of his behavior. It is difficult for me to believe that a young man of such obvious integrity could treat her so badly. It is even more difficult for me to believe that his feelings could change so drastically in such a short time. Where is he, Mrs. Skinner? I want to speak with him myself. I want to hear from his own lips his own explanation of what has happened."

"Do sit down, Mrs. Kempton and have your coffee."

Sybil did not realize she had risen. She stood for a moment looking down into Mrs. Skinner's cool, pitying eyes. Pitying! How dare she patronize me! How dare she! She wished she could tell Mrs. Skinner exactly what she thought of her. She wished she could banish Alfred from her home, forbid him to see Joanna, instead of the other way around. But she had none of Mrs. Skinner's advantages, not one. She sat stiffly in the chair that was offered her and took the coffee.

"We are two sensible adults. You know as well as I that an alliance between my son and your daughter is impossible. I don't think I need go into detail. Alfred, I'm

271

afraid, is taking it badly. He had no idea of your daughter's background—none at all. It came as quite a shock to him. He'll write Joanna, of course, in due time." Her voice was cool and she was quite aware of her victory.

Sybil looked at her and placed her cup on the small round table between them. Looking at that stony, implacable face, she knew she had failed. She felt drained and hopeless. Even her anger had left her. What had she expected after all? She felt she had degraded herself and Joanna by coming. But at least she knew! She knew exactly where they all stood.

"Then there is nothing more to be said," she murmured, as much to herself as to Mrs. Skinner.

"No, I imagine not. However, I would take it as an extreme favor if you'd see that Joanna gives up her efforts to contact Alfred. It will be easier all around that way. And as I said, he will write."

She touched her lips fastidiously with her napkin and put it carefully on the tray.

"Well, Mrs. Kempton, it was good of you to come. I'm glad we had our little talk."

She's dismissing me! She's actually dismissing me! How she relishes her role, her power!

They walked down the broad staircase to the front door together. Neither of them seemed able to think of anything to say, but at the last moment Mrs. Skinner thought to mention Sybil's father.

"How is he? We've been hearing such sad news. A matter of weeks, isn't it? Poor man! I hope he won't suffer much longer."

The words had no meaning for her. She tried hard to put them together. Her father must have become ill since she'd last heard. Surely Ned would have written. The fact that her father's illness was news to Sybil was not lost on Mrs. Skinner.

"I am so sorry, Mrs. Kempton. I didn't realize. Well, they say it's cancer. He was in a hospital, but now I understand he is at home." She looked away quickly for tears had sprung uncontrollably to Sybil's eyes. "Foster, is Mrs. Kempton's cab still here?"

An elderly butler materialized in the front hall. He must have been waiting somewhere just out of sight.

"Yes, madam."

"Oh, good." She held out her hand and managed her slight smile. "So nice to have seen you again, Mrs. Kempton. I'm sure our little problem will work itself out."

Sybil did not reply. She did not take Mrs. Skinner's hand, but left without a backward glance. She'd failed and now she'd learned that her father was dying. Her mind was numb.

"Well, where to now?" asked the driver in a bored tone. "Back to the station?"

She nodded mutely.

"O.K. Gee, you know, we don't get much call to come out this way. Most of these folks have their own drivers. Me? I haven't ever been here before. This is some layout. You can't see these places from the road. All the money they must need to keep this up. Me? I have a little two-family place in the city and it's eating up all I make."

She hardly heard him. They drove along the river road in the direction of the Eldridge estate. She watched with a kind of horrified fascination the scenery that was so very familiar. Could she possibly go on without seeing her father? It might be her very last chance. She could not ignore the fact that her father was dying. If that were true, a visit from her could hardly be considered harmful. The humiliation of Mrs. Skinner's scorn left her weak and trembling. She did not know if she could bear another such confrontation with her sister, but surely it must be her duty to try to see her father. No, it was more than her duty. She wanted desperately to see him.

She directed the driver toward the old stone gates above which the Eldridge crest was displayed on a bronze shield. In the distance between the long rows of elms she could see the white columns of the stately Georgian house.

Home! Had this ever really been home?

"Hey lady, how long do you think this will take?"

The driver was trying to get her attention in the rear view mirror. He pointed to his watch. "I mean, I got to get back to town, you know? Can't make a living out here."

"Oh," she said. "I'll—I'll be glad to make it worth your while. And really, I won't be long."

"Well—" The driver was reluctant. "If I had known this was going to be an all-day thing—"

She reached into her purse and brought out a twenty-dollar bill.

"Please," she said.

The driver stared at it.

"Lady, for that you can stay all night."

He pulled up behind a white Cadillac on the front drive and she got out before he could open the door for her. She ran lightly up the steps. Had they always been this wide? No, the porch had been enlarged. It extended the width of the house.

She looked up at the imposing front door and nearly panicked, but she resolutely rang the bell. A stranger opened the door and stood looking at her expectantly. She felt weak and almost faint, realizing she'd had nothing to eat since breakfast. That, in addition to her emotional turmoil, was almost too much. She took a deep breath.

"I'm Sybil Eldridge Kempton. I've come to see my father."

The maid's eyes grew wide. She was young and inexperienced.

"Yes, ma'am," she said and stood aside for her to enter.

"Mother!"

Ned was just coming down the stairs. He strode across the hall, his handsome features registering his surprise. He kissed her cheek and took her hands, staring as though she were an apparition.

"Mother, I never expected to see you here."

"Who is that, Ned?" Alicia's voice came from the li-

274

brary. "Really, that girl is hopeless. I've told her and told her to announce visitors— Oh, Sybil."

She stood in the wide entrance hall, staring at her sister. "It's you."

"Yes. How are you, Alicia?"

"How am I? Is that really the point?" She was wearing a beige hostess gown. Her red hair was perfectly coiffed and her make-up impeccable. She looked as though she might have been posing for a picture in *House Beautiful*. She was calm, almost content. If her father lay at the point of death upstairs, no one would have guessed it. Her long green eyes seemed to see right through her to Ned.

"Did you know about this, Ned?" she demanded imperiously.

"I came on my own, Alicia. I understand father is very ill."

"Oh, I see." Alicia pressed her lips together. "Well, Sybil dear, you're a little late."

"Oh, no!" she gasped.

She felt weak with grief. Standing here in the entrance hall of the splendid old house, it was as though she had never left. She half expected her father to come down the stairs and chide her for being late to lunch again. Everywhere she looked there were little reminders of her girlhood. There was the old Spanish chest in which she used to hide when the thought of lessons with Madame Hautval became too much for her. To the left was the library where she'd spent so many happy hours. To the right was the entrance to the drawing room where on the night of her debut she had danced with Ronald, with Edward, even with Jason Skinner. Over all, her father had presided, a kindly, loving figure. She couldn't believe he was gone.

"He's still alive," Alicia said belatedly. "Just barely. He won't know you, of course. Go up if you must. A nurse is with him. Ned, show your mother the way," she added as an afterthought.

"I don't need to be shown the way, Alicia."

"Of course. I'll be in the library if you want me. Come

275

along, Ned. You've still work to do on that paper." She turned and left, giving her no more attention than she would a tradesman who had come to perform some insignificant service. Ned gave his mother an uncertain look.

"It's all right, Ned," she said and began to ascend the stairs slowly.

The sun had gone. Slate-gray clouds could be seen through the window above the spring rainbow of cut flowers in the huge vase on the landing. Her knees trembled as she continued to climb the stairs. The house was so quiet, deathly still.

The nurse who came to her father's door did not approve this visit.

"He's sleeping."

"I'll only stay a moment," she whispered.

Beyond the nurse's starched white uniform she could see her father's bed. It looked empty at first, but then she saw the small head on the pillow. All the flesh seemed to have melted away. It would have been difficult to discover Woodrow Eldridge within that parchment-like skin and small, shrunken skull.

"Father," whispered Sybil. "Father!" She sank to her knees beside the enormous bed that held the fragile body.

She could hear the painful gasps for air that passed for breathing. Tears streamed down her face. She was afraid to touch the long, bony hand that curled gently around the white coverlet and yet she must make some contact.

She reached out and finally held the fragile fingers in her hand. They were cold.

"Father! Oh, Father, I wish—" she began.

The eyelids flickered and opened. For a moment the dark eyes roamed aimlessly. She gave a little cry and pressed the fingers urgently.

"Father, Father, it's Sybil," she cried.

Slowly the wavering gaze came to rest on her face and in that moment there was a spark. She thought she saw some sign of recognition and caught her breath in awe.

The dry lips trembled and moved. The words came out in a hoarse whisper. "I'm so sorry," he said.

The eyelids fluttered and closed and that was all. Had he recognized her? She'd never know.

Oh, Father! It is I who am sorry. It would have been better if I'd never been born.

The words were uttered only in her mind. She could not bring herself to say anything. Struck with the futility of life, the unfulfilled desires, she wished nothing more than to die herself here at her father's side. What had she done but cause heartbreak and unhappiness herself? Everyone she touched was hurt by her efforts, her father, Joanna, Ned, Geoffrey. They all suffered because of her. Now she had to go home and face Joanna with news that could only shatter the girl. When the nurse touched her shoulder insistently, she was ready to leave. She bent and kissed her father's hand, saying her good-bye silently.

No one was in the hall when she came down, but she could hear voices in the library. Ned's apologetic tones and Edward's sarcastic ones. They all stopped and looked up when she entered. Edward was standing over Ned, peering at the disarray of papers on the table. Alicia was poring over her magazines near the fireplace. They looked like a family.

"Well, Sybil, your visit was timely if unexpected," Edward said. "Another day and he may be gone."

"I wonder that no one thought to tell me." She looked at them all accusingly.

"Really, Sybil." Alicia threw aside her magazine in a gesture of annoyance. "You haven't seen him in years. He doesn't know you. He doesn't know anyone now."

"But at a time like this," she said.

"Well, you've seen him," Edward cut off the discussion.

"Yes, I have. I shall be going then. Thank you, Alicia, for at least extending me this courtesy," she added.

She felt like an intruder. Even Ned gazed at her oddly. They all looked so at home. She wondered if they were all living here now. No one mentioned Monty.

Alicia rose at last. "Well, let me call the car for you."

"I have a cab."

She felt as though they all should be saying something else, but couldn't think what.

"I could drive Mother to the train," Ned offered, half rising from his chair. He acted like a recalcitrant child forced to stay with his books and chafing to escape. His appearance made the illusion almost ludicrous. He was a man. He'd put on weight in the past year, perhaps too much weight. He resembled his father more than ever.

"Your mother has a cab," Edward observed.

No one walked out with her. She climbed into the cab wearily. She looked up at the windows she knew to be her father's. They stared back blankly and she felt terribly homesick for her own home, her family, and most of all Geoffrey.

The trip back to New York seemed unending, perhaps because she was so anxious to get back.

Geoffrey was home. The door to his study was closed, but she could hear him talking on the phone. All the way back on the train she planned what she should say to him. Nothing seemed right. Nothing! Some day she, Geoffrey, Marlene, even the children would lie in bed, old and ill, waiting to die. And the years would be telescoped and only signal failures would be remembered. Her father's last words to her were "I'm sorry". Why? Why had he said that? What was it he regretted most? She thought she would never forget those last words. What would Joanna regret, the fact that she'd been born at all? What would Geoffrey regret, the fact that he'd married her?

She opened the door without knocking. Geoffrey looked up as he replaced the receiver. There was not a sign of forgiveness on his rigid, handsome face. He half turned away as though to dismiss her without speaking.

She stood in the doorway too weak, too frightened to say anything. After a moment she saw that Geoffrey had turned back and his face had softened. She realized that she was crying, sobbing uncontrollably. Then she was in his arms and he had kicked the door shut.

He held her close, whispering words of comfort. All the pain, humiliation and sorrow of the day welled up in her and she thought she could not bear life without him, without his love. Nothing mattered except that he held her in his arms, that they could face the tragedies of life together.

He eased her onto the sofa, still holding her.

"Oh, Geoffrey, Geoffrey. I love you so. Don't ever leave me, Geoffrey!"

She seemed to be saying it over and over again.

"Darling, I've been such a fool," he said, smoothing her hair and kissing her gently, then passionately. He comforted her with his body. And though they did not actually make love, she felt more cherished than she had felt in years.

Slowly she told him where she'd been that day and what had happened. Light faded from the windows, but they made no move to turn on the lamps. They simply lay in each other's arms in the semi-darkness.

"I should have been with you. You shouldn't have had to do this all alone," he said. "Promise me you'll never go back again without me."

She promised, but she hardly thought there would be an opportunity. She'd hardly be welcome at her own father's funeral should her sister bother even to inform her.

Nothing was said about yesterday's hateful argument. No mention was made of Claudia Barrett, her play, or her offer.

When Mrs. Norris knocked on the door to announce dinner, it was nearly seven o'clock.

She sat up trying to smooth her hair and rumpled clothes.

"I feel rather like a teenager caught necking in the back of the car. What will the children think?"

He laughed and pulled her down beside him again, slipping his hands inside the jacket of her suit, caressing her breasts and kissing the hollow of her neck.

"The hell with the children," he said huskily. "I want my wife."

They needn't have worried about the children. No one was home. Marlene had taken Arthur to Radio City and

Joanna had left early that afternoon and not returned. When Mrs. Norris told her this, she became immediately alarmed, but Geoffrey calmed her.

"It's Monday. She has classes, remember? And she often has dinner at school and stays for meetings. She'll be all right."

"Will she, Geoffrey?"

She stared at him across the candlelit table and tried to believe that. But her eyes swam with tears and she could not eat the baked sole that had been so carefully prepared. He knew as well as she that nothing would ever be the same for Joanna again.

He insisted she take a warm bath and go to bed right after dinner. He even made her take a sleeping pill, though she protested.

"I have to talk to Joanna."

"I'll talk to Joanna tonight and you'll see her in the morning. Right at the moment she doesn't know anything more now than she did yesterday. Trust me, darling. You've had enough of a strain today. Lean on me. That's what husbands are for, you know."

He kissed her and she allowed herself to be convinced. She felt utterly drained and exhausted. He was right. Everything could wait until morning. Everything!

III

When she awoke, it was past noon. Geoffrey had left for the office hours before. She opened her eyes to find Arthur standing beside her bed staring down at her.

"Are you sick, Mother?" he asked anxiously. His blue eyes were sad in the thin, pale face and she remembered her own terror yesterday as she knelt beside her father's bed.

She glanced at the clock and then at him.

"Arthur, why aren't you in school?"

"It's lunchtime," he said. "I thought maybe you were sick."

"Oh, no, darling, no!" She sat up and reached out to rumple his hair. "Shall we have lunch together, just the two of us? Only mine will be a sort of brunch. Would you like that?"

His face brightened, then clouded.

"Ned's here, though."

"Ned?"

She felt groggy and unsure of what she was hearing.

"Yes, he's been waiting more than an hour Aunt Marlene says. They're in the living room talking. Well—" he hesitated. "It's more than talking. I think they're mad at each other."

Ned! Why had he come? It wasn't hard to guess. She didn't really need to be told. Her father no doubt had— He'd been so weak yesterday. Even Edward had said—

She couldn't keep her thoughts coherent.

"Arthur, darling, why don't you run in and tell Mrs. Norris there'll be four for lunch? I'll get dressed as fast as I can. Oh, is Joanna home, too?"

He shook his head.

"She had classes all day. Anyway, I don't think Joanna's going to come home anymore."

She stopped in the act of reaching for her dressing gown.

"What are you saying, Arthur?"

"Last night she told Daddy she wasn't going to live here anymore. She took her suitcase this morning. She said she was never coming back."

She froze. Her lips felt stiff.

"You must have misunderstood, darling."

"No." He shook his head. "If we don't hurry I'll be late for school," he added and left the room.

She went straight to the phone and dialed Geoffrey, her hands trembling.

"Mr. Kempton is in a luncheon meeting, Mrs. Kempton. I'll have him call as soon as he returns," Mrs. McCarthy said.

"When will that be?" she asked impatiently.

"It's hard to say, Mrs. Kempton," came the cool, lilting voice of Geoffrey's secretary. She was older than either Sybil or Geoffrey, silver-haired, attractive, efficient, and always terribly pleased with herself no matter what the emergency. "You see, sometimes—" she began conversationally.

"Never mind," she said with unaccustomed abruptness. "Please have him call me when he returns, Mrs. McCarthy. It's urgent!"

After lunch, after seeing Ned, she'd go to Geoffrey herself if he hadn't called. Whatever meeting he was in, she'd insist on seeing him. Poor Joanna! How unhappy she must be! How desperate! What could she possibly have meant about not coming home again. Was she going to Alfred? Would she try to convince him to elope despite his family's feelings?

Marlene and Ned were indeed having words in the living room.

"You're crazy! You think your mother's going to give you money for that? You're crazy. I wouldn't give you a dime. Who do you think you are anyway? There's a war, an emergency! Everybody does their share, you know? Everybody! What's so special about you? You think you're too good to fight for your country? Who the hell are you anyway? In war everybody's the same? Everybody, you hear?"

Marlene glared across the glass coffee table at Ned who sat with his head lowered and glowered back at her. He said nothing. He wore a white turtleneck sweater that emphasized the plumpness of his face and contrasted with his flushed cheeks.

"Don't give me those cow eyes either," she said. "God, when I think of what your mother went through on account of you, I—"

"Marlene!"

Her tone was sharp and Marlene looked surprised.

"Mother!" Ned rose at once and went to her, embracing her and kissing her cheek. "Mother, I'm afraid I have sad news." He was suddenly all solicitous charm. That was Ned, mercurial.

She looked up into his dark eyes.

"I know," she said quietly.

"He died in his sleep early last night," he went on as though he hadn't heard her. "Aunt Alicia and Father didn't want you to know. But I just couldn't stand by and— Mother, I'm so sorry. Grandfather was a grand old man." He put his arms around her.

She allowed him a brief embrace and then turned away. How much of his feelings were genuine? She'd learned that Ned's emotions were not always what they appeared. He seemed to be unsure of his own feelings or of how to show them. When would he learn to be honest with himself?

"Marlene, will you take Arthur into the kitchen? I'm afraid he'll have to eat right away or risk being late for

283

school. We'll have that special lunch another time, darling," she said and smiled weakly. Arthur always seemed to be forgotten in times of family strife. He gave her an odd look. What must he be making of all this?

She turned back to Ned.

"I think we should sit down."

She took the chair beside the long glass doors to the terrace. They were open slightly and a chill breeze drifted through.

"Thank you for coming to tell me about your grandfather. That was kind of you. But what was that I heard you discussing with Marlene? What is it you want?"

"Want? Why, Mother, I don't—I don't want anything except to be with you now when you need me." Ned sat down on the chair beside her. He looked too big for it and peculiarly out of place. He reached for her hand, but she moved it away.

"The truth, Ned. Please. I'm not in the mood for games."

He paused, his hand hovering aimlessly in midair for a moment and then dropping to the polished cherry wood of the chair.

"I need money, Mother. I need it badly and right away."

"Why?" She gazed at him steadily, realizing that this was the truth. He reached into the pocket of his gray slacks and pulled out an official-looking letter. She knew what it was before he opened it. He was being drafted. Unless he applied for further academic deferment, he'd be called within months of graduation. Most probably such deferment would be denied him. His record at school was poor. Only last Christmas she'd received a letter from Edward blaming her for Ned's apparent lack of industry.

My dear Sybil,

Your cooperation will be greatly appreciated in having Ned devote some time of every day of this holiday to his studies. He has sorely neglected his work and I have been advised by the

284

> authorities that he may not graduate in June. He has repeatedly ignored all warnings and has taken to drinking to excess which earned him suspension during the fall term. This kind of behavior is hardly worthy of the rather substantial investment that is being made in his education at Princeton. Since you so willingly took on the direction of his early development alone which, as you know, is of the utmost importance, perhaps you can now begin to remedy the rather horrifying results of your inept efforts.

She knew he was merely trying to find an excuse for his own failure with Ned. Still, his accusations hurt. And she tried to talk to Ned, but he was beyond reason. He delighted in what he thought was his rightful social position. Since he'd been born to it, he thought there was not another thing he'd have to do to prove himself. She knew he was not assessing his father's nature correctly. She tried to warn him then, but there was little she could say. It took the United States government to bring him to the realization that everything wasn't always going to go his way.

"I don't believe in the war, you see," he was saying.

Isn't that what she had heard Joanna say? How many young people felt like that, or was it an excuse not to serve and protect the safety of their loved ones. Did she herself believe in the war? She wasn't sure. When it came to sending her son, making this terrible sacrifice, could she be strong enough? She had just lost her father. What if Ned were to be killed or maimed? She looked at him now and the years seemed to melt away. He was a frightened child again.

"I can't go."

There was a tremor in his voice.

"You must understand that I can't go, but they expect me to—the minute I graduate." He laughed. "I'm afraid I'm a terrible disappointment to Dad. He wanted a brilliant son and he got me instead. Well, I can't be what I'm not, can I? You of all people should know that."

Ned's shoulders drooped and he glared defiantly at his mother.

What does he see, she thought, noting her son's intent gaze. She was a woman who had certainly handled her own life the way she thought was best for her. And what had come of it?

"Sometimes we are forced to do things we'd rather not," she said. Her tone was gentle. He had a point after all.

"But I can't!" Ned's voice was no longer strong and he turned his head away. "Don't you see, I can't! I have to leave, get out of the country now! I won't be drafted!"

He turned back to her and their eyes met. She was shocked to see tears in his. How terrible war was when it took the best, the strongest of their young men for a cause the boys did not even understand. Why? Who was responsible? Had mankind progressed no further than this? Was violence the only solution to political problems? Had man learned nothing from the horrors of the last war that they were willing to enter into another senseless massacre? The weapons only became more powerful and destructive. Along any street in the city there were constant reminders that they lived on the edge of disaster for there were the common signs directing people to "shelters" everyone hoped would never be used. But draft evaders were considered a disgrace. They were despised for their cowardice. Could she possibly condemn her own son for his fear?

"I have to have money to go away. Father won't advance me any. My allowance is next to nothing and I haven't been able to save. What can I do? Help me, Mother. Help me, please. I can pay you back. It will just be a loan for only a few years. Please, Mother."

He was begging pitifully, shamefully.

She looked into those frightened, troubled eyes. Once she had sacrificed everything for the privilege of keeping him near her. Now it might be a matter of keeping him alive. "But where would you go? You'd never be allowed to come back, would you? You'd lose your citizenship. Ned, you can't run away. It isn't that easy."

"Isn't it? You did it."

"Oh, Ned, that was long ago and I'm not sure anything was solved by running away. If you only knew! There must be another way."

Ned shook his head. His full, sensuous lips, so like Edward's were pressed into a stubborn line.

"No, there isn't. If you don't help me, I'll go anyway myself. Perhaps you'll never hear from me again."

Was it an idle threat? She wasn't sure. She was trying to concentrate on Ned's problem, but thoughts of Joanna kept interfering. She didn't know what to do. If only Geoffrey were here.

"Ned, let's have some lunch and think about this calmly. Why—why, there's your Uncle Monty in Washington. And Geoffrey. They'll surely know of some other way."

"Uncle Monty! Geoffrey!" He laughed bitterly. "Two military men! I'd jump out a window before I went to them. What would they do for me, but insist I do my bit. 'Yes, sir, my boy, do your bit. It's difficult while it lasts. Of course, they may bring you back dead or maimed for life, but a man must do what he must do.' "

His imitation of his Uncle Monty's blustery manner was very good, but his tone was close to hysteria.

He shook his head.

"Well, at least I see now where I stand."

"What do you see?"

"That you're like all the others." He stood up, pushing his chair back with such violence that it crashed against the terrace doors and tipped to one side. He came and stood over her, leaning his hands on either side of the arm chair, his face close to hers. The dark eyes were wild and the mouth curved bitterly.

"To hell with you, Mother. To hell with you and all the rest of them."

He whirled around and slammed out of the apartment.

287

Terrified, she ran after him. Marlene caught up with her in the front foyer and held her back.

"Don't be a fool!" she said. "Let the bastard go!"

"Go? Go where? Marlene, I may never see him again."

"Don't you believe it. This is all part of the act. He'll be back. I know Ned."

She shook Marlene's arm away.

"You don't understand." By the time she reached the elevators, it was too late. She turned back to see Marlene standing in the doorway, her arms folded, her face a mask of disapproval.

She rushed past her and back to her room. She opened the locked drawer of Geoffrey's desk and took out the bank books that were kept there. She'd just have time to make it to the bank. It was the only thing to do. He was pleading for his life. How could she deny him?

She sent the money to Princeton, assuming he'd go back there, but the bank draft was returned within a week. He was gone.

Geoffrey was furious when he discovered what she had done.

"Ten thousand dollars! Ten thousand dollars! Were you out of your mind? Draft evasion is a crime and you would have been an accomplice to it. I can't get over it, Sybil. How you could even have considered, much less carried the idea through?"

"I—I couldn't do anything else. He was desperate. You should have seen him." She tried to defend herself. "I didn't know what to do. Psychologically he never would have made it. I'm sure of that."

"If that were true, the Army would have found out about it. Not everyone is fit for combat. They know that. They're not heartless, you know. Mistakes are sometimes made, but the military are not heartless, nor basically stupid. I've never known you to act so irrationally."

She felt angry and guilty by turns. One thing she was sure of, there were no easy answers.

Three weeks passed without a word from Ned. Edward, in an effort to locate his son, had actually gone to

Geoffrey's office and announced that the boy had made off with over five thousand dollars from the office safe.

"Ashford acted as though he expected me to supply the missing funds," Geoffrey added indignantly. "You simply have to face the fact that the boy's turned out badly. He never was much good. I should have guessed that the first time I met him when we visited that mockery of a school, remember?"

"I remember that you said Ned reminded you a lot of yourself," she said unhappily.

"Yes, but, God, I had some sense of decency! I'd be the last man to advocate war. I'd hate like hell to have to send our son, but there is such a thing as honor. Ned's a thief and a coward."

"Don't say that! You have no right, no right at all. He's only a boy and—and he's afraid. Is it a crime to be afraid?"

"Yes, if you can't face your responsibilities! Who the hell does he think he is?"

She shook her head and said nothing. It seemed to her that she had failed miserably as a parent. As the weeks went by she was more and more convinced of this. Ned had disappeared, apparently left the country and Joanna, with substantial financial help from Geoffrey, had taken an apartment with her friend, Regina. Arthur had been right. She never did come home again.

"She'll be back," Geoffrey predicted. "She just needs time." The day she went to Philadelphia she learned that Alfred was seeing her against his parents' wishes. He went up to Barnard to find her. When she came home that night she talked to Geoffrey. He told her where her mother had gone and what she had tried to do. She listened, but it made no difference. She simply packed her things. She wanted to get an apartment and he promised to help her. She didn't want to see her mother then and she asked that Sybil not try to see her. Geoffrey thought it would be best to leave her alone for awhile.

Leave her alone for awhile? Just like that. She was out of it. But what did Joanna really think? Did she under-

289

stand what had happened? Shouldn't she know more about the Skinners? Shouldn't Sybil try to explain why she hadn't warned her? Did she know how much her mother wanted to help her? She wanted to see the girl herself, talk with her, make her understand that there was nothing she wouldn't do, if she could. How could she possibly leave her alone as Geoffrey suggested?

But it soon became obvious that she had no choice.

Geoffrey saw Joanna regularly, but she wouldn't even speak to her mother on the phone. Sybil lived from day to day in a lethargy, a kind of hopeless stupor. Nothing interested her. She spent long hours in bed sleeping or simply staring into space. She refused social invitations, begging off at the last minute and sending Geoffrey on alone. She completely neglected Arthur. Marlene had to step in and take over there. It was too much of an effort for her to do anything. All she could think about was the fact that she had apparently failed both Ned and Joanna.

Then Claudia Barrett called.

"Sybil, darling, I imagine you thought I died. Well, hardly. I've been everywhere, to London, to Beverly Hills, even to the Bahamas. But I've rounded everybody up at last. And we're all meeting at Twenty-One at one today. You must come. It will give you a real *feeling* for the production. See you then."

She hung up without waiting for a reply. Sybil didn't intend to go. She even tried to call her back, but received nothing but a busy signal. She hadn't even read the play. What had happened to it? She didn't remember seeing it since that awful morning she and Geoffrey had that terrible fight. That seemed so long ago. She thought she remembered seeing it on the floor. And then she found it in the drawer of the night table. She idly flipped open the manuscript and then surprisingly she found herself interested. It was eleven by her bedside clock. An hour later she'd read half the play and was very favorably impressed. It was a clever comedy about an aging but still attractive actress whose son-in-law falls deeply enamoured with her or his dream of her. The actress realizes that she is hardly indifferent to the boy, but fights her inclination in a humorous way.

The part was perfect for Claudia Barrett and the lines sophisticated and clever. For the first time in weeks she found herself thinking of something other than her own failures. She could imagine the clothes the heroine would wear. With the songs and large production numbers there were ample opportunities for costume changes, glamorous, striking costumes!

When she finally began to dress for lunch she told herself it would be just to meet the cast and to see Claudia and tell her regretfully in person that she couldn't consider doing the designing, that Geoffrey had been adamantly opposed to the idea. But it would be interesting, fun really to meet so many theater people.

"Well, thank God! You look like yourself again."

Marlene approved of Sybil's lime green linen suit and smart, wide-brimmed hat.

"You're too thin, though. You'd better start eating again. What's up anyway?"

Once she began to tell Marlene about it, the whole idea seemed more exciting than ever.

"A musical! She wants you to do the costumes for a Broadway musical! Oh, honey, do you know what this could mean? We'd be on our way again, right back in the mainstream. God, how I've been hoping for this! It's just what you need, what we both need."

She hugged her excitedly, knocking the hat askew.

"Wait a minute, please, Marlene! I'm just going today as a favor. I—I'm not going to accept."

"Not going to accept? Are you crazy? Something like this gets dumped in your lap and you're not going to accept?" She stared incredulously at her. "Why not?"

She turned away.

"It's Geoffrey. He won't hear of it. When I first told him a month ago, he was furious."

For a moment Marlene said nothing.

"That was a month ago," she observed finally. "A lot has changed since then."

"Yes, but I don't think Geoffrey's attitude has changed."

"You never can tell. It might have. He's been worried about you."

"I know."

"Well, then, it could be a possibility. If I were you, I'd keep an open mind. I don't mind telling you, I'm itching to get back in."

"Oh, Marlene, I know that. I think you should. Maybe something can be worked out with Claudia. I'll speak to her about it, if you like," she offered.

Marlene shrugged and the excitement left her eyes. "You can if you want, but it's not me she wants, it's you. Look! All I ask is that you keep an open mind. Don't be so quick to say no. Will you?"

"All right, Marlene."

She avoided her eyes. What Marlene was saying only echoed her own thoughts. But she had to think of Geoffrey. Her marriage was precious to her. For the past month Geoffrey had been the soul of kindness. She needed that now—needed him to lean on. "That's what husbands are for," he'd said.

Yes, thought Sybil. Yes!

And then she found herself caught up in the excitement of meeting Claudia and her friends and their euphoria communicated itself to her. Twenty-One seemed to be filled with theater people, but it wasn't hard to locate Claudia, who had evidently been watching for her.

"There she is! There she is!"

The rich voice carried across the dining room as she singled her out among the guests. "Harry, bring her over here, she looks positively lost." Harry obediently escorted her to his wife's side.

She allowed herself to be petted, flattered, introduced, and praised and found she enjoyed every minute of it. Everyone talked at once and no one really listened to anyone else at all. She was confused by the number of new names and could not for the life of her connect them with the proper faces, except for one, the young playwright. What a surprise that was! She knew him instantly and she could see he was pleased.

"Well, I wondered if we'd ever meet again." He took her hand and looked deep into her eyes. He had dark hair and yet his eyes were light, so pale a blue they seemed to have no color at all. His gaze was arresting.

"Hello, Carter!"

She smiled up at him. She hadn't seen Carter Hayes in three years, not since he'd been the cause of the jealous argument between Geoffrey and herself. He seemed older, even more attractive, but there was still that charming modesty.

"You remembered my name," he said. "I was afraid you wouldn't know me at all."

"Nonsense," she said. "I even remember what you said about Chekhov. You said he was too dated for modern audiences."

"And you said he was timeless," he reminded her. "I'm terribly flattered that you do remember."

He sat beside her, keeping her hand in his and she could feel again the excitement she'd first felt the evening they'd met. Carter Hayes was younger than she, by about eight years, she judged. He was intelligent and flatteringly attentive. He listened to everything she said with profound interest and asked questions as though he valued her opinion. Geoffrey, she knew, would be just as upset by Carter's attentions now as he was when they'd first met at that supper club.

It was *his* play! How terrible that she hadn't even noticed the author's name! She had skimmed so quickly through those first pages that morning. Then she'd been feeling listless and useless. But now—

"Well, what did you think of it?" He raised his brows quizzically and he looked a bit anxious.

She knew she must be careful about what she said. He looked so vulnerable.

"I've only read half. I can't wait to finish the rest."

"Tell me more," he said, grinning boyishly. "That's music to a writer's ears."

293

"I discovered him," Claudia announced, suddenly turning her attention to them.

"We discovered each other," he said. "I wrote the play for Claudia Barrett."

"And you won't be sorry! We'll have a smash on our hands. You'll see. The entire production will be a smash and a joy to the eye with Sybil's costumes. Did you bring anything along? Sketches or anything?"

She realized then that she'd waited too long to explain. She should not have come at all. Claudia was taking for granted that she was accepting the offer. How could she tell her now? And did she really want to? That was the real question.

Claudia simply launched into a discussion of her own ideas on costuming. Sitting at her table, Sybil realized she was in the midst of people she'd only read about or seen in the theater or the movies. There was the moment when a silver-haired gentleman responded to her gasp of recognition and smiled directly at her. Delighted, she smiled back for she felt she knew him. Only afterwards did she realize he was Grant Bremmer, a musical comedy star she'd fallen in love with years ago in Philadelphia. Claudia fed her excitement at meeting these star-touched show people. She pointed out directors, actors, and writers, calling to them across the room, insisting upon introducing her as a dear friend and a most talented designer. She was flattered and found that she very much liked the attention suddenly showered upon her. It made her feel real and important and, best of all, needed.

By the time she was riding home in the cab she had half begun to believe in her own part in the production. Perhaps she'd been too quick to write it off. Perhaps Geoffrey could be persuaded. Oh, she would persuade him! Suddenly there was nothing that she wanted more than to do this play.

He came in very late. He'd gone to a dinner party without her again. She stayed up to finish the play and was awake when he arrived.

"Well," he said. "You look chipper for this hour of the

294

night, or should I say morning." He bent and kissed her forehead. "Everyone missed you."

"Did you enjoy yourself?" she asked.

"It was the usual. The women ended up in their corner and—well, I did have an interesting go-round with Paul Marsden about the Lafferty case. You know it could go as far as the Supreme Court?"

"Who's Paul Marsden? Do I know him?" she asked.

"Oh, I don't think so. He's one of the Harvard wonders we have clerking for us. Quite bright and well-informed, as Harvard wonders go."

Geoffrey sat down on the edge of the bed and began to talk excitedly.

"I'd like to have that chance to bring the case before the highest court, not just for the prestige, but because an important point concerning individual liberty is at stake. It's time the courts recognized that."

She listened with attention. Lately Geoffrey had taken to telling her about his interest in the changes taking place in the courts. She was pleased and flattered that he did this. She thought she had some very pertinent comments of her own to make, but he seldom gave her an opportunity to express them, though when he did he was almost always impressed. He seemed to run true to form here, too. He acknowledged her ability to assess a problem and recognize the basic point of difficulty. But he never liked her to join in these erudite discussions at parties, no more than he liked to see women lawyers in the courtroom. He always found some flaw in their approach to any case. As far as he was concerned, women did not belong in the profession. Even informal discussions were out of bounds for them. She wondered what exciting topic the women had found to discuss at the party, their children and private schools no doubt. What Geoffrey could not seem to understand was that women might have interests outside the home. What would happen if she told him now where she had been today? He seemed pleased with himself and in a particularly tolerant mood. Perhaps she could broach the subject of her own need to be creative, to have something vital and interesting as a part of her life, too.

But she could not bring herself to do this and risk disrupting this period of comparative tranquility in their marriage. He never once complained of having to go to parties alone while she was depressed. He had not, since the very first, chided her about Ned. He gave her cheerful, hopeful reports of Joanna, reassuring her, when she had lost hope.

He seemed to want to make their marriage work as much as she did. Lately he'd been more affectionate. There were kisses, caresses, and other little signs of affection. But how did he really see her? Who was the person behind Sybil Kempton, wife and mother? She felt somewhat like a pampered pet.

The loss of her father, Ned's desertion, and Joanna's refusal to see her made her need for Geoffrey stronger than ever. She accepted her role without protesting. She was afraid to give up what she had for something that might not last. And so she said nothing about Claudia and the afternoon at Twenty-One. But she could not forget it and she put off calling Claudia and telling her the truth.

She never deliberately planned the deception. She never wanted to fall into that trap again and yet she did. She even told Marlene she wasn't going to do the play. Marlene had been disappointed, but she understood.

"You're going through a bad time now. I know. You wouldn't want to create another problem. Well, I'm just sorry for your sake. It could have helped take your mind off things."

That, in effect, was exactly what it did do. It began as something to occupy her thoughts. For the next week during the long, idle hours of her days, she worked on sketches for the play. Just for fun, she told herself. When she was concentrating on her designs for Claudia's wardrobe, she had little time to think of anything, even her daughter. Twice she dialed Joanna's number just to hear the girl's voice. She needed to know Joanna was all right, needed to know she was there. What the poor child must be suffering! How desperately she wanted to help!

Joanna did nothing more than say hello. The moment she recognized her mother's voice, she broke the connection. The experience was shattering and after the second time she knew that Geoffrey was right and she simply would have to wait for Joanna to come around on her own. Would that day ever come?

She lived with the pain and despair only a mother who has lost a child can know. She drowned herself in her work, exhausting herself in a fever of creativity.

She began to go out to museums with sketchbook and crayons to get ideas from paintings. She liked the ultra-feminine dress of Renoir's women and found they inspired her most. Marlene guessed what she was doing and seemed pleased, but she said nothing until she actually saw the work.

Sybil spread the sketches out on bed, carpet, chaise, and desk in her room and called Marlene in. She was as anxious as if the designs were to be used. Of course, they were not, but she wondered if she had lost her touch. To her the gowns were exciting. What would Marlene think?

There were so many costume changes that her ideas had to range as widely as they would for a new collection. There was a cocktail dress with a slim skirt and bouffant panels. The neckline was open and wide in a cuff around the bosom like the bodice in a painting she'd seen. Leather was now fashionable and she'd used a leather vest in a stunning sports outfit with tapered Edwardian trousers. There were smart tailored sheaths and little dresses with beautifully decorated sweaters to be made up in brilliant colors. There were bouffant skirts for more festive scenes.

She stood back and watched Marlene study them critically. She seemed surprised by the amount of work Sybil had done in so short a time. She said nothing until she had examined every one. Sybil found she was literally holding her breath. She felt as flushed and excited as a schoolgirl waiting for the results of an exam. Marlene's first remark was a terrible letdown.

"What are you going to do with them?"

"Do with them? Why—I— Nothing! It was just the problem, the challenge, I suppose. And I enjoyed doing them. Oh, Marlene!" She caught her friend's hand. "Are they any good?"

"You have to ask? Don't you know? They're knockouts, every one! What a shame nobody's ever going to see them but you and me! What a waste!"

"You think Claudia would really like them?" she asked uncertainly. She felt desperate for Marlene's reassurance.

"Are you kidding? She'd be crazy not to."

Until that moment, she wasn't sure what she would do with the sketches. But having come so far, it seemed a sin to turn back. She'd give the sketches to Claudia. Marlene could work on the actual production, finalizing details, but she herself would have nothing to do with it. That was the solution. The sketches would be a gift and Geoffrey need not know anything about them. She wouldn't be taking on a job. She wouldn't even be accepting money from Claudia, but she would have the satisfaction of creating and seeing her work on Broadway. She brought the sketches to Claudia the next day.

"You're mad! Positively mad!"

She couldn't believe Sybil's proposition, but she loved the designs, wanted to see more, and wanted her to start work on actual production at once.

"We'll set up a studio here for you at my hotel. Hire anyone you like, but you'll have to supervise. I can imagine the disaster we'd have on our hands with anyone else in charge. You'll have to select the fabrics and make last minute changes. No, Sybil, I want you. If you're going to insist on keeping this secret, then go ahead. I won't give you away. With Geoffrey out all day and sometimes far into the night it should be easy. I won't take no for an answer. There'll be a check in the mail tomorrow morning. I'm putting you on retainer."

She was adamant and Sybil wavered. She'd been to

several of the preliminary rehearsals, been buoyed again by the excitement of the theater. The truth was she didn't want to withdraw. She went home and told Marlene the news.

"Oh, honey, I've been hoping, praying! It's the smartest thing you ever did." She grinned broadly.

"I couldn't do it without you, Marlene. You'll help, won't you?"

"Are you kidding? Try to keep me away." She rubbed her hands together gleefully. "This is going to be real good for you. You're even beginning to sound like your old self again."

Efficient and confident as usual, Marlene began to make plans for the actual management of the gowns' production. "I'll look up the best contacts we had. Somebody will still be around. You leave all that to me."

She paused in her planning and looked at her almost shyly.

"It's like starting all over again, isn't it?"

Sybil smiled and nodded. Marlene's enthusiasm had infected her.

"Yes, it is!"

"And this time the sky's the limit," Marlene predicted, excitement mounting. "The sky's the limit."

She didn't have the heart to discourage her, not then. She didn't have any plans beyond Claudia's play. Really she didn't have any right to that either and the secrecy plagued her.

In the weeks that followed, she was out a good deal of the time. She'd forgotten how busy she'd always been when she was working or how satisfying her work was. Often she was out in the evenings. Claudia and her entourage were night people. They seldom rose before noon and Sybil began to follow their example, often coming in very late at night, even after Geoffrey had returned from dinner meetings. The odd thing was he didn't seem to mind at all. He accepted her explanation of volunteer work and the new friends she was making. The lies seemed to come so easily, too easily, and Geoffrey wanted to believe her.

"I'm glad you're getting out more and thinking of something other than Joanna and Ned. They have their own lives to lead and so do we. It's probably the hardest truth a parent must accept."

Yes, she thought. But how many parents were so bitterly parted from their children? No one had heard from Ned in two months, not even his father, who continued to blame her for the boy's behavior. Presumably he'd left the country as he said he would. But where was he? Was he well? Was he happy? Would she ever see him again? At least Joanna was nearby and she never ceased to hope that eventually the girl would come to her. In June, Geoffrey learned that young Alfred Skinner planned to waive his academic deferment and go into the Army.

"Joanna's terribly upset. He's asked to be assigned to Korea," he said.

"Asked! Oh, Geoffrey! Those poor, miserable children."

For several days she thought she couldn't bear the burden of her own guilt. She had chosen to bring Joanna into the world without a father. She had sent Jonathan away. It was her choice that so affected Joanna and Alfred, who wanted nothing more than to be themselves and to love each other.

Marlene blamed society and the rigid mores by which the Skinners and their circle of friends lived.

"Goddamn snobs! It would serve them right if that kid of theirs never comes back," she said viciously. "But don't you worry about Joanna. She's stronger than you think. She's getting along just fine."

She looked at her friend closely and saw at once what she had not seen before and what Marlene had carefully kept from her.

"You've seen Joanna! You've been seeing her, Marlene! And you never told me," she accused. She felt a sudden, furious surge of jealousy. Geoffrey and Marlene! Marlene, whom Joanna felt unworthy of even meeting

300

Alfred Skinner! Marlene was permitted contact with Joanna.

Marlene shook her head unhappily.

"I never meant to—to do anything behind your back. It just seemed easier if you didn't know. I mean, she's only a kid yet. She needs someone. I—I've been going over about once a week just to make sure everything's all right. They have fixed the place up real nice. That Regina always was a nice, sensible kid. They have four rooms, two tiny bedrooms, but it looks like a palace compared to that dump we had in the Village. Don't get upset! I talk now and then about you when she lets me. And, well, someday she will come back. Honest! I believe it. In the meantime—" Marlene opened Sybil's portfolio of sketches and began concentrating on them, obviously too painfully aware of her friend's emotions to go on.

Only with tremendous effort did she overcome her feelings. Marlene hadn't meant any harm. It probably was better that she hadn't known. Isn't that exactly what she was doing with Geoffrey, keeping something from him that would only upset him if he knew? Still, it seemed to her she was being left out of her own family, punished over and over again for something that happened so long ago she could hardly remember why she had acted as she did.

At least her relations with Geoffrey were going along smoothly. There were no more angry outbursts or unreasonable accusations. Their marriage was far from perfect, but they seemed compatible, and Geoffrey in the past months had developed a kind of inner contentment with her. They seldom made love, but Sybil, who had in the past found this frustrating, was now so busy with her work on Claudia's play she hardly noticed. She made no overtures herself and this might have accounted for his calm good spirits, though she didn't think of that at the time.

Summer came and she accepted Mrs. Kempton's invitation to bring Arthur for a month's visit in August to the Cape Cod home. She had completed her designs to Claudia's apparent satisfaction and there seemed no reason not to go. They hadn't taken a real vacation all together since Arthur was a baby. The boy was delighted.

"This year I'm going to learn to sail. I'm old enough now. Grandmother said last year that if I could swim well enough this would be the year!" His eyes glowed with anticipation and he talked of nothing else. He went to the library and took out stacks of books on sailing over which he pored every evening.

Even Geoffrey was enthusiastic and spent time with Arthur discussing his favorite sport. It was a pleasure for her to watch them looking over the books together. Polite and formal as ever. Arthur gazed up at his father with admiring eyes and Geoffrey patiently instructed his son with obvious pleasure and an attitude of surprise at the boy's unusual intelligence and understanding. She thought sailing might finally bring them into real contact with each other.

And then at the last moment, to Arthur's deep disappointment, Geoffrey didn't go with them.

"Remember I spoke to you about the possibility of my presenting oral arguments before the Supreme Court?"

"Of course I do! Oh, Geoffrey, do you mean there's a chance?"

"Every chance," he said proudly.

"How wonderful! But that wouldn't be until the fall, would it?"

"Darling! How naive you are!" he said hugging her. "It takes months of preparation. But don't you worry. I'll get off for a few weekends. Perhaps even a whole week. You go. You enjoy yourself. Mother's bought a horse for you. You can ride again. I'll expect you to come back all tanned and healthy and more beautiful than ever." He kissed her and seemed to think that would make everything all right.

If anything, she was more disappointed than Arthur. She'd been looking forward to this vacation, to having Geoffrey to herself. And when he was all relaxed and happy, she planned to tell him everything and make him understand just how much her going back to work meant

302

to her. But that was not to be and it worried her. When would she be able to tell him?

The major portion of her work on the designs was completed, but Marlene's work had just begun and she was relishing it, though she'd be left behind in the city. She planned to move right into a part of the suite Claudia had taken at the Commodore.

"It will be like a vacation for me," she said. "Room service for every meal and all free!"

Sybil felt almost guilty about leaving at all. Perhaps Marlene might need her. And what of Geoffrey? Wasn't her place with her husband? She'd be gone a whole month. But her mother-in-law was anxiously expecting her and Arthur really wanted to go.

They took the train, leaving the city physically and spiritually behind. Being on the beach every day was like living in another world. She did ride every morning on the hard-packed sand. She soon felt a part of the endless blue skies and the eternal sea. It gave her a new perspective and she grew calm and hopeful about her life. Even reunions with Ned and Joanna did not seem impossible here. She and Arthur tanned beautifully and Mrs. Kempton, who hardly ever ventured beyond the terrace, pronounced them both the joy of her life.

"I watch you jealously from the windows. Two such marvelously attractive creatures and you both belong to me!" she was fond of saying.

Arthur spent his mornings learning to sail at the yacht club and his afternoons on the beach with his mother.

Though Geoffrey never did find the time to join them, he called several times a week and spoke at least part of the time with Arthur about his sailing, to the boy's immense satisfaction.

"Thank God Geoffrey found you, Sybil," Mrs. Kempton said.

She had changed little since they had first met. She was, of course, confined to her wheel chair, but her face never lost that lively, interested expression which had so impressed Sybil from the first.

303

"You've been so good to him. I hoped someday a beautiful, sensitive woman like you would arouse in him the devotion I always knew was there."

She looked up at her mother-in-law quizzically. They were having tea on the terrace overlooking their private beach and watching Arthur race his grandmother's Irish setter over the sands.

Mrs. Kempton laughed lightly at Sybil's expression. "I don't mind telling you I worried about my second son. It's no secret he was a playboy and seemed destined to throw away his life on things that did not really matter. But then he found you, a loving and very beautiful woman. Still! Any man worth his salt would find you irresistible. How old are you now?" She shook her head and held up her hand. "No, don't say it! No one would ever guess. You look as young as you did the day I met you. I think you have the kind of skin that ages very slowly. And in those yellow shorts you look like a teenager. Slim legs, perfect figure! My dear, does Geoffrey know how fortunate he is? Probably not or he'd have moved heaven and earth to be here at least one weekend. Do you miss him terribly?"

"Yes," she admitted. She was glad they only had another week here. She did want to be with Geoffrey. Ned, Joanna, Claudia Barrett, the production of the costumes, all the turmoil of the past year had been erased by the pleasant, restful weeks by the sea. She thought she was ready to go back and be a wife to her husband again. Perhaps they'd needed this time apart, she and Geoffrey, to see, as Mrs. Kempton put it, how fortunate they were.

She was determined to tell him the truth about her work as soon as she got back. They would have a long talk. She'd make him see that she needed this outlet to add meaning and dimension to her life.

They returned on Saturday of the Labor Day weekend. They took an early train and wired Geoffrey their arrival time. She was surprised when he did not meet the train. She called the apartment, but there was no answer. They waited for him nearly an hour before taking a cab home.

Perhaps she should have realized then that something

304

was very wrong. It was only when they got home and found everything closed as if it had been that way for days that she began to be uneasy. She hadn't spoken to Geoffrey on the phone for over a week. Mrs. Norris told her he was working day and night. Still, he should have returned her call. Now there was no one home, not even the housekeeper, and no note to explain his absence.

"We should have stayed another week," Arthur said. To him the city seemed deserted and he had been looking forward to seeing his father who was nowhere in evidence.

"School, darling, school. We have to get you ready for the fall term." She rumpled his hair affectionately.

He grinned sheepishly. "I wouldn't mind missing the first week or two. I'm hungry, are you?"

"We'll raid the refrigerator," she promised. "But we ought to change our clothes first. Come on. I'll race you. Last one in the kitchen is a monkey's uncle."

She was halfway to her own room when she heard Geoffrey come in.

"Father!"

Arthur raced down the hall to greet him.

"Wait till you hear about the sunfish Grandmother bought me! It was a present for doing so well at sailing school. I never expected—"

"Where is your mother?"

Geoffrey's tone was curt. He cut the boy's spontaneous recital off without bothering to make any kind of pleasant comment over the news he'd just been given. She could imagine Arthur's face. He must feel crushed. How could a father be so insensitive? She strode rapidly toward them. Something must be bothering him. Even he wasn't usually that impatient.

He heard her coming and told Arthur to go into the study.

"Turn on the TV if you like. But don't come out until I call you. Do you understand?"

"Yes, sir."

He went, shoulders drooping.

"Oh, Geoffrey! How could you? He was so anxious to see you. No wonder you feel you can't get along with him. You can't even meet him halfway. That's no way to handle him."

"Really? And you're an expert at handling people, aren't you? At handling me, for instance?"

He looked at her with icy blue eyes and she felt the chill of disaster, but she walked calmly past him and sat down in the living room.

"What's wrong?" Really she didn't have to ask. She knew. Somehow he'd found out.

He followed her. She could feel his anger, feel the way he was holding himself in check.

"Well," he said at last. "Don't you have anything to say at all?"

If only she had told him herself!

"How? How did you find out?"

"How did I find out?" he exploded. "Will you look at yourself sitting there so primly, hands folded in your lap. Don't you know what you've done to me? To us? Why? Why? You knew I didn't want you to get involved with Claudia. I told you that quite clearly. You have a career as my wife. Isn't that enough for you?"

He began pacing the room.

"And don't give me that wounded look. I'm the one who's been wronged, not you. When that letter come ten days ago, I thought I'd lose my mind. I didn't believe it at first. But there it was in black and white, a check for thousands of dollars and a plea for you to hurry back to work the minute you returned. Back to work! Back! That meant you had been at work. You'd been deceiving me for months."

"I meant to tell you," she cried. "I—I wanted to. Oh, Geoffrey, can't we talk about this calmly. Let me tell you how much I've enjoyed being back at work again. Let me tell you what it means to me."

She went to him, holding out her arms in supplication. He turned on her angrily.

"My God! What it means to you! What about what

306

it means to me? Claudia Barrett is my client, if you'll remember. You've made me a laughing stock in her eyes, allowing her to be the central character in this intrigue. She made me sound like an emotional imbecile in that letter. 'Darling, Sybil, when will Geoffrey come around so we can use your name? I want everyone to know my designer,'" he mimicked her voice. "'He's such a dear, but so Victorian in his thinking!'"

"You shouldn't have opened a letter addressed to me," was all she could think to say.

"Oh, don't be a fool! I'm not in the habit of opening my wife's mail. I thought it was for me, that there'd been a mistake. She's my client! And now evidently she thinks she's your client, too. Well, I won't have it! I won't. You'll tell her at once. You're through. You don't need a job. You're well taken care of by your husband and you have plenty to do right here. You're not interested!"

"But I *am* interested. That's just the point. I am interested. I want this job." Her voice was clear and firm. It was important that he know the truth. "I don't think you're being fair to me."

"Fair? Look who's talking about fair! You call running out of here behind my back and consorting with that— that woman, when you knew how I felt about it— You call *that* fair?"

"I didn't say that. I said you weren't being fair to me now. Will you for once listen to me? Please. Even the worst criminal has the right to be heard. Where's your sense of justice?"

That got to him. He could hardly deny her a hearing, but it was obvious from the beginning, from the way he sat puffing angrily on cigarette after cigarette, that he was not prepared to be an impartial listener. She thought she exhausted every possible argument. She told him of her loneliness, her depression over Ned and Joanna. She tried to describe her need in terms he would understand. After she was through all he said was, "I take it you are determined to continue with this project."

"I won't walk out on Claudia now. It's a little late for

307

that. Besides, I want to stay. You asked for the truth," she said before he could interrupt. "I enjoy my work and—and I'd like to continue, perhaps in some other way in the future."

"Then your future has nothing to do with me. Nothing! Do you understand that? Think about it, Sybil."

It was the last thing he said before he stalked out of the apartment. He was off to his club, his sanctuary. Whenever he wanted to punish her, he went to his club. Probably he'd been staying there since he'd opened Claudia's letter. That's why the air in the apartment had seemed stale. The place had been closed for days. He'd only come to issue his ultimatum, not to listen or try to understand. In a day or two he'd come back and expect her to give in completely to his way of thinking. What gave him the right to have everything his way?

For the first time she knew she couldn't accept that any longer. She was more than a wife and mother. She was a person with needs of her own. She didn't want to lose Geoffrey. Her marriage was precious to her. But if being his wife meant she was to have no identity of her own, well she would not be able to go on that way.

She was angry when he left and she came to a quick decision. She sent Arthur down to wait for her in the lobby.

"Are we going to dinner? Is Father coming, too?" he asked doubtfully.

How much of the argument had he heard? The walls in the apartment were not sound proof.

"No, you're father won't be coming. Run down, darling. Tell Bert we want a cab."

She wanted him out while she gathered together some of the things they'd need. She didn't want to answer the inevitable questions while she packed.

Just before she left she thought of leaving a note, but decided against it. If he really wanted to find her, that was up to him. She stood in the doorway and looked through the foyer at the spacious living room of her home. If she left now, would she be able to come back? Would Geoffrey want her back? She might be doing the wrong thing, handling him in the wrong way. He didn't take well to shock treatment. But how could she stay?

She turned resolutely, tears stinging her eyes as she closed the door. The cab was waiting and she sat beside Arthur, willing herself not to look back at the building.

"Mother, what's wrong?"

He put his small, sun-browned hand over hers.

"I—I'm not sure, dear."

He looked puzzled, but did not ask why.

"Where are we going?"

She tried to smile at him through stiff lips.

"We're going to be staying at a hotel for awhile with Aunt Marlene and some friends."

He looked at her with wise old eyes.

"My friend Peter's parents are divorced," he said finally. "He says it's not so bad. He sees his father more now than when they were married."

"Oh, Arthur! Oh, darling!"

She pulled him to her, hugging him close and fighting her tears.

"It doesn't have to be that way. Don't even think about it."

She wished she could believe what she was saying. She wished there were someone to comfort her. Oh, Geoffrey! Geoffrey!

Had she been wrong to marry him in the first place? She had not been madly in love with him, not the way she'd been with Jonathan. But she could remember quite clearly her need to be married and how she promised herself that she would make a good marriage. Affection had deepened into love. But she'd done most of the adjusting. Wasn't that always the way it was in marriage? If so, she wasn't sure now that it should be. They would have to reach some kind of compromise, if she were to be a whole person again. Was she strong enough to do what she must do? She ached to be in Geoffrey's arms again, to know that he loved her. Did he love her? Wouldn't a man who loved a woman try to understand her?

The cab made its way to the Commodore through relatively empty city streets. It was the last holiday weekend of the summer and she realized for the first time that Marlene might be away or at least out. She'd written often about her progress on the costumes and how busy she was, too busy to get up to the Cape. Still, she thought this weekend it would be a miracle to find her in.

But she was. She was sitting alone in her suite, watching television and putting the finishing touches on a salmon colored gown Claudia would wear in the third act.

She took one look at Sybil and called room service for brandy. She sent Arthur down to get a soda at the coffee shop in the lobby.

"My God! What's happened to you?"

"I—Geoffrey and I have—have— Oh, Marlene, I'd like to stay here for awhile."

It was all the explanation she felt she could manage at the moment and Marlene, bless her, understood.

"O.K. O.K. Look, it's none of my business." She held up her hand. "Don't say another word. You want to stay here, they'll find room. Claudia has two floors."

She got the manager on the phone and made the necessary arrangements. When the brandy came, she made her drink it down in one gulp.

"Whatever it is, it can't be as bad as you look. It'll work out. You can't let yourself go to pieces. There's Arthur to think about, you know, and there's work to do. We've got plenty of work. We're opening in New Haven in less than a month. Boy, will Claudia be glad to see you."

Marlene kept up a rapid running commentary describing the many problems that had come up. She seemed to know instinctively that Sybil would break down if she was forced to think of something else. Only that night when she was alone in bed with the door to Arthur's connecting room slightly ajar, did she weep. They were silent sobs for she did not want to awaken and frighten the boy. But her loneliness for Geoffrey was so great she almost weakened and called him at his club. This was to be the night of their reunion. She would have told him every-

310

thing tonight. But even under the best of circumstances, would he have understood?

She slept badly, waking a dozen times before dawn. They had Sunday breakfast in Marlene's suite. Arthur looked subdued, though Marlene did everything she could to make him smile.

"Tell me again about sailing school, Sport. What was that stuff about yawing? Sounds more like mule school to me," she added laughing.

Arthur politely explained the term and described some of his activities, but he looked as though he wanted to run to a corner and cry. She thought she must look the same.

Marlene, on the other hand, looked well. Working day and night seemed to agree with her. She was animated and excited. She looked like a woman who was right where she belonged, organizing, cajoling, directing, creating a smoothly operating team of professionals. She promised to take Arthur to the Central Park Zoo later that day and then to a movie.

"After your mom and me get some work squared away, O.K., Sport?" She grinned at him, lifting his chin so his eyes met hers.

"Work on Sunday?" he asked, looking uncertainly at his mother.

"In show business everyday's a work day."

"Are you in the movies, Aunt Marlene?" he asked with awe.

She laughed. "Not exactly, honey, but that's close. Tell you all about it this afternoon. The TV is in there," she told him, pointing to her bedroom. "Think you can keep busy till lunch time?"

He nodded and stood up. Before he left he came around to his mother.

"I suppose we're not going to see my father today."

"Not today," Sybil said and kissed his forehead. She didn't know what to tell him.

He left without another word.

"Do you feel like talking about it?" Marlene asked.

She shook her head and took a long, shuddering breath.

311

"O.K., then. You feel up to working? You look like hell, you know. Even with that tan you look like hell."

"I'm going to be all right."

Marlene gave her a long, steady look. "Yeah," she said. "Yeah, maybe."

The sitting room had been turned into a workroom. Bolts of fabric lined one wall. In front of the long windows stood a cutting table. She went to the desk and picked up her sketch of the black taffeta cocktail dress. Red arrows pointed to the panels.

"What's wrong with this?"

"Oh, that!" Marlene shrugged. "La Barrett's hips. She's got hips. She diets and exercises religiously, but she's got hips. We're going to have to modify those panels somehow. From the back she looks like a Mack truck in that one. Uh, her description, not mine. I made some suggestions, but she doesn't want to hear it from me. You're the one she wants. I had all I could do to keep her from calling you back home over that one. And she wants to wear red silk pajamas in that bedroom scene with her hips! There's a challenge for you."

Sybil smiled wryly. "Yes, the hips are a problem. Where is Claudia?"

"Out on Long Island at somebody's estate with the rest of the cast. A couple of seamstresses and me were left to hold the fort, as they say. I've been paying the girls double time and they seem happy enough. Everybody will be back tomorrow night."

She was glad. That would give her time to collect herself. Together they could iron out some of the difficulties. They worked most of Sunday and all of Labor Day. Concentrating on her work kept her mind from drifting to Geoffrey all of the time. By late Monday she wondered if he'd been back to the apartment, if he'd found her gone, and what he'd thought then.

On Monday evening they had dinner in the hotel dining room. Arthur had become very interested in what his mother was doing. At first he thought she was drawing pictures. He soon came to understand that she was a dif-

312

ferent kind of artist and he was impressed when Aunt Marlene showed him how a picture was translated into a gown. He was fascinated, too, by the models he'd seen of the sets.

"Will I see the real play when it's ready?" he asked his mother.

"I don't see why not. It will be your first grown-up Broadway play. Just think, you'll have met all the stars beforehand."

"I will?"

"Certainly. That's quite a privilege, isn't it?"

He was impressed and the excitement of the idea seemed to keep his mind off his father temporarily at least. She forced herself to act cheerful for his sake. She thought she was carrying everything off very well until Carter Hayes arrived.

He came in from the bar with several people she recognized as being part of Claudia's production. They must have just gotten in.

"I don't believe it," he said, hurrying across to her. "Sybil!"

She managed to smile for him. He looked so genuinely pleased to see her. He took her hand and gazed at her with those pale blue eyes. He, too, had been away. He looked tanned and rested.

"I feel like an anxious schoolboy. I've been looking forward to your return each day and been bitterly disappointed when you did not come. Sybil, it is good to see you."

She introduced Arthur and he drew up a chair and was perfectly charming to the boy, who was flatteringly impressed when he realized what it was that Carter did.

"We write stories in school," he said. "It's the hardest thing we have to do."

Carter laughed. "Believe it or not, I used to think that, too. But there's a difference between writing what you have to write and writing what you want to write."

When Marlene took Arthur upstairs, they stayed behind to have a drink. They sat for a time in silence in the

313

all but empty dining room. The few waiters on duty lounged against the wall as though they, too, were guests with nothing more pressing to occupy them than casual conversation. There were only two other couples dining in the large room. None of the huge crystal chandeliers was lit. Only the soft glow of candlelight illuminated the tables in use. It was as though they had wandered into a place of half life.

With Arthur gone her resolve to remain cheerful seemed to collapse. The atmosphere was as dismal as she felt. Carter was a perceptive person. It would be useless to try to hide her feelings and she was really too tired to try.

"Can you tell me about it?"

"Do you want to hear?"

She felt suddenly very close to him. They had been brought together here tonight in this almost empty city, joined somehow in a common destiny. What she had not been able to discuss with Marlene, who was a part of the situation, she was able to talk over with a relative stranger. In the weeks she'd been working with Claudia she had been aware of Carter's interest in her. She had always found him attractive. Tonight she found him to be an understanding friend. She told him everything as objectively as she could, hoping he might offer some advice.

For a time afterwards he said nothing and she was calmer than she had been. Talking about the problem did seem to help.

"I thought it might be something like that. I hardly know your husband, but he never struck me as the kind of man who'd be willing to share you with a demanding career. I wonder if I blame him."

"Surely you don't object to women having careers? It doesn't mean I love my husband less."

"I know. I know. It's hard to say how I would behave in a similar situation. Perhaps that's why I haven't married. Some men feel threatened by their wives' careers. They look upon the career as a rival with whom it is impossible to compete, don't you see? And if the woman is successful—" He spread his hands.

She answered in a whisper.

"Are you telling me there's no hope?"

"No, no! I'm telling you what you already know. That it's very difficult. You know as well as I that there is always hope. And you love him. I can see that," he added wistfully.

He took her back to her room. Before he left, he gave her a long look. "You'll make the right decision. Good night, dear Sybil."

The right decision! She did not think there was any further decision for her to make. It was up to Geoffrey now. She was terribly afraid he had already made his choice.

But she was wrong. He arrived three days later in the middle of a hectic scene. Claudia was difficult at any time, but she was particularly restless and critical during fittings.

"Look at the line of this suit, Sybil. It's laughable. I look lopsided. What have they done to your stunning design?"

It was a black suit with a mandarin collar. At the shoulder and the hip were sudden shocks of yellow satin forming a dramatic diagonal line.

"You see! You see what they've done while you've been gone. And the green dressing gown. Surely the train should be tapered. One can hardly move without tripping over it."

She swept about the workroom, picking up gowns, pointing out defects, and dropping the clothes carelessly in a heap, sometimes on the floor. Marlene had all she could do to coax her back to the platform so that whatever she was wearing could be fitted.

Her hairdresser had not yet arrived that morning and the platinum locks were wild. She was simply helpless when it came to doing her own hair or pretended to be. She expected things to be done for her, sacrifices to be made. She never once questioned Sybil's staying at the hotel, assuming arrangements had been made for her own convenience. Nothing mattered now but the production.

"The salmon gown is perfect, especially with that set,

but what about the panels on the cocktail dress? Oh, Sybil! Thank God you're back! I'm surrounded by incompetents when what I'm paying for is genius! We're opening in three weeks! Three weeks!"

Her voice filled the room and sent the two young seamstresses into nervous spasms. They bent their heads diligently over their work. Claudia's mere presence was imposing enough. Her outrage was devastating.

Marlene, on her knees to adjust the hemline, rolled her eyes in mock horror and Sybil spoke soothingly.

"Marlene and I have never missed a deadline yet. There's nothing to worry about, Claudia."

"And, oh, darling, would you do *something* about the ingenue's clothes in the first act? I know they're supposed to be impossible, but good God!"

She assured her that she would look into the problem and was rewarded with one of the star's dazzling smiles.

"Thank God for you, Sybil! Thank God for you! Geoffrey! Geoffrey darling! It's been ages."

The words all seemed to come in one breath and, at first, they seemed meaningless and irrational. But Claudia was gazing with such animated interest towards the door that she had to turn. Geoffrey was there and the sight of him sent a shock through her. She felt her hands trembling and she put them behind her. He'd come. This was what she wanted, wasn't it? He'd come to her.

"Darling Geoffrey!" Claudia left the platform and rushed toward him, throwing her arms about him and kissing him on the mouth.

Marlene stuck the pins she'd been working with back into the cushion on her wrist and swore softly under her breath. Her eyes met Sybil's briefly, but she looked quickly away in embarrassment.

She didn't know how she would feel when she saw Geoffrey again. She did not expect to feel frightened, but she did. She watched him stoically suffer Claudia's affectionate greeting. She had thrown herself at him with such abandon that any wife might have felt a twinge of jealousy. His good manners were impeccable and only his

316

tight-lipped smile betrayed his distaste. Claudia slipped her arm through his.

"You must come have coffee in my suite away from this mayhem. Darling, it's so good to see you again. I thought perhaps you were angry with me."

She pouted prettily.

"Angry with you?" he asked, trying desperately to catch Sybil's eye. But she found she could not look at him directly. Now that he had come she didn't think she was ready for this encounter. She wished she could bolt from the room like a schoolgirl and refuse to see him at all.

He looked tired, but nothing else had changed. There were the same handsome features, the same commanding figure, even the same husbandly appeal to his wife's social aplomb. He wanted her to extricate him from the unpleasant position in which he found himself. It was her duty, his look told her, as though nothing at all had happened.

"Sybil, dear, come along. You didn't tell me Geoffrey knew! Here I've been keeping your part in the production a deep, dark secret," she added accusingly. "Come along both of you."

She began to usher them toward the door and Sybil found she was powerless to do or say anything to stop her. It was Geoffrey who made the move.

"I don't like to seem a bore, Claudia, but I've come to see my wife. We have something rather pressing to discuss. Perhaps another time." He pulled away and left her standing there looking surprised and rather annoyed. One look at Sybil told her there was more to this meeting than met the eye and she quickly reversed her assault, taking on an aspect of generous equanimity.

"Oh, darlings, nothing terribly, terribly serious, I hope. Do take all the time you need. Oh, Sybil, don't forget your meeting with the set designer at two and Geoffrey, dear, don't be such a stranger." She leaned toward him, kissing his cheek and brushing her breast deliberately against his upper arm.

"There's no one in the conference room," she added, as she left.

They went there and only when the door was closed behind them did Geoffrey speak to her. He still held his hat and briefcase in his hand.

"I waited to hear from you," he said.

She wanted to cry, to throw her arms around him, to beg him to take her back, but she walked to the far side of the long polished table. She needed the safety of something solid between them.

"I wanted to—to call," she admitted.

"But you didn't. It's been five days."

"I know."

He sat down opposite her. They must look ludicrous, she thought, sitting opposite one another at this long table. Two people who had shared the same home, the same bed, the same life were meeting like strangers.

"We have to talk, Sybil."

She met his eyes. Yes, they were Geoffrey's eyes, steady and honest. They were not angry now. Was there a spark of understanding there? He'd come to her. That was a good sign, wasn't it?

"I don't know what to say," she told him.

When she looked at him all she could think about was being in his arms, feeling his lips on hers, his body pressed close. She wanted that terribly now, but she knew it wasn't enough. They had to come to terms with their problem.

"I love you, Sybil," he said quietly, gazing at her intently. "Nothing can change that. Even your joining Claudia's troupe cannot change that. It took me awhile to realize it, but I have."

When she said nothing, he sighed.

She was afraid to speak. Her voice would give her away and she'd never know what he'd come to say.

He slammed his fist against the table. Lines deepened in his forehead.

"Damn it, Sybil! Do you know what you've done to me? When I found you'd gone, I nearly lost my mind.

318

What do you want me to say? I love you. I need you. I want you back on your terms. We'll take it one day at a time, only for God's sake, come home," he finished huskily.

His eyes were filled with pain and a desperate longing.

"Oh, Geoffrey!"

Tears streamed down her cheeks. She was trembling with relief and joy. She never thought she'd hear him say those words. She'd almost given up hope. He hated to apologize for anything and seldom admitted to being wrong. What a tremendous effort he had made! Surely that was all that was necessary.

He pushed back his chair impatiently and was beside her, pulling her to her feet, holding her, kissing her. He brushed away her tears and she clung to him. It wouldn't be easy. She knew that, but they'd taken a first step and they loved one another. That's what mattered.

They hardly heard the insistent knocking at the door, but finally it penetrated.

"Madam, Madam Sybil. Can you come?"

Renée one of the young seamstresses always addressed her in this way. She couldn't seem to manage the last name.

Reluctantly he released her, glancing at his watch.

"I suppose it's just as well. I have to be in court. But darling—" He caught her to him again. "I can be home by three. Will you be there?"

She kissed him again and blew him another kiss as she reached the door.

"I'm sure we can both be there by three," she said.

PART FOUR

I

The view from the penthouse suite atop the thirty-fourth floor of Hampton Towers was spectacular. The east and south walls of the living room were floor to ceiling windows that revealed the panorama of the city. On clear nights such as this one in January, 1966, you could see the Verrazano Bridge, a graceful string of lights, a diamond necklace suspended above the black waters of the river.

"Stunning!" Roslynn Stevens, editor of *Woman's Way*, broke away from the crowd of photographers, newsmen, and television people to stand at the windows beside her.

"There's nothing like New York anywhere, is there, Sybil? Especially when you're on top."

"No, there isn't."

Her voice came from some distant place. She was feeling the strain of the past few days. There were the interviews, the television spot, and plans for the testimonial dinner tomorrow. All were taking their toll. The House of Madame Sybil was being honored by *Women's Way* magazine and Sybil herself named the designer of the year.

"You must be numb and I don't blame you," Roslynn was saying. "Your success is as stunning as the view from this room."

Stunning! Probably that was the word to use in describing her success. Even she felt that it was. How much things change and yet how they remain the same!

The view had been just as stunning six years ago when

she and Geoffrey bought the penthouse apartment. But the bridge across the Narrows hadn't been there then. It was 1964 when it was actually opened to traffic. It had only added to the beauty of the city. But what of all the other changes in her life? How many of them had added happiness? Sometimes she wondered what she really wanted from life.

What constituted happiness? Security? Love? She'd thought both were necessary once. Now she had more than security and something less than love.

She saw her dark reflection in the windows against the blackness of the night. It was a clear enough outline, though the features were indistinct, confused by the number of bustling people who had turned her living room into a television studio.

"Once we go, you won't know we've been here at all," the producer promised her. "We're very experienced."

She had every confidence in the television people. They seemed to know just what they were doing. She was much less sure of herself. In the thirteen years since she and Geoffrey had agreed to give their marriage another try, she had found that she was not so certain where her happiness lay or what direction her life should take. She thought her role, like her image in the glass, was confused by the many demands made upon her.

It was hard to keep her own identity in focus. A feeling of near panic seized her now as she tried to see herself clearly amid the confused reflections. It was like a child's game she vaguely remembered playing.

"Don't step on the crack, or you'll break your mother's back."

How studiously she'd avoided cracks in the sidewalk for an entire day! What must she now avoid to remain whole?

She saw Geoffrey come in. He, too, was a dark reflection in the glass and he would have fused with the others and been lost entirely except that he was so tall and his white hair so striking. It didn't make him look older than his fifty-six years, only more distinguished.

At fifty-three she herself was especially youthful. She did nothing to hide her age, though she might easily have done so.

"Why? What's wrong with being fifty-three?" she asked in reply to a recent interviewer's question on that subject. "Why shouldn't a woman look youthful at any age and be proud of it? I have three grown children and I hope one of them will make me a grandmother soon. I'd be very proud to be a grandmother."

Her figure was as lovely as ever and her dark hair frosted with gray. She had good skin and her face was hardly lined at all. She had caused quite a stir at her last fashion show by appearing along with the models in one of her own gowns. She had been reluctant at first to do it, but Marlene persuaded her.

"Give them all something new to talk about in the reviews," she'd said.

It had and favorably so. She'd worn the gown to the party afterwards. Everyone commented that evening on what an attractive couple Madame Sybil and her husband, the prominent attorney, Geoffrey Kempton, made. "Everyone" consisted of some of the biggest names in the communications media because both she and Geoffrey were so well-known in their fields.

If anything, Geoffrey's success was even more stunning than her own because it had happened so quickly. His first book, *Beyond the Letter of the Law*, came out in 1955, two years after his work on the Supreme Court case which gained so much attention because of the landmark decision it produced. She had gone to Washington and been in court every day during the oral arguments. She had never been so proud of her husband. He was quoted in the papers. He was in constant demand for talk shows. The prestige of his name alone attracted important clients to the firm.

It was apparent from the first that his book was a best seller and he was easily persuaded to begin another. They'd bought the condominium penthouse apartment largely from the proceeds of his second book.

325

In those days they'd sit for hours, arms around each other and marvel at the view.

"Can this possibly last?" he'd asked.

"What, the view?" she teased him.

"You know what I mean. Everything! Even my brother treats me with respect. No, no," he corrected himself. "It's more like reverence. I think he actually believes in the possibility of my being named to the High Court one day."

"Don't you?"

He shrugged and then smiled self-consciously.

"The idea has crossed my mind. I find I'm really very ambitious."

"Oh, darling! I'm so very, very proud of you."

She said that over and over again that year, at first simply because she felt it and later because he needed to hear it. Not once had she heard the same words from him.

He was ambitious, compulsively so. It seemed at times he was driving himself beyond endurance.

His ambition was not a simple thing. His sudden drive seemed to stem from competition. He seemed to be trying to keep one step ahead of "Madame Sybil". She hadn't admitted this to herself until recently. Perhaps she'd been too busy and caught up in her own career to notice.

The publicity from Claudia's play encouraged her to re-open the shop with even greater success than before. After the second year Marlene convinced her to expand.

"We can have retail shops in Chicago and Los Angeles. They'll carry dresses with your name on them, not the exclusive models from the custom shop, but moderate priced dresses might be a terrific idea right now. I got some ideas for merchandising."

Marlene had a genius for management. Once they started, there was no holding her back. She'd kept up her contacts in the industry and had been waiting for a chance to get back in.

"For a kid who's been on her own since she was fifteen and never had much schooling to speak of, I'd say I do all right," she was fond of saying.

Marlene had her own penthouse apartment now. She'd gone on a strict diet and taken off thirty-six pounds.

"Fashion and fat don't go together so good. I'm gonna keep it off, even if I have to stay away from the booze and you know how that'll hurt. But we're gonna show them this time, honey. We're gonna show them all."

She looked younger at fifty-eight than she had at forty. With her new figure, some of the old, unconscious flirtatious gestures returned. She had two men very interested in marriage, but she insisted she was considering neither one seriously.

"One of them's a two-time loser. Divorced twice! What do I need to complicate my life for? I like it fine the way things are."

It was an exciting, rewarding life Marlene led, traveling a good deal of the time to make sure all their operations ran smoothly. Twice a year they both went to Paris for the showings, more to keep an eye on trends than anything else. They always stayed at the same hotel and frequented the same restaurants where they became known. Sybil had the respect of many of the French designers, one of whom came without fail each year to her showings.

Two years ago she'd been asked to do a movie. She'd had to spend three months on location in London. She'd known from the beginning how long she'd be gone and begged Geoffrey to join her for at least part of the time.

"London! You want me to go back to London! How can you ask such a thing?" he demanded impatiently. "I should think you'd know better."

"It's hardly a war-torn country any longer. I hate to think we'll be separated all that time."

"There's an easy solution to that. Don't go."

She hadn't been able to answer him right away. She'd been too angry. Suppose she had asked him to give up one of his speaking tours when his first book was just beginning to catch on? What would his answer have been? It always seemed that her career must be viewed as secondary. His was the one that counted. The movie was something she had always wanted to do. She and Marlene

327

had dreamed of it when all they had was a portable sewing machine in a walk-up apartment.

Later she told him about the director and the artistic mood he was trying to develop. She was enthusiastic and hoped she could make him see why.

"I can tell we'll work well together. We see things in much the same way. It's a love story about two terribly sensitive young people. Each scene is like a still life awaiting the magic of motion. It should be a beautiful film, one I want to be part of. He could have asked anyone, but he chose me. Don't you see? It's an honor really."

"You know I find art films pretentious. I like a good, old-fashioned story. I suppose you'll do it no matter what. Oh, go ahead! What's the use of talking? Do what you want. I won't stop you."

She knew he wouldn't. That's what they had agreed. She would have a right to her career without interference. But was that enough? There was no shared joy or satisfaction in her achievement. When she had to travel, he did not actually complain, but she felt his resentment and gradually they seemed to be making less and less contact. They seldom talked seriously and she hardly knew what he was thinking any more.

For two years now, ever since the movie, they hadn't even shared the same room. When she came back from London, he had arranged everything.

"It's better all around, you see. We're both so busy. We don't keep the same hours. It's more practical."

It had been practical, but far from satisfying. She missed her husband, but he gave no sign of missing her. It was then she began to think they'd gone beyond the point of no return. They were married in name only. They still entertained. They were still thought of as a couple by their friends. But there was so little left of their marriage, she sometimes wondered why they bothered with the charade.

"The cameras are ready for the taping, Madame Sybil."

The young assistant director wore a worried look and carried a sheaf of papers covered with detailed notes. He was just beginning to make his way in the world of television and could not afford mistakes.

"You're not nervous, are you?" he asked in a lower, more confidential voice. "Just be perfectly natural. I can tell you'll photograph beautifully."

She smiled and assured him she was not nervous at all. This was her home and even the cameras could not obliterate the familiar surroundings. She was to sit on her own sofa and chat with Roslynn Stevens as she had often done in the past. She saw nothing particularly nerve wracking about accepting the gold plaque honoring her work from her good friend, even if the event was to be telecast later to millions of homes all over the country. She had wanted the award, coveted it for years in fact, as the highest symbol of success. Now that it was hers, she wondered if the cost of achievement was not too great.

The actual taping took only minutes and when it was over the very efficient television people went about packing up their equipment. True to their promise an hour after they left, it would have been difficult to know they'd been there at all.

Roslynn stayed for a drink, but did not linger long. She was a vivacious brunette who never put off what could be done today.

"I've a million things to do before tomorrow night's dinner," she said. "I imagine you'll want to go over your remarks, Sybil. Try them out on Geoffrey. I hear husbands can be the severest critics. I hope someday to find that out for myself when I locate the right man."

She looked wistfully at Geoffrey.

"Why are all the most attractive men married?"

He escorted her to the door and came back carrying his own coat.

"I didn't know you were going out," she said.

"Can't be helped if you want me to make that dinner tomorrow night," he said testily. "You do still want me to be there, I suppose."

She should not have been surprised by the edge his

words had. She went to him, looking up into his eyes. They seemed so distant.

"The dinner would have very little meaning for me without you, Geoffrey. We've come such a long way together."

She wanted him to know that, to think about it. She thought his gaze shifted guiltily. He could not share even this special moment.

"Don't wait up for me. I'll be late," was all he said.

She was alone, more alone than she'd been in years. Tomorrow she'd be the very center of everyone's attention. Her family, all three of her children, her friends and colleagues, all would be with her tomorrow, but tonight she was completely alone. She took one last look at the "stunning" view, which so closely resembled her success, as Roslynn said, and then rang for her housekeeper. She ordered dinner on a tray in her room. Anything else would be too depressing.

She kept herself busy the next day, too busy to think. When Carter Hayes turned up at her studio, she should not have been surprised. The publicity she'd been receiving brought calls and telegrams from old friends everywhere.

He blithely by-passed her secretary and two assistants saying, "No, no! Don't announce me. I want this to be a surprise."

She and Roslynn were going over last minute details for the dinner when he barged in. He closed the door and stood looking past Roslynn at her, a slow smile on his lips.

"You can't imagine how often I've thought of you or how many times I've wanted to write," he said reproachfully.

She had forbidden him to write. He'd made his feelings for her quite clear that fall of '53 and she had been just as open with him.

"I love my husband. I want our marriage to work."

"But we can be friends. Surely we can be friends," he insisted.

"We'll always be friends."

"But you don't want me to write. You don't want to see me again."

"It's better that way for both of us."

"Safer, you mean," he said bitterly. "You won't allow yourself to admit the truth."

The truth he spoke of was the attraction between them, more on his part than on hers. She was too busy that fall trying to prove to Geoffrey that she could keep him just as happy, though she'd gone back to her career. For a time she thought she had succeeded. Carter's constant attentions presented a possible problem until he decided reluctantly to leave.

"If you ever need me, or think you need me, don't hesitate to come to me. You know how I feel."

He thought he was in love with her. She was flattered at first to think she could inspire the love of a younger man. Her feelings toward him were hardly love. She was fond of him, but that was all. She told him he'd quickly forget her if he gave himself a chance.

He'd gone to Los Angeles that December. Some time later she'd heard he had married a young actress and she was happy for him. But it was a tempestuous marriage. After several years the inevitable divorce was difficult. There'd been a child, a daughter, and he'd sued for custody and won.

At forty-five he was eight years younger than she, but he looked years older. It was hard to find the enthusiastic, boyish charm she'd found so appealing beneath the bitter façade. There was a puffiness around his pale blue eyes that suggested he'd sought relief from tension in alcohol, too much alcohol. She embraced him, kissed his cheek and introduced Roslynn, whom he vaguely acknowledged. He'd hardly taken his eyes from her.

"I read about the award," he said. "In fact I've seen this month's issue of *Woman's Way*. It was at the airport. There you were smiling out at me from a dozen covers. I'm sure the newsstand attendant could think of no better way to beautify America. Sybil! It's been too long!" he finished fervently.

She felt a rush of affection for him. He had been so kind during those wretched days she'd been separated from Geoffrey. She wished now that she could do something for him. He looked depressed and lonely, a disillusioned man. Some spark had left him, perhaps that firm belief that there was little in human behavior that could be condemned.

"I don't know if I can get you into the dinner tonight, Mr. Hayes, but I am having a cocktail party this evening for some of Sybil's friends. Can we count on you to come?" Roslynn asked graciously. "Had we known you were going to be in town—" she began. He looked at her then and smiled wryly. He waved the generous suggestion aside.

"You would never have thought of me, not an insignificant has-been playwright."

"Oh, Mr. Hayes, I would—"

He shook his head. "I know what's being said about me, Miss Stevens. But I should like to come to your cocktail party. May I, Sybil?"

"I'd be hurt if you didn't," she replied quickly.

The party would be good for him. There were contacts he could make that might prove invaluable. But would Geoffrey understand? He had recognized Carter's obvious interest in her even before she did. She hoped after all these years this would not add another problem to an already difficult situation.

Geoffrey came home that evening in a tense mood. She could hear him beyond the door of their adjoining rooms preparing to shower and change. He banged drawers and doors, swore impatiently and finally called to her that he needed a drink. Now! She made it herself and brought it to him.

She was almost dressed, leaving until last the lemon yellow silk gown she'd designed for the occasion. Her short hair was styled in elaborate waves with curls of a hair piece high on her head. Intertwined was her favorite

332

string of seed pearls. Beneath her billowing blue chiffon dressing gown she wore a long taffeta slip which rustled softly as she walked.

"A very dry martini, just the way you like it," she said, smiling up at him, trying to coax away the resentful look in his eyes.

He took one sip of his drink and made a face.

"Lord, Sybil, will you never learn to mix a martini? I should have done it myself."

She reached for the glass.

"I'm sorry. Let me ask Lamarr to make another."

Their domestic staff had grown over the years to a live-in couple who acted as housekeeper, cook, butler and chauffeur.

He gave her a look of sheer disgust.

"Don't bother! I said I needed a drink now and I do. Any kind of drink."

He drained the glass and set it down. She watched him apprehensively.

"Well, what is it?" he demanded impatiently. "You're staring. Don't you approve?"

"It isn't that—"

"It never is," he growled. "I know what you're thinking. I always know what you're thinking. That lovely face is very easy to read. But you needn't worry. I'm not going to disgrace you this evening by drinking too much. I know my place!"

"Your place?"

"Of course my place. What else? Madame Sybil's husband!" He spat out the words viciously. "That's how I'm introduced. Did you know? It happened today at a business meeting. Madame Sybil's husband! I could have torn the bastard apart with my bare hands. He even had that stupid magazine with him. I could cheerfully have shoved it down his throat, but I didn't. No, you would have been delighted with my restraint. I told them how proud I was of my beautiful and talented wife. Proud, I said. And every man at that conference table was wondering how Madame Sybil was in bed and laughing at me.

She gasped and felt the blood rush to her face. She knew he was deliberately baiting her, trying to belittle her by attacking her femininity because he felt threatened. She knew she mustn't take his words seriously. She turned to go, but he wasn't through.

"Do I shock you? Don't you think it's true?"

He hurled the words at her rigid back.

"Believe it. It's true. I'm the joke of New York."

"Please, Geoffrey, not tonight."

"Not tonight! Not tonight!" he mimicked. "Why the hell not tonight? You're my wife, aren't you?"

In two strides he'd reached her, grasped her shoulders roughly and spun her around to face him.

"My wife!" he repeated, his eyes blazing with dangerous fury.

She tried to pull away, but that only served to enrage him. His arms tightened around her and he bent towards her and crushed his mouth against hers, deliberately smearing her careful make-up. She struggled, but he held her head with one hand, digging his fingers into the thick waves of her hair. His mouth was hard and he gripped her with merciless strength. She felt the entire length of his body against hers, could feel an unaccustomed and fierce desire rise in him. She knew instinctively she would be helpless against it, though she tried one last time to break free. Instead, the twisting of her head simply broke the delicate string of pearls that had been so carefully arranged in her hair. The pearls fell to the carpet unheeded as he half-carried, half-dragged her to his bed. Jealousy and anger had made him lustful and she felt him grow hard against her.

He threw her onto the bed and raised himself above her. She was too weakened by shock and fear of his unreasoning fury to speak above a whisper.

"Please, Geoffrey. Please," she begged breathlessly. "Not this way. Not in anger!"

She reached up to touch his cheek, but he pushed her hand away.

His brows arched and slanted quizzically.

"Why not? I have a right, don't I? You're my wife. My wife!" he told her hoarsely, his eyes narrowing.

With one swift movement he tore the material of her slip, stripping it from her breasts leaving them bare. She cried out, but he didn't seem to hear.

"Ah, here we have the real Madame Sybil, the mother, the wife."

His mouth seemed to attack her breasts. He moved across them sucking, biting, and at the same time tearing with his hands at the long slip until he'd succeeded in freeing her body of it. She gasped as he thrust himself into her, lifting her hips to meet his. He rolled over and over with her on the huge bed and then knelt above her drenched in perspiration.

"Well, Madame Sybil, you are, after all, only a woman." The words were cold and his eyes mocked her. "Don't worry, my dear, I'm through with you this evening. You won't have to bother about me again."

She closed her eyes and wept. They were bitter tears of regret for all they had been to one another and what they might have been. She remembered the tender moments when they'd made love out of their mutual need and desire. Tonight he had meant only to demean and hurt her. He had succeeded.

She did not try to move until she heard him leave. She felt bruised and badly shaken. Slowly, dragging the spread with her, she stood before the mirror, saw her ravaged reflection and looked quickly away. What was to be done? In little more than an hour she was expected at Roslynn's party. What sort of image could she possibly present feeling the way she did now. Her husband in a fit of jealous rage had humiliated her in the only way he could.

She was trembling with an anger she could not control, but it inspired in her a determination not to be defeated. She would not let him do this to her. If she had to go on alone, then she would. It was useless to attempt to redo her hair and make-up alone. She'd need help and so she called the one person she could trust.

Marlene sounded as though she'd begun her celebrating

already. There was music and male laughter in the background. Derrick Hughes had probably already arrived to escort her to the dinner.

She listened as Sybil tried to give a circumspect explanation of her sudden need for help and was relieved at the speed with which she recognized the fact that her need was urgent.

"Turn that down a minute, will you, Derrick honey?" she called sharply above the sound of the Beatles.

"You want me to come over?" she asked in a more confidential tone. "Is that it?"

"Yes, yes, please." She fought the sobs that rose in her throat.

"I'll be there. Right away. Whatever it is, don't worry. I'll be there," Marlene told her fiercely.

She sat beside the phone and waited. She didn't know where Geoffrey was. She didn't think she'd see him again tonight. What explanation could she give to her friends? Anything she said would be suspect. She raised her chin resolutely. She'd manage. She'd carry off her role well and no one would know of the emotional turmoil she would carefully hide. He wouldn't expect her to manage so well, not this time.

How often she'd borne his jealousy in the past. She'd ignored the sarcastic phrase, the barely veiled attempts to hurt her. Never had he demonstrated his feelings so dramatically as he had tonight. He'd gone too far and perhaps he'd meant to.

Something had died between them, a depth of understanding, of caring, of respect. He had taken her as he might have taken any woman of the street, savagely and without consideration. It was as if he'd meant to destroy her. In a way perhaps that's what he wanted to do. He wanted to destroy what she had become. Perhaps he thought he still loved and wanted the Sybil he had married. She couldn't go back to being that docile, pliant woman now, no more than he could accept her as she was.

Marlene came and with dazzling skill and efficiency

helped to repair the damage. They removed the ruined hairpiece and brushed her short hair into a becoming casual style. She was finally able to handle the make-up herself while Marlene altered another slip to fit beneath the yellow gown. There was no need for explanations or even words between them. Marlene worked in tight-lipped silence. She did not intend to have this evening spoiled for either of them.

Before they went into the living room to face Derrick, she took Sybil's hands and looked anxiously into her face.

"You want a drink or something first? Something stronger than sherry, a real drink?" she suggested.

"No, no. I'll be all right, thanks to you." She still felt shaky, but she knew that the moment she had to face her family and her friends her pride would take over. For their sake she would want to appear well.

"You look terrific. Every goddamn man in that room will fall in love with you if he hasn't already. And every woman will envy you."

Marlene spoke with the angry authority of one who dared anyone to think otherwise. She did not refer to Geoffrey, taking it for granted that she and Derrick would be escorting her.

The lemon yellow gown was a great success. The delicate material clung to her figure, molding every soft curve suggestively. The neckline plunged nearly to the waist. The only jewelry she wore was the diamond drop earrings Geoffrey had given her for their twentieth wedding anniversary. She'd briefly thought of casting them aside, of wearing others, but she knew that would be a childish gesture. There'd been enough childish behavior for one night and the diamonds were the perfect touch. Tomorrow she'd have to deal with Geoffrey and what was left of their marriage. Tonight was Madame Sybil's.

Arthur was driving down from Cambridge where he was in his last year at Harvard and would meet them at Roslynn's. Joanna would be there, too, with her fiancé, Wilfred Balfour. It seemed as though she had finally

337

found someone she could love in the widower who was thirteen years her senior.

Even Ned was flying in from Chicago with his wife of four years. Ned! How different he was today from the angry, frightened boy who had tried to run away from his military duty! The Peace Corps had changed him, the Peace Corps and Diane.

She thought she could manage the cocktail party and the dinner. Very little was required of her. She'd accept the award calmly, speak only a few short sentences honoring Marlene, her indispensable right hand, and her family for their encouragement. She would not have to mention Geoffrey by name. The audience would simply assume the rest. The television interview was scheduled to be shown tomorrow. Then it would be over except for having her picture on the cover of *Woman's Way* for an entire month.

To her own surprise she felt relieved to be arriving at Roslynn's without him. All along she had known what a strain it would be to have a tense, angry husband beside her. With him there the evening would have been more of an ordeal than a triumph.

In place of her husband, her son was beside her. Arthur played his part admirably. He was, at twenty-one, a handsome man, serious and thoughtful. He had inherited his mother's coloring: black hair and deep blue eyes. He had his father's strong, classic features. His wide mouth was gentle and there was a hint of shyness that made him particularly attractive to women. He seemed unaware of this himself, which only added to his charm. As a student he had always been outstanding, a fact that only seemed to irritate his father.

"When does he play?" Geoffrey once asked impatiently. "It isn't normal to be so dedicated. By the time I was his age I'd been thrown out of more schools than I can remember. But I enjoyed myself. God! He makes me nervous. I'm afraid I'll make a mistake in front of him, some blunder in elementary law or even in grammar. I can't talk to him anymore."

338

The truth was they'd never been able to talk. At eight, the boy had been hopeful and anxious to win his father's approval through their mutual interest in sailing. But that had come at the height of marital difficulties. The turmoil of the household did not escape him. He became resigned to his father's lack of interest in him.

Roslynn's party was much as Sybil expected, crowded, noisy, and filled with celebrities.

"Is that long-haired, bearded creature really your son, Sybil?"

Claudia Barrett always said exactly what she thought and her rich voice, heavy with consternation carried across the room to Ned who stood beside his equally long-haired wife, Diane. They were drinking fruit juice, having refused anything stronger.

He looked up, recognized the speaker, and made his way across the room. His dark eyes sparkled with humor.

"You know, Miss Barrett, I often ask myself that question only in reverse. Is my mother really that brilliant, beautiful, vital woman? It doesn't seem possible. May I present my wife?" he asked, slipping his arm around the slim girl beside him. The top of her head barely reached his shoulder.

"Good Lord! Your wife!" Claudia raised the back of her hand to her forehead and the four heavy gold bangles on her arm clanked noisily. "She doesn't look old enough to be married."

Diane's natural, blonde beauty was untouched by any kind of make-up. She did look like a clean-faced child.

"I'm thirty-two," she volunteered, smiling her warm, gracious smile. She had an unself-conscious grace that was beautiful to see. "The same as Joanna. We discovered we were born within days of each other."

"Unbelievable!" Claudia murmured. "Sybil, dear, I'm going to drown amid all this youth," she added in an aside. "I feel positively crotchety. What a shame Geoffrey couldn't be here tonight!" she added, taking her arm and leading her insistently away so they could speak privately.

She steeled herself for what was to come. Claudia could

be terribly persistent, as well as perceptive, and she was the last person to whom she would want to confide her troubles.

"What actually happened, my dear? Do I detect the effect of the green-eyed monster? Two careers in one family are difficult to manage and don't I know it! Or, is it something else?" she asked pointedly. "There has been talk, you know."

"Talk?" Her heart froze, but she went on smiling. "What sort of talk? Geoffrey's simply been working too hard. He's overextended himself, that's all."

Claudia patted her arm and was patronizing.

"All right, darling, if that's the story you're giving out, I'll support you. You can count on me. But I shall never understand how a man like Geoffrey Kempton could see anything in that mousey Lisa Atkins."

The blood drained from her face. Nothing had prepared her for this.

"Who is Lisa Atkins?"

"You're joking." Her large eyes widened in genuine surprise. "No, my God! You aren't, are you? But surely—" She stopped helplessly. "You mean to say no one's told you?"

She didn't say that no one had been that unkind. Or, was it being unkind to let her know what apparently was common knowledge? Perhaps it was the very thing Geoffrey had counted on. She didn't even ask how Claudia knew. Who else knew, she wondered. Did Marlene know? Did Roslynn? What about her daughter? Did Joanna know?

Why hadn't she guessed there'd been someone else? Why shouldn't there be someone else? He was seldom home. For months they'd had little to do with one another. Since she'd done the film, she'd known there was something. Perhaps even before that.

"Who is Lisa Atkins?" she repeated more calmly.

Claudia took her arm again and lowered her voice.

"Some clerk in his office, a little nobody. I don't think she's thirty. Younger than Joanna! But then that's the

340

way with men Geoffrey's age. Believe me, I've been through it all. The best thing is to ignore it. They only do it for attention. A man like Geoffrey is worth a little annoyance now and then. It never really means anything much to them."

But it means something to me, she wanted to say. She'd heard women talk of their husband's affairs in this way before and she never quite understood the attitude. Was it a posture everyone expected, or did they really believe that?

Claudia gave no more than a minute's thought to her dilemma before something more interesting caught her attention.

"Oh, look, isn't that— Why, it is! Carter Hayes! I didn't know he was back. He looks terrible!" She made a face. "That bitch he married ruined him. I wonder if there's anything worth salvaging. After all, he did give me my greatest success. Do you think he's still capable of writing anything at all? I must speak to him."

With the train of her cerise gown trailing behind her, she left Sybil standing alone and numb with the knowledge that she'd been a fool. Geoffrey had been unfaithful to her and she hadn't even guessed.

The rest of the evening went by in a haze. She scarcely knew what she said or did. She went through the motions of accepting the congratulations of her friends. She was witty and charming for the press. And all the while she was thinking of Geoffrey and that other woman. Was he with her now? He must be as he'd been night after night when the "demands of business" kept him out so late. It was the oldest story in the world and yet it was unique because it was happening to her.

Was she jealous? Hurt? They had drifted so far apart she didn't know if she felt either. He was her husband. His loyalty was a habit. No, what she really felt was anger and she was bitter, too, because he had chosen this way, another more public way to humiliate her. If there was someone else, why couldn't he have told her? She would not have stood in his way.

When Arthur finally brought her home in the early hours of the morning, he insisted she take a sleeping pill and sat with her until it took hold.

"You look exhausted, but far too wound up to sleep. And Father's not here?" he asked. "Still? What was it, a business trip? Surely it could have waited one night."

His dark brows drew together as he eyed his mother shrewdly. Had he guessed part of the truth?

She sat in bed, propped up by pillows. The rainbow colors of the satin quilt made an island of pleasant unreality of her bed. She avoided his question. Actually, she was surprised he had not asked it before.

"What time will you be leaving in the morning?"

"Hours before you're up. I have a two o'clock class. But I won't miss the television spot in the evening. You can count on that. Mother—" he began tentatively.

She knew what was coming and cut him off.

"It's nothing I can talk about just yet, darling," she told him, reaching for his hand. "And it's nothing for you to worry about."

She met his eyes, saw his concern and was grateful. More than that, she saw his pain. What must he really think of his father? He'd always been particularly close to her. She didn't know how he saw his father now, or if any gossip had reached him. She didn't want to prejudice him in any way.

"Good night, darling," she said. "Thank you. It's been a long night. I couldn't have done it without you."

He was sensitive enough to know that this was partly true and he seemed reluctant to leave her.

"I'll call you tomorrow after I see the show," he promised. "I'll let you know what I think of you as a television personality."

He kissed her.

"I love you, Mother. You won't forget that?"

"I never do. Now run along. You need your sleep."

Alone, she tried to think of everything but Geoffrey. She looked back on the evening, the proud moments, the happy moments, and found they were completely overshadowed by him. What was she to do? How could she face him again?

She couldn't relax. The pill didn't seem to be helping and then suddenly sleep overcame her.

The moment she awoke she thought of Geoffrey and felt leaden with depression. She listened for a time for sounds of movement from his room, but it was past ten. If he had come in at all last night, he would not still be here. She remembered the violence of his love-making yesterday. Only a driven man would have behaved that way. She thought she could understand him, but she could not forgive. She'd gone beyond that. And perhaps he did not want her forgiveness.

They would have to talk and she wasn't sure how to arrange this. Should she call him at his office? She seldom did that except in cases of extreme emergencies because it annoyed him. This emergency was certainly extreme.

He made it easy for her. He came in while she was having a solitary breakfast in the dining room. He threw his coat and hat over a chair and sat opposite her, his back to the window so that he was outlined boldly against the winter sunlight. She saw him quite clearly, knew everything about him, and knew beyond question that it was over between them.

He refused coffee.

"I'm not going to apologize," he said. His strong jaw was tilted at a belligerent angle. He didn't wait for her to reply. "I don't think either of us wants to continue with this marriage. Get a divorce. Get it any way you like. Do it quickly. I won't contest anything. I can't go on living this lie."

"Then it is true," she said. "There is someone else."

She hadn't meant to say that. Another woman could only be an effect, not a cause. There were too many other problems.

He looked surprised, but only briefly.

"You've been talking to my brother," he said. He bent his head to light a cigarette, inhaled once or twice, and crushed it out.

"No, not your brother. Claudia told me last night."

She thought she was speaking with admirable control, as if they were talking about turning in their old car for a new one instead of altering their entire lives.

"Ah, yes! Dear Claudia! Bitch!" he growled. "Sorry," he apologized immediately. "I thought we could be sensible about this. I thought you would want the divorce every bit as much as I do. Lisa, or no Lisa, there's nothing left, is there?"

"But— Do you love Lisa?"

She found the words hard to say, but she wanted to know. From the depths of her feminine pride, she had to know.

"Well, I wouldn't have expected that of you. Do I love her more than you?"

His tone was tinged with sarcasm and she wished she hadn't given him another opportunity to belittle her.

"Obviously, I find her more compatible. She makes no demands on me. She appreciates my work. She tries to understand it. That matters to me, you know."

He hadn't answered her question directly, but she knew the answer and was unexpectedly sorry for him because he needed the reassurance of an adoring woman. She felt sorry for herself because she had not found a man who was equal to having a woman be herself.

She thought she should feel something more, but she didn't. She had no idea what life would actually be like without Geoffrey after twenty-two years of marriage. She'd lost him, not to another woman, but to his pride. It wasn't something she could fight. There didn't seem to be anything else to say.

She thought he would go then. He pushed back his chair and got up, but he stood looking down at her. She remembered him as she'd first seen him in his uniform, remembered the effect of his voice and recalled how little time it took to realize she was attracted to him.

"Never doubt that I loved you, Sybil. I did love you. But you— I don't know if you ever loved me."

He couldn't have said anything that would have hurt

344

her more. She closed her eyes. She didn't think she could bear to hear another word.

"Oh, Christ, what's the use? I'll send for my things. You don't have to bother about the locks."

He emptied his pockets, dropping his door key on the table. It made a cold, final clatter, the ultimate insult. When he finally left, she found she was gripping the arms of her chair so tightly her hands ached. There was no other sound in the vast expanse of the lavish, empty apartment except that of her own carefully measured breathing.

II

She went to a lawyer Carter Hayes recommended. She couldn't possibly involve her brother-in-law. He didn't even want to know the details, no one did. Everyone took the divorce for granted. She felt foolish and annoyed with herself for not having taken the initiative long ago. The humiliation of realizing she'd waited too long was difficult to bear.

She heard after a month that Geoffrey was no longer with his brother's firm. He'd gone to Washington with the promise of a government post. Lisa Atkins had not gone with him. Perhaps he was being particularly discreet in view of the possibility of a Supreme Court appointment. Or perhaps, as Claudia suggested, it hadn't meant anything after all.

Their separation caused some snide comments in the columns.

"Divorce for Madame Sybil? Proof positive that marriage and a successful career don't mix?"

But the divorce itself caused little interest and in no way affected business. How different from the scandal in the forties when she'd gained her freedom from Edward!

Arrangements were made for her to establish residence in Reno. She hated the idea of going there again, but she was able to spend a good deal of the time in California at the Los Angeles shop. Marlene flew out to join her and it was all over faster than she expected. She was back in time for Arthur's graduation in June. How proud she was as she watched her son receive special awards for his high academic achievement! Geoffrey did not come. Instead he sent a gift. He was financing a summer camping trip across the country complete with a new car. It would give Arthur a chance to relax before going on to law school in the fall. But he wasn't sure if he wanted to go. He thought she'd need him at home. It was tempting to keep him with her. She was lonely. A sense of failure pervaded her life. She'd married twice and both times had met with failure. She was lonely. She, who had any number of friends to call upon, was often lonely these days, but she insisted he go. Geoffrey had always said Arthur was too close to her. She did not want to make that mistake, too.

Marlene suggested a trip.

"It would do us both good to get away. Not a business trip, just good old-fashioned fun," she said wistfully. "What do you say?"

"Someday, someday I'd like to travel for fun, but I can't think of going anywhere now. There's Joanna. I think she needs me now."

Joanna could not seem to make up her mind. Since January she'd broken her engagement to Wilfred Balfour three times and then finally agreed to set a date in December. She wanted a quiet reception in her mother's home.

"I'm too old for a fuss. I just want the family and a few close friends."

Her relationship with Joanna was amicable, but rather formal. They'd never recovered the closeness they'd once had, but they had established a kind of truce oddly enough after news reached them that Alfred Skinner died late in 1953. He'd enlisted immediately after graduation but the war in Korea was over before he could see action. It was a freak accident at a base in Hawaii that killed him. His body was flown back and buried in the family plot. Joanna read about it in the newspapers and went to the funeral services in Philadelphia, where she confronted Mr. and Mrs. Skinner.

"They killed him," she told Sybil afterwards.

She came to see her mother straight from the train. She stood in the living room, holding the black hat she'd worn, turning it over and over in her hands, her tear-stained face marked forever by tragedy and despair.

"All this time I blamed you. I—I was wrong, Mother. *They* killed him. They wanted him dead rather than married to me. They were triumphant in their grief, if you can imagine such a thing. Triumphant! Triumphant!" she cried hysterically. "Narrow-minded prigs! They're inhuman."

She broke down then and Sybil went to her, holding her, comforting her as best she could. She spent the night in her old room and Sybil sat up beside the bed. The next morning they talked for hours. For the first time she was able to understand something of what had happened in her mother's life and of why she had not permitted herself to marry the girl's father and destroy his career. There was never the old camaraderie of the past between them, but Joanna no longer tried to shut her out.

She liked Joanna's fiancé. He was attractive in a quiet, charming way and his affection for Joanna was apparent in everything he said and did.

Not long before the wedding date, the couple came to dinner. There would be just the three of them to go over last minute preparations.

Will brought her flowers, a colorful fall bouquet.

"How thoughtful! They're lovely," she said, brushing the delicate blossoms against her cheek.

"Not half so lovely as my celebrated mother-in-law to be."

He had an engaging smile and a way of fixing his hazel eyes upon the person to whom he was speaking, making her feel that at that moment she was the most important person in the world to him.

"Now you know why all the girls at Barnard are a little bit in love with him," Joanna said. "You should see the

348

hordes of sweet young things I must compete with. They study political science for the sheer pleasure of being near Dr. Balfour!"

Will put his arm around her and kissed her cheek.

"You forget. There is no competition. I'm already very happily committed."

Sybil liked the sound of his voice. It was deep and pleasant and always calm. Will was a man of infinite patience and he would need patience. Joanna was an independent woman with ideas of her own. Sometimes she complained to Sybil of his lack of sophistication.

"Those tweed jackets he wears look—well, seedy, and that ever present pipe! Sometimes I think he's an ad for a road company version of *Good-bye, Mr. Chips*."

But the complaints were always accompanied by a fond look in her eyes and Sybil thought that her daughter really rather liked the image she was painting.

Tonight Joanna's eyes were stormy.

"Don't get carried away with Will's thoughtfulness, Mother. The flowers are by way of apology. He can't stay to dinner." Her voice was brittle.

"Oh?" She raised her brows inquiringly.

"My oldest daughter, Rene, is about to have her first child. I thought the least I could do would be to try to comfort her husband. I hoped you would understand. I just received word an hour ago."

"But of course! How exciting for you, Will!"

She leaned forward and kissed his cheek impulsively. "You must go."

"Thank you, Sybil." He cast an anxious glance toward Joanna. "I'll call you here as soon as there's any news, darling."

She allowed herself to be kissed, but said nothing and when Will had gone, she threw herself onto the sofa and began to cry.

"Oh, Mother, I—I can't. I can't go through with it. I just can't marry him."

Sybil thought it could hardly be anything more than nerves. She sat down beside the girl and tried to quiet her.

Eventually the storm was over and she suggested they both needed a drink. Joanna went to the bar and mixed them herself.

"Now tell me what this is all about," she said.

Joanna sat stiffly beside her.

"I think I've made a terrible mistake."

Joanna was a beautiful, desirable woman. She had looked particularly lovely that evening aside from the sullen expression and the tears.

Today, she wore a green wool dress with a wide band of embroidery at the hem and cuffs. The rope of pearls she wore around her neck was looped into a knot. She wore her dark hair chin length with long bangs that emphasized her large eyes. All Sybil's children had large, expressive eyes like their mother. Joanna's were filled with confusion. The uncertainty was a familiar story. She had not been able to commit herself totally to anyone since Alfred.

"I—I don't know what to say or where to begin. It's the life Will expects me to lead first of all. He expects to go on with his teaching career in New Jersey, of all places. I've never even heard of the town we'd live in. Imagine! Political Science Chairman of a small college in New Jersey! Thank God he's published some books. What would we do for money? And then there are those daughters of his, already dowdy married creatures, and not out of their twenties. Now he's about to become a grandfather. What does that make me?"

"Do you love Will, Joanna?"

"It's not enough! It's not enough!" Her words came in a nervous rush. "Perhaps I shouldn't marry at all. Perhaps it's simply not for me. Marriage, I mean. How many marriages are really successful? It's an awful chance. The idea of falling into some miserable situation terrifies me. Look at you and Geoffrey."

She caught her breath sharply and Joanna's eyes met hers. Once again they filled with tears.

"Oh, Mother, I didn't mean to say that. Please forgive me. It's just that I do think of it."

She groped for Sybil's hand blindly.

"And—and I think of my own father."

"Your own father?"

She had told Joanna very little about Jonathan. In fact, they had not spoken of him in years. When Geoffrey adopted her, giving her his name, he became for all intents and purposes her father. He got on better with her than he ever had with Arthur.

"Yes, yes, my own father," she continued, a sob in her voice. "I don't really know who I am, do I?"

"That's an odd thing to say after all these years, isn't it?" She hadn't expected this. Doubts! She knew Joanna would have doubts. Everyone did before marrying. But this— This had not occurred to her.

"I don't think it's odd at all. Other people have thought of it," she added pointedly.

"The Skinners, I suppose you mean."

"And Ned."

"Ned? Why? What does he have to do with this?"

"I had a long talk with him on the phone last night. He made me see what I'm doing."

She frowned. "I don't understand. What are you doing?"

"Looking for a father."

The words hung between them. She often thought that Joanna's interest in older men was prompted by this need, but she'd never voiced her opinion. If Joanna could resolve her problems by marrying an older man she genuinely loved, well, why shouldn't she? At 45 to Joanna's 32, Wilfred was hardly old enough to be her father.

"And that's all you see in Will, a father?"

"No— But I— Perhaps what I need is another kind of life."

She shifted uneasily on the smooth cushions.

"Ned says each of us has a duty to his fellow man. Ned says we must be givers not takers. Only then can we be happy. I believe him. Look how different he is now. Why, he'd give you anything, anything at all. Look how he spends his money. Not on himself or Diane, but on others. Mother, he's happy. Really happy. Did you ever think we'd see Ned like this? Did you, Mother?"

"No," she admitted.

Ned had changed. But she thought he was not the person to advise Joanna. He saw life from an entirely different angle. He'd found salvation in a truly personal God. Years ago he'd stolen money from his father, run away, but returned in time to register with his draft board only to be turned down. A heart murmur they said. The result of a childhood disease probably. Ned was relieved and grateful for the reprieve, but restless. He finished college only at his father's insistence, worked for a time for Edward in San Francisco and then in Detroit, where he'd met Diane. For the first time he'd had to face the truth about himself.

"I won't marry you," she'd told him. "I'll sleep with you because I'm attracted to you, but I won't marry you. I won't commit myself to someone who doesn't know what love really is!"

The refusal shook him. Very few women could refuse him. Handsome, wealthy, possessed of a reckless sense of his own sexuality, he'd had his share of women. Diane surprised and intrigued him. Eventually he became a convert to her faith, a kind of Unitarian approach and they were married. At Diane's suggestion they began to work for the civil rights movement, participating in marches and sit-ins. Admirers of Martin Luther King, Jr., they gave much of Ned's income to the NAACP and even attempted to integrate one of his father's more affluent housing developments.

Furious at what he considered Ned's sudden fanaticism, Edward refused his son employment.

"You're no son of mine," he wrote Ned. "Go to your mother, or the devil, whichever suits you."

"I'll go to Africa," he wrote back. "The Peace Corps needs volunteers."

And he did. He had a good income from his grandfather's estate, but most of it went for his charities. The life he and Diane led was one of dedication and sacrifice. She thought it would hardly suit Joanna, whose small salary for teaching French at Barnard was generously supplemented by her mother. Joanna spent every cent she had on herself, going to the theater, keeping up with wealthy friends, and enjoying what New York had to offer a young woman with money. She even found it difficult to give up what she called "her city" for a month's vacation every summer. Will was not a wealthy man, but his textbooks did very well and they would have more than enough for a comfortable life together.

Sybil looked at her daughter's profile as she brooded silently, staring into space. Perhaps she was picturing herself as a fastidious martyr to some imaginary cause. Joanna had little knowledge of the realities of life.

Perhaps she needed realities. Perhaps what she did need now was the father she'd never known. Certainly her sudden interest in Ned's way of life was a whim, an excuse to put off the wedding and the inevitability of facing the test of marriage, of learning to give herself totally to another human being and consequently seeing herself as she really was through Will's eyes. Perhaps she'd already glimpsed herself and found she did not like what she saw.

Men did find her terribly attractive, but she seldom allowed them to get to know her. She built an impenetrable wall and no one, not even her mother, was permitted to see the real Joanna.

Was it possible that all this stemmed from her basic uncertainty about who she actually was? Considering all this Sybil decided to break the silence of years. She decided to tell Joanna who her father really was. It might make all the difference.

Joanna accepted her father's name gravely, writing it down in a small blue leather notebook she carried in her purse. That was all. She asked no further questions. What the girl would do with the information Sybil wasn't sure. She might do nothing at all. But the information itself seemed to calm her.

Sybil was somewhat less than calm. Speaking Jonathan's name after all these years unnerved her. She'd often wondered about him. Where was he now? What would he do if he learned that he had a daughter whose existence he'd never suspected? Could it really make much difference to him? He must have his own life, his own family. Would Joanna try to reach him? She wondered if she should ask her not to, started to say something, and then changed her mind. The girl should be free to do what she chose. It was out of her hands now.

They ate a quiet dinner and waited for Will's call till past eleven.

"What could be keeping him? He's always so careful to be punctual and considerate. Too punctual and too considerate. There are no surprises," Joanna said with distaste.

"Count your blessings, my dear. And I do think that Will is a blessing. I think in many ways he's right for you."

"But am I right for anyone?" the girl asked and then shook her head. "Oh, Mother, please don't worry. I haven't made up my mind yet one way or the other. I'll—I have to think," she sighed. "It's not the end of the world."

She left and Will called not ten minutes later.

"Was she angry, annoyed, I mean, about my not calling? It was a difficult birth, but everything's all right now. Oh, it's a boy," he added.

"Congratulations! You must be very proud and happy."

"I would be if Joanna were here."

"Go to her," she advised him impulsively. "Tonight. She needs you, Will, whether she realizes it or not. Go to her."

"Do you honestly think I should? Joanna and I have never—" Will hesitated, obviously embarrassed.

She was surprised. She'd taken it for granted that Joanna, like her other friends, was particularly free in her attitude toward sex. Was that, too, a problem?

"She needs you tonight, Will, for whatever reason," she said and hoped this was true.

There was no more talk about postponing the wedding. The days went by and Joanna seemed content if not actually joyous. She never mentioned her father again, or whether she'd made any effort to look him up. Sybil did not ask. She thought Will looked particularly happy and decided that was a good sign. Invitations were sent out and Joanna dutifully came into the salon for fittings on the wedding suit and the other clothes she was planning to take to Hawaii on her honeymoon.

"Who's going to give the bride away? I wouldn't mind being a stand-in father," Carter Hayes offered.

"Ned's doing the honors. Joanna hasn't even written to Geoffrey, I'm afraid. Frankly I'm surprised. I thought she'd want him at the wedding."

Carter laughed.

"How terribly civilized! Would you want him there?"

"I honestly don't know. It's Joanna's wedding."

She had been seeing Carter for the past few months. He had done some television work and was now working on a new play. She found he was comfortably undemanding and he understood her.

"The play's for Claudia. Not that I've told her yet, you understand. I'm playing hard to get and it's driving her mad," he confided. "She's been begging me to do something for her and I keep putting her off."

"Why do you do it?"

"Oh, Lord, I don't know. After so many years of not being in demand I rather like the idea of being sought after. Besides, if we could repeat that first success, I'd be made all over again. My ex-wife took me for just about everything I had except Tracy, which I'm sure is no secret to anyone. Want another drink?" he asked and then laughed as he looked down at her untouched glass. "Now Stephanie would have downed that within the first minute and several others before the first course. Waiter! I'll have another one of these," he said, holding up his glass. "It takes two before I get to feeling anywhere near relaxed. This is the place to be, isn't it?" he said, looking around appreciatively.

The small exclusive restaurant was not far from Broadway and was a meeting place for people in the entertainment world. During the evenings they spent there, a number of well-known people stopped by their table usually to greet her and stayed for a drink at his insistence. She found the evenings interesting at first, a diversion from the unremitting loneliness of her personal life. She saw people from time to time, even went to several dinner parties. They were always the same. People were kind. They never mentioned Geoffrey. But she always had to go back to the empty apartment and the empty life. After Joanna was married next week, even the excitement of preparing for the wedding would be over.

"You don't have to go back alone," Carter told her once. "You could let me come with you." He held her hands and looked urgently into her eyes.

He said it only once because she withdrew immediately. There was nothing she wanted less than that kind of involvement now. She felt empty and cold since Geoffrey left. She thought she would never love again.

"Bring Tracy to the wedding, Carter. She'll be home for holidays then, won't she? I'd like to meet her," she said suddenly.

He couldn't have been more surprised.

"Do you mean it?"

The guarded look left his eyes. He had assumed a cool, sophisticated, almost belligerent manner since he'd been back. He seemed to expect people to challenge him or perhaps belittle him. He'd fallen from grace, after all. His reputation was of someone less than dependable. He'd begun numerous projects during his decade of marriage and finished nothing other than one terrible movie for his former wife.

"I'm surprised anyone speaks to me at all," he'd told her, "except you, of course. You've always been so generous, more than generous."

Now he looked at her hopefully.

"You'd really like to meet Tracy? No one ever asks

356

about her. It's as if she didn't exist. That's my fault as much as anyone's, I suppose. She's been at a school in Connecticut ever since I won custody. She was the one thing I was able to salvage from my marriage. Stephanie wanted her, wanted her badly to spite me. They never got along. Here," he said producing a dog-eared picture and pushing it across the table. "That's Tracy. She's older now and changed some. What do you think?"

She was a wispy, wan child of six or seven in the picture. Her wide blue eyes looked tragic. She wondered if he realized that.

"Bring her to the wedding. I'd like to get to know her," she said.

Perhaps there was something she could do for the child.

He smiled and gave her a curious look.

"Funny, you like children, don't you?"

"Most people do."

"Nonsense. They don't. They find them nuisances. You don't. You like them. I'll be damned if I can say the same. They're all a mystery to me, one I don't particularly care about unraveling. Even Tracy— She's—well, hard to get close to. We're strangers. When she was very small, I was mad about her. She trusted me completely. Now I can't even imagine what she's thinking."

"But she's away so much, Carter. You can't hope to know her when you see her so seldom."

She remembered the year Ned spent at boarding school and how little she thought she knew him when he came back. But all children changed. They grew away from you. They did become strangers. But they needed you still, needed guidance. You were responsible for them. They were a part of you. And you loved them. No matter what they did there was always that emotional tie.

"There are many things I wish now I could have done differently," she said thoughtfully.

"I wonder what I shall regret most," he said. "Bringing her into this crazy world perhaps."

He shrugged. "Here's my drink. What shall we drink to this time? It helps to have an excuse, you know."

"To Tracy then," she said and wished he did not need to drink quite so much.

His moods were erratic and tonight he had gone from gloating over the progress he'd made on his play to depression over his daughter. He'd admitted to her that at one time he'd even tried drugs to lift his moods.

"Just marijuana. That was at the height of my Hollywood despair. I thought it might enhance the creative powers that were so successfully hidden for so long. It simply relaxed me into a hazy stupor and I didn't care if I ever got another word down. This is safer," he added, tapping his drink.

"Sybil, what are the chances Claudia can raise enough money for another production? I mean, does anyone take her seriously anymore?"

She didn't expect the question.

"Why, her reputation as an actress has always been—" she began.

He shook his head impatiently. "I don't mean that. What I want to know is, could she get the backing she needs? My agent doesn't seem to think so. I know she looks like she's living well, but there's very little left. She'd need someone to believe in her. Do you believe in her, Sybil? Do you believe in me?"

He leaned across the table, looking anxiously into her eyes.

"I've always believed in you both."

He sighed and sat back, patting her hand. He smiled suddenly, disarmingly. "Didn't I say you were generous? There aren't two people in this room who would say the same. I love you for that, Sybil."

Dear, romantic, impulsive Carter, she thought. He made her days less lonely. She was fond of him. She'd always been. But love? No, there was too much of the temperamental boy in him.

She wondered if there ever would be another man in her life. She hadn't allowed herself time to think very

358

much about it. After the wedding there would be time and she dreaded the moment when she must face the truth about herself. She had all the things she'd ever wanted and no one with whom to share her life.

III

The wedding was planned for Sunday afternoon and on Monday the roses began to arrive, a single red rose every day. No card was enclosed. There was only the rose each day. By Friday everyone at the studio had noticed and Sybil herself was intrigued. It was such a lovely thing to do for the mother of the bride.

"Who is he?" Marlene asked. "You sure can pick 'em. No one sends me flowers, not even on my birthday, not that I want to remember my birthday. Who's the charmer?"

"I honestly don't know who it could be unless Carter— I'll have to talk with Carter," she said.

But it wasn't Carter. She was sure of it. He would have given himself away. He was not the type to make anonymous gestures. She thought of Will. It would be like him to be so thoughtful and he knew she loved flowers.

Friday evening, after an exhausting day, she retired early. She took a book and a glass of warm milk to her room and prepared to relax. She was much more tired than she thought, so that when the phone rang she was just drifting off to sleep. The voice came to her as part of a dream from the past.

"Sybil, my dear, I was almost afraid to call, but our daughter gave me courage. And then I thought if I sent the flowers— You always did like flowers even when you couldn't really afford them."

It couldn't be. She must be dreaming. She hadn't heard that voice in years and it stirred memories she thought were dead.

"Jonathan!"

"Yes. It's Jonathan." His voice was low, nearly a whisper.

She found she was trembling.

"Joanna said nothing. I didn't know—"

"I didn't want you to know. I didn't know if you would care to see me. It was difficult for me to accept the fact that we had a daughter all these years and I'd known nothing about her. I wondered and waited and debated with myself. Joanna wants me at her wedding. May I come, Sybil?"

"Oh, Jonathan, of course. How—how wonderful for Joanna!" She spoke automatically, knowing how much this would mean to her daughter and not fully comprehending what it would mean to her.

"And for you, Sybil? How will it be for you? It's been so long. I hardly know what to say. I— Could I see you? Before the wedding, I mean. Tomorrow perhaps. There's so much— Please let me see you tomorrow, Sybil."

He wanted to see her.

"If you like," she said slowly and sat up, looking about her room, seeing everything with great clarity, the mauve carpeting, the pale pink walls, the very feminine French provincial furniture, the rainbow quilt. She was wide awake now and gripping the receiver with both hands as though to hold on to the sound of his voice.

"Dinner then, if you haven't any plans, the night before the wedding, I mean."

She had no other plans she cared to keep.

"Do you think that restaurant is still there? You remember, the one near the park. I'm not so familiar with New York anymore."

"It's there."

He sounded so different. They might have parted yesterday and yet there was a lifetime between them. What would he be like? What should she expect? Surely he'd changed in thirty-three years. Lord, was it really that long ago? Thirty-three years! How had she changed? What would he expect to find?

"Until tomorrow then. Shall we say eight?"

She didn't even think to ask where he was staying. She sat staring at the phone long after she'd replaced the receiver. She saw him in her mind as she had left him, standing underneath the street lamp watching her cab. She'd thought she'd lost him forever that fall evening and now he'd come back. Joanna must have meant what she said about needing to know her father. She'd found him, gone to him, and yet she'd said nothing.

She hesitated. Then began to dial her daughter's number. Before it could ring, she hung up. She was meeting Joanna for lunch tomorrow. She'd wait until then. What was there to say after all?

Jonathan! Jonathan! She'd see him tomorrow night and that was all that mattered. She had planned to have dinner with Carter and he was annoyed when she cancelled their date.

"I had something very special I wanted us to do."

"We can do it another time."

"It was meant for this time," he said coldly. "Oh, hell, I'm sorry, Sybil. I don't mean to sulk like this. It's just that Tracy's here. I went up and got her from school in Connecticut. I'm not much of a parent. I was counting on you."

"Don't worry, Carter. I won't let you down. We'll do something special for Tracy next week." She felt especially generous. She meant to do what she could for Tracy.

"All right, if you say so," he told her grudgingly. "But it's not like you to break dates."

"I'm sorry, Carter. It can't be helped, not this time." She thought she sounded too cheerful to be really sorry, but she wasn't thinking of Carter or Tracy. She only thought of Jonathan. His name sang in her mind all morning as she directed Edith with plans for the wedding. It was to be a simple ceremony, one that Joanna and Will had half-prepared themselves with Ned's help. She suspected the do-it-yourself plan was mostly Ned's and Diane's. Even the young minister was a Unitarian friend of

Ned's. Well, it would be different and modern and perhaps more meaningful than a traditional service.

At lunch Joanna was hardly as relaxed as a morning at Elizabeth Arden's should have made her. The massage and facial always quieted Sybil. Joanna was tense and irritable and for a time, she thought the girl meant to make some startling announcement about calling everything off, but she didn't.

She didn't know whether she should mention Jonathan or wait for Joanna to say something. She didn't have to wait long. They were no sooner seated than Joanna began.

"He called you, didn't he?" she asked.

"Yes," she said, delighted to talk about him. "I'm glad you went to him, Joanna, really glad. Please don't be concerned about that."

Joanna gave her mother an odd look.

"Concerned? Why should I be concerned when you're obviously glowing?" she said.

"Glowing? Am I?" she asked. But she needn't have asked. She felt as she hadn't felt in years. Just the thought of Jonathan stirred her.

"Your father is very proud of you, Joanna. It was the first thing he said to me. We have a beautiful daughter."

"Your father", "we". They were words she liked using.

"Did he?" she asked. Tears sprang unexpectedly to her eyes. "I—I liked him, too," she confided shyly. "He's—he's very well-known and respected in his field, isn't he?"

Sybil nodded.

"You know, he was hardly surprised when I told him who I was. Oh, there was the initial shock, but then almost at once he—he accepted me. He made me tell him all about myself and you. Mostly he wanted to hear about you. He likes Will. He came here to meet him. He told me he approved." She laughed self-consciously. "Well, I asked him that, if he approved, and he said he did. He's been to dinner with us twice. He kept saying he wanted to see you and yet he was actually afraid to call. He wouldn't let me say a word. He called me after he spoke to you last night and do you know what he asked? He asked if I approved."

She was obviously flattered.

"And did you approve? Do you approve now?"

For a moment Joanna said nothing. She carefully arranged the silver beside her plate. When she looked up a deep line appeared between her large eyes.

"Mother, you should be the one getting married tomorrow, you and my father."

She became alarmed by Joanna's tone She sounded defeated. It had been weeks since she'd mentioned any doubts.

"Oh, don't worry," the girl said, reading her expression. "I could do much worse than Will and I don't know if I could do better. I suppose he needs me. I suppose we need each other."

Suddenly she felt terribly sad. She remembered Joanna in love, the excitement, the sheer joy she obviously felt in being near Alfred. But that had been a younger, naive Joanna.

"Don't worry, Mother," she repeated. "I'm going to go through with it. Who knows, maybe I'll even be happy?" She smiled brightly and opened her menu. "What wonderful, lo-cal thing can I have to eat? You know, I suspect I shall let myself go the moment we move out to the wilds of New Jersey. I'll probably become fat, comfortable, and complacent. So don't worry about me."

She couldn't help worrying, but by evening even her concern was displaced by the delightful anticipation she felt. She had asked Joanna nothing really about her father. She knew little more now than when he had called. It was the way she wanted it. She found she couldn't talk about Jonathan in relation to herself. It was something she had to experience.

She chose her dress with great care, a simple blue wool with a soft wedding-ring neckline. It was not as simple as the one she'd worn when she'd last seen Jonathan, but perhaps he'd remember the blue. She laughed at her own romantic foolishness. She was going to see someone she cared for very deeply long ago. They'd talk about old times, of course, but they weren't young and free as they had been then. Jonathan, in all probability, was a grandfather by now.

Jonathan, a grandfather! She could hardly imagine it. She felt no different herself as though no time had passed. She could still recall the pain of their parting when he began to assume that she did not care for him at all and she could not tell him the truth. She could tell him now, or could she?

Through all her pleasant reminiscing she neglected to think of Jonathan's wife! It gave her pause. What sort of woman had he chosen? Unexpectedly she felt a stab of jealousy. Jealousy! What right had she to feel jealousy? She had sent him away without hope or explanation. She had no right to think of him now as anything but an old friend, an old and very dear friend.

Her eyes stared back at her in the dressing table mirror. She'd sat here hundreds of times preparing to go out with Geoffrey. And Geoffrey seemed now more remote than anyone else. It was as though the years of her marriage had been erased. They had no substance for her. She knew in her heart she had truly loved only one man in all her life.

She fastened seed pearls in her ears. She looked younger than she was, she knew that. The careful make-up and the smooth, youthful hair style helped. But how would she look to Jonathan? She turned off the dressing table lamps, brushed her cheek against the single full-blown rose that had arrived that morning and went to the living room to wait. She'd sent Edith and Lamarr off for an evening of rest before tomorrow's festivities so she would greet him herself.

She opened the drapes completely so that he would get the full effect of the view and then he hardly noticed it at all. When he arrived promptly, she had to calm herself deliberately before she opened the door.

They stood for a moment without speaking. He wore a tan cashmere coat and held a brown hat in his hand. His hairline had receded somewhat. There was gray at his temples and his brows were sprinkled with white. He seemed taller than she remembered and not so painfully slim. The laugh lines around his brown eyes deepened as he smiled down at her. His wide generous mouth was just as she remembered and the cleft in his chin even more pronounced. She could see herself mirrored in those gentle eyes. For a moment neither of them spoke.

"My word, you're beautiful," he told her huskily.

And they both laughed softly remembering the very first words he'd spoken to her.

"You are exactly as I remember you. Dear Sybil," he said, taking her hand and kissing it. His eyes never left her face.

"Come in, Jonathan. Please, come in."

She took his coat and offered him a drink. He watched her every movement as though he were afraid if he looked away she might suddenly disappear.

"Nothing seems real," he said. "Nothing! When Joanna came to me, I couldn't believe it."

"She insisted on knowing. I—I didn't know if she would go to you. I think I might have tried to stop her."

She came to sit beside him on the sofa. She felt irresistibly drawn to him. Suddenly she wanted to touch him, but she did not dare.

"Stop her? Thank God you didn't. Didn't you think I would want to know?" His eyes reproached her. "If I had known then, I never would have let you go."

She turned away. His gaze was too penetrating.

"I couldn't have let you do that, Jonathan. There was— There was too much at stake. Your career—"

"My career!" His words mocked her gently. "Oh, my poor, noble, foolish Sybil! Do you think I would have cared about my career? Didn't you know how much I cared? How much I still care?"

She turned to meet his eyes again. They were gentle, but insistent.

"You've made another kind of life for yourself. Joanna and I—" she stopped because her voice was shaking.

"You and Joanna are part of my life," he said.

She did not know what to say. They were the very words she wanted to hear and yet she was afraid to acknowledge them.

"Well," she said at last, smiling at him, "you know a good deal about me."

"I always have," he said.

"Ned's married. Did Joanna tell you?" she asked trying to keep her tone light. She wanted to reach out and caress his cheek.

He nodded. "Good old Ned. And you've another son."

"Yes, Arthur. He's going to be a brilliant lawyer. I'm very proud of him." Her voice was enthusiastic.

She tried not to think about his mouth and how it had once felt on hers. He had taught her about love and she remembered the lessons well. How she had hurt him! How she had hated to give him up! Did he know? Did he really know what he had meant to her? What could he possibly feel toward her now? Kindness? He was always kind. Compassion? Perhaps.

"And Marlene! Marlene is very well. She'll be so surprised to see you again."

Their conversation seemed stilted. She felt she was saying all the things required of her and nothing that really mattered.

"And you, Jonathan? Tell me about your family." She couldn't seem to keep her hands still. She arranged and rearranged the cigarette box until he reached out and caught her hands in his. She looked up at him questioningly.

"I love you, Sybil," he said. "I have always loved you."

She caught her breath painfully.

"Jonathan!" she whispered.

She couldn't help herself. His arms encircled her with strength and authority. His mouth sought hers and she yielded joyfully, giving in to her own passion with an abandon that surprised and shocked her a little. When he drew back to look at her, her eyes were wet with tears.

He brushed them away with his fingertips.

"What do children know of love?" he asked. "Perhaps it was wasted on us then. We'll make up for it, Sybil. We'll make up for it and more."

She believed him, trusted him, loved him. She put all thoughts of his family from her mind. There were no doubts, no questions. She felt she could and would do anything he asked. They dined at the restaurant they both remembered so well. It had changed hands several times since they'd been there last, but they knew it, not so much from its appearance, but from the ghosts of memories. They lingered for hours over dinner until they were the last patrons in the room and the waiters began to hover anxiously about them. He tipped them outrageously for their patience.

"The last time we left here, I thought I couldn't go on living. Now I want to live forever," he told her.

They kissed under the red and white striped awning. They kissed again in the cab downtown. And when they reached her penthouse she didn't want to let him go. He came in and they sat talking till the early hours of the morning. It was then he told her about his life. He'd married. He was thirty-eight at the time and Claire only twenty-four.

"In a way, she reminded me of you, but it was only a surface illusion. Young, vulnerable. Her parents didn't approve at first. I was so much older. And she was—oh, delicate in many ways and completely dependent. She needed me. We had two children, Paul and Beth. We almost had a third child, a boy, but it was stillborn and Claire died then of the most extraordinary complications, mostly emotionally induced. She was a child. I thought for a time it was my fault, but she was a child. I thought having our own children would help. I thought she'd develop a sense of responsibility, a maternal instinct. There is none, you know. It simply does not exist in some women. Claire was one of them. She wanted to be a little girl all her life. We lived in Washington during the war. I never went overseas. I was assigned to Walter Reed Hospital. The hours were long and difficult. It was hard for

Claire because I was seldom home. She simply couldn't cope with the loneliness and two small children."

For a time they sat in silence. Claire had not been real to her, but she could feel his distress. She was sorry he had suffered, but glad he was free. What would she have done if he were not free? She did not think she could have given him up a second time.

"I was very fond of Claire, sincerely fond of her. But there was really no one else but you. Sometimes I read about you, about your success. Have you been happy?"

She didn't answer. Had she been happy? There were times of happiness, yes. She'd sometimes been supremely happy for a day, an hour. Did anyone have much more?

"I'm happy now," she said.

He kissed her hand. "So am I."

They talked of the past.

"Whatever happened to Mrs. Philips and Mr. Barbarini?" he asked.

She shook her head. She didn't know. She'd never gone back.

"I want you to know I won't compromise you tomorrow," he said. "Ned will give Joanna away, of course. And I? Well, I'll be the close family friend. I promise you. There'll be no problem."

"Oh, Jonathan, I'll be so glad to have you there."

His eyes told her he knew how she felt and understood.

"Can you stay in the city long?"

"A day or two, but then I'll have to go. But I can come back. I will come back if—"

"If what, Jonathan?"

She knew what he would say and waited breathlessly to hear the words.

"There's still time for us, Sybil. We can have now what we should have had years ago. I want to marry you. I've always wanted that. I don't pretend to be the same person I was, but neither are you. It only means we have so much more to bring to one another. Marry me and we'll go away for a time and get to know one another all over again. I'd like to visit every lovely place there is in this world with you beside me."

He pressed her hand to his lips and waited with head bowed for her answer. She could hardly speak.

"Jonathan, if we only could!"

He gazed at her tenderly.

"Why not? If you feel as I do that there's been a bond between us all these years, why not? We had something very precious once. I don't think it was ever really lost. All it needs is a chance to flourish."

Could they begin again? She believed in their love. It transcended every barrier. She knew him as she knew no one else. He seemed to know all about her. He'd learned a good deal from Joanna, but he'd been following her career himself. She wondered what Arthur would think of him. She wanted Arthur to know and like him. But in the end that wouldn't matter. Arthur would marry someday and she would accept the girl because he loved her. But she had been divorced from his father only a little more than six months. Could he begin to understand? He would eventually. He'd have to because this was what she wanted, what she'd always wanted.

She didn't give him her answer then, but she knew what it would be. He seemed to know too.

IV

The next afternoon they stood together and listened as their daughter and Will repeated the words from the sonnet they'd chosen as part of their wedding ceremony.

" . . . I think on thee, and then my state.
Like to the lark at break of day arising
From sullen earth, sings hymns at heaven's gate;
For thy sweet love rememb'red such wealth brings
That then I scorn to change my state with kings."

Will's voice was firm and clear as he spoke of his love. He saw no one but Joanna. She recited her passage from the Book of Ruth with equal fervor.

Without their having consciously thought about it, she and Jonathan moved closer together. He slipped his arm about her shoulders. When the ceremony was over, everyone kissed everyone else. Jonathan held her and she knew they belonged together and told him so.

"If we're not careful, we'll outshine the bride and groom," he said. His eyes told her how happy he was.

They spent the reception carefully avoiding each other, seeing that the guests were comfortable and enjoying themselves. It was as if they'd been married all along. Every now and then their eyes would meet and there would be some joyful, unspoken communication. She'd turn back to her companion with a radiant smile and say something charming. It was a lovely reception and everyone seemed to be enjoying it.

Joanna took her mother aside.

"Thank you, Mother. Thank you for everything. But thank you most of all for my father."

She looked beautiful in her beige satin suit with her veil a halo of tulle with tiny green velvet ribbons in her hair.

"Be happy, darling. Be very, very happy," she whispered.

Tears touched Sybil's lashes. She hadn't meant to cry, but her emotions overwhelmed her and she couldn't help herself. Now she was being the typical mother. Well, perhaps she was. She wanted the best for her child, wanted it terribly.

Marlene was surprised beyond words to see Jonathan.

"Doc! Hey, Doc! I can't get over it. You look— Gee, you look almost the same. Except maybe for this," she touched the gray at his temples. "I would have known you anywhere."

She took his arm. "We need to talk. I still can't believe you're real. What do you think of old Ned?"

Only Tracy Hayes seemed lonely and out of place. At nine she was introverted and terribly shy. She stood on the edge of the small circle of friends and family like a homeless waif. Once Carter had a drink or two he ignored her. She looked miserable. Her pale blonde hair hung limply to her waist. The dark red velvet dress with the wide lace collar was much too long for her. Sybil did what she could to make the child feel at home and a part of the celebration.

"What you need is a ribbon in your hair, like Joanna's."

"I don't have a ribbon," the child said solemnly. She was startled by her suggestion.

"I know where there's a ribbon just like Joanna's. Come with me and I'll show you."

Ned's wife Diane came, too. Together they brushed Tracy's long hair up and back and fastened it in place with green velvet. The child was delighted and couldn't stop staring at her reflection in the mirror.

"Someday I want to be a bride, too," she said.

Sybil hugged her.

"You will, darling. You will. But you have to smile more often."

She touched the corners of the thin mouth and the lips quivered into a smile.

"Let's go in and circulate," Diane said, taking the child under her wing and talking to her as though they were equals. "I hardly know anyone here at all either."

Later she said, "The poor thing needs someone to love her. Doesn't her father care at all?"

"In his own way, I think Carter loves his daughter," she said. "Some people don't know how to express love."

Everyone was curious about Jonathan, but Carter was more perceptive than most.

"Who is he?" His face was flushed. He'd had more than his share of champagne and was starting on scotch.

"A very old and dear friend," she said, as she'd been saying to everyone.

"Something more than that," he said, frowning. "I think I'm beginning to feel left out," he added pointedly.

She was too happy to take much notice of his aggrieved tone. He'd been talking more seriously about their friendship lately.

"We're good for each other. Your career complements mine. There wouldn't be any problem. And I'd work hard. I'd want to make you proud of me. You inspire me, Sybil. Do you know that? You bring out the best in me."

Being "good" for each other was hardly a romantic basis for marriage. She was fond of him. That was all. And she'd told him so. What she wanted and needed was a man like Jonathan. She smiled at him across the room. He was talking to Tracy. He knew how to make her smile. He charmed her as he used to charm Ned. She watched them, remembering and smiling herself.

"He's a rather special person, isn't he?"

Arthur was standing beside her. He had been particu-

373

larly quiet today. But she'd seen him watching Jonathan, a bemused expression on his face.

"He seems to know everybody, Aunt Marlene, Ned, Joanna. But I don't know him."

She thought he sounded hurt.

"I want you to know him," she said, slipping her arm through his.

She almost told him her news then. He would be the first person to know. But she decided to wait until they were alone and could talk more privately.

It was past midnight by the time the last guest left. Jonathan had to leave earlier to get back to commitments in Philadelphia. "I'll call you tomorrow," he promised.

She hated to see him go. They'd had so little time together, but he would call her tomorrow. She'd count the hours. Maturity should have brought patience, she thought, laughing at herself. She couldn't help it. She couldn't wait to be with him again.

She and Arthur sat alone over the last of the champagne. She felt relaxed and comfortable, but not ready to sleep. She wanted to talk about Jonathan and she told him her news.

At first he said nothing, but busied himself lighting a small cigar, a habit he'd lately acquired. She was prepared for him to be surprised, upset, or even resentful. But he said nothing to suggest any of these.

"I'm glad, Mother," he said. "I never thought you were very happy with my father."

So that's what he thought! She was sorry because it wasn't true and it must color his thinking, giving him a distorted understanding of marriage.

"You're wrong, darling. There were times when I was very happy."

His wise eyes met hers. They'd always seemed wise beyond his years even when he was a small child.

"That happiness doesn't last though, does it? I've wondered about that, you know. Can you commit yourself forever to one person? People change. How can you promise something like that? I listened to Joanna and

Will. They promised. I wonder if I could ever promise to love one person forever."

He looked so vulnerable, so very young.

It was hard to know what to say and what she said now would be very important to him. What could she say about love? She knew she wanted to give Jonathan all her love, to commit herself to him totally. But love was not a simple thing. She'd loved others.

She remembered now with great clarity how she had become attached as a child to Ronald Baldwin, or rather how they had become attached to one another. After her mother died, she had been a lonely child with only her father to depend upon. She adored him, but he was remote in his suffering. The loss of his wife shattered him and at first he had neglected her. Ronald had been kind to her, but kind out of his own loneliness. He had lost his father and his mother was often ill. They were two children in a world of unresponsive adults and they clung to one another. Neither of them understood the sacrifices real love required.

Then she met Edward. She thought she was in love with him and that he loved her. She could look up to him, admire him as she did her father. She was too inexperienced to recognize his motives then and later the realization nearly destroyed her. She turned her fierce need for love upon her child. Ned! Poor Ned! How many of his difficulties had she herself caused in those early years?

But another love had come, Jonathan's love, just when she'd stopped believing in love. It gave meaning to every breath, to every thought and yet she had given it all up. All! And why? The desire to protect him from scandal, to save his career, to allow him to be what he could be sounded noble and self-sacrificing. If it were really there, it was secondary. She had been protecting herself and her son, whom she knew she would most certainly lose in the chaos that would follow should she choose Jonathan. She gave up his love in favor of the safer commitment to Ned. Ned was utterly dependent upon her. He could not withdraw his dependence and affection, not then. But eventually he did, as all children do.

She turned to Geoffrey who thought her docile and submissive. For a time she had been thus to please him and because she knew she would lose him if she showed herself to be anything but the way he expected her to be. For a time she seemed to lose herself, but only for a time.

What had she become then? Who was Sybil Eldridge Kempton? Madame Sybil? Her public image only seemed to mock her. It was something she and Marlene created. Two frightened, lonely women had built a small empire in the fashion world and they, too, were dependent on each other, she, no more than Marlene herself. Between them there was another kind of love.

She looked at Arthur now, his dark head bent over his glass. He was so young, too young to be so serious. How much did he have to remember?

She laughed softly and he looked up at her quizzically.

"What's funny?"

"I am, I suppose. My whole life just seemed to flash before me. I was wondering if it was a sign of maturity or, heaven forbid, age."

"Oh, Mother, you'll never be old, not in that way."

She leaned over and kissed him. "Thank you, darling. You're my number one fan." She sat back and gave him a long look. "I was trying to think what to say to you. I know what it is now. You mustn't be afraid of love, Arthur. Don't be afraid to commit yourself. I think I've known many kinds of love and that includes my love for you, for my children. Without any one of these my life would have been sterile.

"Love doesn't always remain the same, but that doesn't mean you should avoid it. There's no point in living if you're going to go through life without letting yourself feel. All love has the potential for joy as well as sorrow. When you commit yourself, you commit yourself to both. There's no such thing as perfectly joyous love that lasts forever, not among mere mortals, I suppose."

He was silent for a moment and she watched his face

carefully. He was her youngest, her last child. She thought guiltily that perhaps she had loved him more than the others. He'd always been sensitive, too sensitive for his father's tastes. The sensitivity only added dimension to his character. Someday he'd be a particularly understanding husband and father if he had the courage to love.

He looked at her and smiled.

"I think you and Dr. Rogers are going to be very happy," was all he said finally.

But she knew he'd remember what she'd told him and think about it. She wasn't worried. He'd find love someday and he wouldn't be afraid.

Marlene was far less confident of her happiness. They spent most of the next morning discussing her plans.

"You sure you're ready for this? You made up your mind awful fast. You've only been free, what is it, six months? What does he think about your career? Where are you going to live? Is he going to drop everything and come here? Or is it going to be the other way around." She shook her head. "Don't get me wrong. I like him. I always thought he was right for you. But now? You're not just two simple kids, you know. How's all this going to work out?"

It was almost embarrassing because she had not considered any of the practical aspects.

"I honestly don't know," she admitted. "We didn't discuss that, so I don't know. I haven't stopped to think. But we're not children. You're right. He knows about my work and admires it, as I admire his. He wouldn't ask me to give it up. Don't ask me how I know, I just do. Oh, Marlene, I never thought I'd have this chance. Be happy for me, please. We'll work things out. Just be happy for me."

"Honey, who could help it?" she asked. "It's not every day a miracle changes your whole life. I'm all for miracles."

They couldn't be married for another month, but they spent as much of that time together as they could. He called her every night and spent every weekend in New

377

York. They rediscovered the city together—theaters, concerts, museums, and walking together in the Village. Mrs. Philips' building was gone and in its place was a parking lot.

"Nothing stays the same," Jonathan mused. "In a way I'm glad. I don't like to think that other people lived in rooms we lived in. Somehow I feel they belonged to us. You know, I never went back to get my things after that last night with you. Not that I left much behind, a sweater, two shirts and some books, I think. But I couldn't go back."

They walked through Washington Square Park in the cold winter air. She turned the mink collar of her coat up against the wind and leaned towards him.

"Well, that's still there," he said, stopping. "Our bench!"

"It can't be," she protested laughing. He was as sentimental as she.

"Even if it isn't, I'm going to believe it is. It looks old enough. Let's sit down."

They did and the cold wind blew about them, but they hardly noticed. She remembered how in another time in another season he'd told her that they couldn't go on as before. She could almost smell the warm fresh air of that summer day. They stayed until her toes grew cold inside her fur-lined boots and laughed at themselves for being foolishly romantic.

"Do any two people have the right to be so happy?" he asked. Briefly the thought frightened her, but he teased her gently into smiling again.

"Don't tempt the gods? That's what you're thinking. Darling, we make our own happiness, our own fate. And I thought you'd reached the age of reason. Methinks you're younger than you look." He kissed the tip of her nose and she promised to be ever so reasonable.

He told his children about their plans at Christmas.

"How did they react?" she asked, anxiously, remembering Arthur's doubts about love. Ned had been as pleased as Joanna.

378

"They think there's life in the old boy yet," he joked. "Beth had given up all hope. She's married herself, you know, and thinks everyone should be. Paul's philosophy is a little less orthodox. He has quite a way with the ladies, inherited my charm, no doubt. But he says he's not against marriage as long as it's mine and not his. They want to meet you, of course. I told them you'd come the week after New Year's, though I neglected to ask you first. Will you?"

Would she! When she was with him, she delighted in his presence. She liked introducing him to her friends. He charmed everyone and she liked to sit back and watch him and know that the smile he gave someone else would soon be hers. She lived each day in an enchanted world. New York had never looked so beautiful. She had never felt so well. Even when they were apart, she was not lonely. He was always with her, would always be with her.

It rained on the morning she was to leave for Philadelphia.

"Wouldn't you know?" asked Marlene. "Who likes to travel in the rain?"

"I don't mind. I like the rain as long as it doesn't keep me from Jonathan."

She stopped at her studio only briefly. She wanted to get to the travel agent before catching her train. They were planning a honeymoon trip, a cruise around the world. They'd be gone three months. There were so many things to do before they left. But nothing seemed to be a burden. Everything would be done in time.

No one who saw her, none of her friends, could help being happy for her. She wished she could share something of what she had with everyone.

She walked in the rain down Fifth Avenue to the travel agent. She passed Cartier's and, on an impulse, went in and bought a pair of gold cuff links with Chinese symbols on them. They stood for long life and happiness, the discreet clerk told her. It was his first sale that morning.

"That's perfect," she said and left him smiling, a little

379

awed by her shining happiness. She tucked the small package inside her purse and went on her way.

She could imagine Jonathan's face when he saw them. She imagined his face now. He must be leaving for the hospital. There was a staff meeting this morning and he'd go there before picking her up at the train. The rest of the day would be theirs and soon the rest of their lives. Was he thinking of her now as she hurried to him?

Jonathan was in a more than usually pleasant mood despite the rainy weather. Sybil was coming today. He'd be meeting her train at one. There was the possibility of snow later, if it turned cold. He liked the snow. It reminded him of Christmas and a small, dingy flat in the Village and Sybil.

He drove as far as Market Street, seeing not the road, nor the other cars, but Sybil, his Sybil. He could imagine her now waking to the winter day. Or perhaps she was up and at work already. She was an early riser, or at least she used to be. Was she thinking of him? Was she smiling the slow, lovely smile and thinking of him? He concentrated, sending his thoughts to her, his love, his desire.

"I wish a beautiful, glorious day for you, Sybil, my dearest Sybil."

He used to think of her every morning like this. He hoped somehow his thoughts would reach her. He used to imagine what it would be like if she came to him. He couldn't get over the fact that she apparently did not love him. He loved her, was obsessed by her and for years could think of nothing else. The pain of his loss was with him all the time. He grew to know it as one knew a constant companion. Gradually the pain grew less sharp, though it never left entirely. She did not come to him and he had to accept defeat. He turned at last to someone else, someone who seemed to need him.

Once he was married to Claire he sternly forced thoughts of Sybil away. He was committed to his wife and Sybil was inaccessible. He had no right to think of her. But now he had every right. His thoughts never left her.

She'd loved him all along. He knew that now and cursed himself for ever having let her go. He could always see her in his mind. He saw her just-kissed lips, her eyes soft with desire and he smiled, remembering. She was his now and soon they'd be together as they should have been all along.

He passed Wanamaker's and saw in the window a mannequin draped in a Dresden blue gown and he saw her at Joanna's wedding, standing beside him, her lips parted in wonder and joy as their daughter repeated the words she had chosen for the ceremony.

"Entreat me not to leave thee, or refrain from following after thee. For whither thou goest I will go—"

"Whither though goest, Sybil," he thought.

Sybil smiled as she waited to cross 52nd Street. It was almost as though he had touched her cheek. She'd lived a lifetime learning about love. She knew there were no certainties, that her present joy might not last, but she was not afraid. Their love rose beyond all else and she rushed toward the future, toward his waiting arms with a hopeful heart. She did not look back.

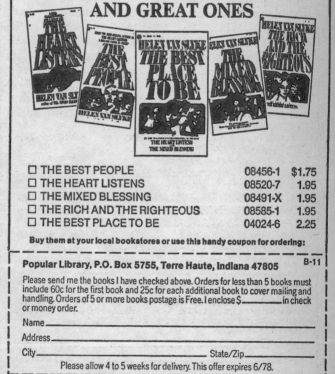

Reading Fit For A Queen

QUEEN-SIZE GOTHICS are a new idea. They offer the very best in novels of romantic suspense, by the top writers, greater in length and drama, richer in reading pleasure.

☐ THE FOUR MARYS—Rinalda Roberts	00366-9	1.25
☐ GRAVE'S COMPANY—S. Nichols	00252-2	1.25
☐ GRENENCOURT—I. Charles	00264-6	1.25
☐ THE HARLAN LEGACY— Jo Anne Creighton	03206-5	1.50
☐ THE HEMLOCK TREE—E. Lottman	00235-2	1.25
☐ INN OF EVIL—J.A. Creighton	00224-7	1.25
☐ ISLAND OF SILENCE— Carolyn Brimley Norris	00411-8	1.25
☐ ISLAND OF THE SEVEN HILLS—Z. Cass	00277-8	1.25
☐ KEYS OF HELL—L. Osborne	00284-0	1.25
☐ THE KEYS TO QUEENSCOURT— Jeanna Hines (Empress)	08508-8	1.75
☐ THE LAZARUS INHERITANCE (Large type)—Noel Vreeland Carter	00432-0	1.25
☐ THE LEGEND OF WITCHWYND (Large Type)—Jeanne Hines	00420-7	1.25
☐ LET THE CRAGS COMB OUT HER DAINTY HAIR—J. Marten	00302-2	1.25
☐ LUCIFER WAS TALL—Elizabeth Gresham	00346-4	1.25
☐ MIDNIGHT SAILING—S. Hufford	00263-8	1.25
☐ THE MIRACLE AT ST. BRUNO'S— Philippa Carr (Empress)	08533-9	1.75
☐ OF LOVE INCARNATE—Jane Crowcroft	00418-5	1.25

Buy them at your local bookstores or use this handy coupon for ordering:

Popular Library, P.O. Box 5755, Terre Haute, Indiana 47805   B-10

Please send me the books I have checked above. Orders for less than 5 books must include 60c for the first book and 25c for each additional book to cover mailing and handling. Orders of 5 or more books postage is Free. I enclose $_____ in check or money order.

Name_____

Address_____

City_____ State/Zip_____

Please allow 4 to 5 weeks for delivery. This offer expires 6/78.

Anne Tyler

*"To read a novel by
Ann Tyler is to fall in love"*
—People Magazine